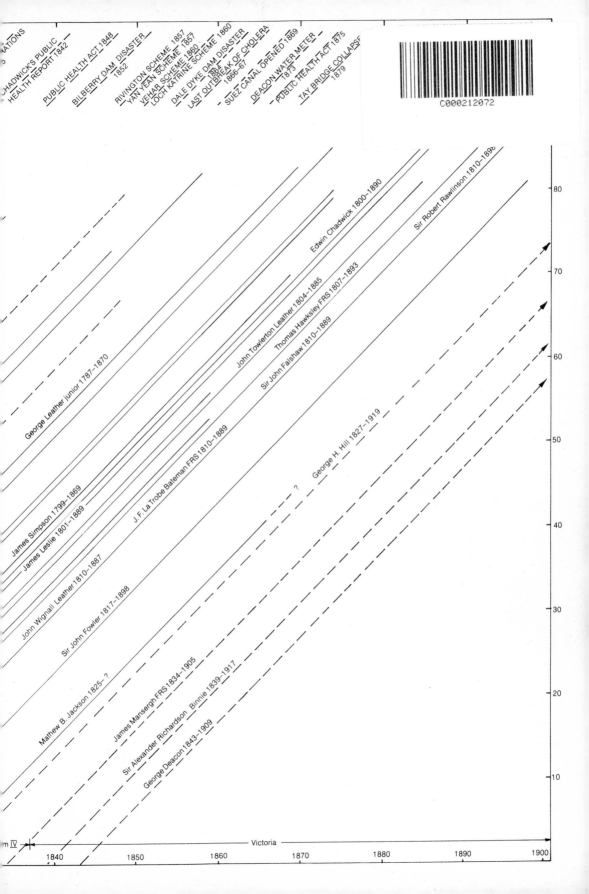

RMATIONS
S

CHADWICKS PUBLIC
HEALTH REPORT 1842

PUBLIC HEALTH ACT 1848

BILBERRY DAM DISASTER
1852

RIVINGTON SCHEME 1857

YAN YEAN SCHEME 1857

VEHAR SCHEME 1860

LOCH KATRINE SCHEME 1860

DALE DYKE DAM DISASTER
1864

LAST OUTBREAK OF CHOLERA
1866–67

SUEZ CANAL OPENED 1869

DEACON WATER METER
1873

PUBLIC HEALTH ACT 1875

TAY BRIDGE COLLAPSE
1879

C000212072

Sir Robert Rawlinson 1810–1898

Edwin Chadwick 1800–1890

John Towlerton Leather 1804–1885

Thomas Hawksley FRS 1807–1893

Sir John Falshaw 1810–1889

George Leather junior 1787–1870

J. F. La Trobe Bateman FRS 1810–1889

George H. Hill 1827–1919

James Simpson 1799–1869

James Leslie 1801–1889

John Wignall Leather 1810–1887

Sir John Fowler 1817–1898

Mathew B. Jackson 1825–?

James Mansergh FRS 1834–1905

Sir Alexander Richardson Binnie 1839–1917

George Deacon 1843–1909

m Ⅳ

Victoria

80

70

60

50

40

30

20

10

1840 1850 1860 1870 1880 1890 1900

Early Victorian Water Engineers

Early Victorian Water Engineers

G. M. BINNIE

THOMAS TELFORD LIMITED
LONDON 1981

Published by Thomas Telford Ltd, Telford House, PO Box 101, 26–34 Old Street,
London EC1P 1JH

ISBN: 0 7277 0128 2

Photoset, printed and bound in Great Britain by REDWOOD BURN LIMITED Trowbridge & Esher

Contents

As this is an historical book, dimensions in the main text are quoted in Imperial units, but in the Appendix metric units have been used.

Preface

The fame of Smeaton, Telford, George Stephenson, Rennie and other civil engineers of the pre-Victorian era was assured by Samuel Smiles who wrote their lives. The fame of Jessop, who was overlooked by Smiles, has recently been restored by Hadfield and Skempton.[1]

About the time when Smiles's classic was published, in 1861, waterworks for town water supplies on a far bigger scale (excluding London) than had ever been attempted before had been successfully completed for Glasgow and Liverpool and were in train for Manchester. However, neither Bateman nor Hawksley, the two engineers responsible for these great pioneering works, became household names like their contemporaries, Robert Stephenson and I. K. Brunel, whose fame owed much to the intense public interest and speculation in railways which reached its climax with the Railway Mania in 1844–47. They were also the sons of famous fathers. Today, outside the water industry, Bateman and Hawksley are quite unknown; yet their achievements have withstood splendidly the test of time. When one considers the destructive energy that is released when a dam fails, the density of population which already existed at that time and the primitive state of the art of dam-building when they began their careers, their success in constructing some 50 dams between 40 and 100 ft high which – with only one exception – are still in use after 100 years or more, deserves to be better recognized. Even the exception (Daisy Green dam) was not demolished until it had been more than 100 years in service.

As the third generation in a family of waterworks engineers, I was prompted to try and see justice done to Bateman, Hawksley and other pioneers of my profession; but engineering history that merely lists the achievements of the period under review can only excite superficial interest and tells one little of the men responsible. For a fuller understanding and appreciation of what was achieved, one must study the conditions under which those engineers worked; what they did; how, and why – with the knowledge and facilities available to them – they often succeeded; and also why they sometimes failed.

Chadwick, a civil servant, has his biographers; but for an understanding of the great stimulus he gave to water supply it has been necessary to make him the principal character in the first two chapters. The remaining chapters deal with the engineers. The durations of their lives, in relation to the history of the period, are shown on the chart at the end of the book.

In carrying out my historical and engineering research I have been helped by an enormous number of people, not all of whom can be named; besides those persons mentioned in the text and in the notes, I am much indebted to the following: Mr A. S. Riley, Director of Operations and Mr N. Hoyle of the Headquarters Staff, Mr H. W. Elton, Director and Messrs M. Baird, R. Clayton, A. K. Craig and T. Quale of the Eastern Division, Mr D. G. Milroy, Director of the Northern Division and Mr P. L. Birtwistle of the Pennine Division of the North West Water Authority; Mr G. T. Calder, Director and Messrs G. Brewin and P. Tandy of the Southern Division, Mr R. Wood, Director and Messrs R. M. Lee and J. France of the South Western Division, Mr H. C. Godden, Director of the Western Division and Mr R. W. Hustwit, Director and Mrs J. C. Day of the North Central Division of the Yorkshire Water Authority; Mr J. W. Thomas, General Manager and Messrs G. Robinson, J. Watt and P. W. Lisle of the Northumbrian Water Authority; Mr J. A. N. McGeoch, Director and Mr R. J. Rennet of the Tayside Regional Council; Mr J. P. Williamson, Director and Messrs J. N. Merrieweather and M. A. Scott-Dodd of the Lothian Regional Council; Mr W. T. Deveney, Director of the Strathclyde Regional Council; Mr W. J. Whitehead of the Thames Water Authority; Mr D. N. Earp, Manager and Mr G. Howe of the Gower Division of the Welsh Water Authority, and Mr L. Kerr of the same Authority; Messrs C. Cash, A. Hodgson and R. F. Everard of the Bristol Waterworks Company; Messrs G. Reid and G. A. Wilford of the York Waterworks Company; Mr A. J. H. Winder of Watson-Hawksley; Mr R. D. Robinson of G. H. Hill and Sons; Mr R. E. Summerfield of Leslie and Reid; Mr W. M. Cormie of Crouch and Hogg; Professor A. M. Neville, Principal and Vice Chancellor of Dundee University; Mr I. Flett of the City of Dundee District Council; Mr J. D. Galbraith of the Scottish Record Office; Mr R. Gillespie of the Mitchell Library Glasgow; Mr P. Cohen of the University of Manchester Institute of Science and Technology; Dr D. Postles of the Sheffield City Libraries; Ms K. G. Jones of the Royal Society of Health; Ms R. Evans of the Geological Society of London; Mrs E. M. Foster of the Thoresbey Society; Mr M. R. Bailey of the Manchester Ship Canal Company; Mr I. McNeil, Secretary of the Newcomen Society; Mr C. A. Chester of the Ryhope Engines Trust; Dr J. Percival and Ms J. Belsen of the library of University College London; Mr B. J. Dangerfield of the Institution of Water Engineers and Scientists and Lady Wilson of High Wray. In addition I must also thank the many members of the Institution of Civil Engineers, in particular Miss D. J. Bayley and her assistants in the library, also my colleagues F. Law, I. M. Kirkpatrick and L. N. Martin.

I acknowledge with gratitude the permission I have been given to reproduce illustrations, drawings and photographs as follows from the archives and collections of the following organizations:

Bristol Waterworks Company—Figs 5.3, 5.4
Cumberland and Westmorland Antiquarian and Archaeological Society—Fig. 9.4
The Geological Society of London—Figs 13.4, 13.6
Illustrated London News Picture Library—Fig. 4.3
Institution of Civil Engineers—Figs 6.3, 9.1
Institution of Water Engineers and Scientists—Figs 8.5, 9.9
Leslie and Reed—Figs 6.4, 6.5
Library of University College London—Fig 1.2
Lothian Regional Council—Fig 6.2
Melbourne and Metropolitan Board of Works—Figs 12.1–12.3
The Newcomen Society—Fig 5.1
Northumbrian Water Authority—Fig 8.11
North West Water Authority—Figs 5.5, 8.4, 9.2, 9.3, 9.16
Punch—Fig 2.1
The Ryhope Engines Trust and Rob Matheson/*Sunday Times*—Fig 8.1b
Sheffield City Libraries—Figs 13.7, 13.8
Strathclyde Regional Council—Fig 9.12
Watson–Hawksley—Figs 8.2, 8.6–8.8, 8.10, 8.13, 13.10
Welsh Water Authority—Figs 10.1–10.6
Yorkshire Water Authority—Figs 3.1, 7.2, 9.5, 9.6, 13.2, 13.3
York Waterworks Company—Fig 5.6

As regards portraits, I am indebted to the Council of the Institution of Civil Engineers for permission to publish the portrait of James Simpson and to Mr John Bolton of the Department of Health and Social Security for permission to publish the one of Sir Robert Rawlinson.

I am very grateful to Mr R. W. Rennison of the Newcastle and Gateshead Water Company for reading the proofs.

Finally, I thank my wife Elspeth, without whose help and encouragement this book would not have been written.

Introduction

In the years following the Battle of Waterloo the quickening pace of the economic development and technical innovation known to us as the Industrial Revolution, together with a sudden and rapid increase in the population (from about 10 million in 1800 to 19 million in 1837) brought unprecedented changes to the country, more especially to the valleys east and west of the Pennines where plentiful supplies of water provided power for mills and enabled canals – then the most advanced form of transport – to be constructed. The opportunities for employment thus produced brought to these areas a large influx of people from other parts of England, and in Lancashire from Ireland as well. Between 1821 and 1831 the population of Manchester and Salford grew by 47 per cent, and Bradford by 78 per cent. Housing had to be provided rapidly and economically: whole 'working-class' districts grew up outside existing towns and villages where there were mills or factories. The centres of the towns, even outside the main industrial areas, grew more congested and more run down as the poorer workers crowded into them. Those who could afford to do so moved out to more salubrious situations and often remained ignorant of the dreadful conditions in the courts and alleys of the towns they had left. Water supply and sewage disposal, which had been barely adequate for small communities, became by sheer pressure of numbers totally inadequate. When cholera first reached England in 1831, and struck again in 1848 and 1866, it found in those overcrowded warrens the ideal breeding ground. Private water companies or improvement commissioners existed in some places but they usually only supplied water to the more prosperous citizens on the basis that only those who could pay the annual rates could expect to be supplied.

The problems posed by these changes would have taxed the resources of any government, but in early nineteenth-century England government – both central and local – had hardly changed since Elizabethan days, was generally blind to what was needed, and was largely incompetent to do anything about the problems.

The landed interests which ruled in Westminster, and in the counties, and the self-perpetuating oligarchies in the old municipalities, were chiefly concerned with maintaining the *status quo* and only took notice of the industrial districts when

1

law and order appeared to be threatened. The 'two Englands' might have continued to grow steadily apart, with serious social consequences; fortunately other processes and new ideas were at work and, by the 1830s were beginning to influence public opinion.

The great Reform Bill of 1831 left the landed interests as the ruling class at Westminster, but this was the beginning of a shift from over-representation of the small and often decayed boroughs of the South and West to fairer representation of the new big urban centres of the North and Midlands. Even if the franchise still excluded all but the more prosperous citizens, many aspiring politicians must have seen for the first time the reality of 'Coketown', even if only from one of the new railways. Likewise the Municipal Reform Act of 1833 did little to alter the qualifications of voters or councillors but it did give many towns municipal status for the first time and encouraged an often bitter rivalry between factions on councils. Earnest young reformers, such as the doctors who had seen local conditions at first-hand, now had a platform; a vigorous and rapidly growing local press gave full publicity to local news and scandals.

In London and some of the big provincial centres serious-minded groups of young men, such as those that gathered round Jeremy Bentham and the rising number of political economists, discussed and urged more efficient and often more positive government. Here again the doctors were often to the fore with their first-hand knowledge and missionary zeal. In Government itself efficiency had its advocates, notably Sir Robert Peel, and the creation of local police forces provided those in authority with servants whose local knowledge was both first-hand and trustworthy.

The established Church had done little for the new industrial areas but a number of earnest young men whose serious commitment to religion led them to concern for the spiritual welfare of these neglected places were forced by what they saw to agitate for better working conditions. A man such as Lord Ashley (afterwards Lord Shaftesbury) almost single-handed goaded successive Governments into appointing numerous commissions and committees to enquire into the conditions in which women and children especially worked; the subsequent publication of the evidence submitted and the reports thereon were an eye-opener to many on how their fellow-countrymen lived. By the 1850s the new popular novelists – Dickens, Disraeli, Mrs Gaskell – were giving life and immediacy to the facts recorded in Blue Books and Parliamentary Papers.

However, one man in particular deserves credit for perceiving a fundamental improvement – which was needed before any other social or physical ameliorations could have any real effect. Edwin Chadwick, remembered today as the author of a harsh and inhuman poor law, should rather be revered for insisting that proper sanitation was an essential prerequisite to any improvement in living conditions. He realized that aid must be sought from 'applications of the science of engineering, of which the medical men know nothing; and to gain power for the applications, and to deal with local rights which stand in the way of practical improvements, some jurisprudence is necessary of which engineers know nothing'.[1] His stubborn advocacy of the necessary measures for public health, against an uninterested or at best lukewarm Government and public opinion, gained him many enemies. His crusade only triumphed after he had left the centre of the stage, but it did triumph – and surely few have done more to put into practice his master Bentham's precept, of the greatest happiness of the greatest number, than Edwin Chadwick.

The first two chapters of this book tell the story of Chadwick's realization (in the 1830s) of the importance of cheap self-cleansing water-borne sewerage systems coupled with constant water supplies, and the rebuffs and opposition he encountered from engineers and others before there was a general acceptance of the need for both these facilities, by the 1860s.

The book also covers the careers of the civil engineers who were mainly responsible for the early water-supply schemes in this country (most of whom came into contact with Chadwick in one way or another), and describes their achievements. It also describes some of the design difficulties they experienced, in particular with the outlets from reservoirs, which often caused problems. Although water supply for towns rapidly grew more important, the water requirements of mills were important when Queen Victoria came to the throne, and the story of Bilberry dam is of a supply solely for the use of millowners. The book ends with the inquest on the Dale Dyke dam failure, the worst of its kind in British history, and the subsequent enquiries in which several waterworks engineers, each the subject of a chapter, became involved.

1   *The underground revolution*

One of the first tasks confronting the Whig Government which came into office after the passing of the Great Reform Bill was the revision of the poor law – the country's social welfare system – which had remained almost unchanged since the days of Elizabeth I and was now both inefficient and inequitable. A Poor Law Commission was set up in 1832 and one of the Assistant Commissioners was a young lawyer named Edwin Chadwick (1800–90).[1] Chadwick for a short time had been secretary to Jeremy Bentham (1748–1832), a voluminous writer on administration and jurisprudence. From Bentham Chadwick had gained an interest in these matters and had as a 'penny-a-liner' journalist written articles on social questions, particularly with regard to London whose slums and poorer quarters he knew well. Chadwick was a friend of the Mills, father and son, the political economist Nassau Senior and other serious-minded people like the doctors Neil Arnot and Southwood Smith who were deeply interested in questions of public health.

A man of great ability, with the clarity of mind to deal with a great mass of evidence and with an immense capacity for work, Chadwick soon masterminded the Poor Law Commission and was generally held responsible for its Report, also for the contents of the Act which followed. When a new Poor Law Board was set up in 1834 he became Secretary, and in the public mind much of the rigour and harshness of the new system were attributed to him, a judgement that was not altogether fair since many of his proposals were never put into effect by a parsimonious Government.

London, though not directly affected by the Industrial Revolution, was growing rapidly; and in the less affluent parts of the capital there were numerous workshops and small factories. With no public transport the workers necessarily lived near their places of business and congestion grew, made worse by the large numbers of unemployed and underemployed who thronged the already crowded courts and alleys. In 1838 there was a serious outbreak of typhus and Chadwick persuaded the Board to authorize an enquiry, which was carried out by his medical friends Neil Arnot and Southwood Smith, and a doctor from Manchester named James Kay (afterwards Sir J. Kay Shuttleworth), with similar interests. This was the

4

first time in the history of England that physicians were employed to study systematically the sanitary conditions which might contribute to ill health, and their report revealed to Chadwick at least the relationship between environment and health. The new unit of poor law administration was the union, and to obtain further information he therefore sent out a questionnaire to all union medical officers of health and all assistant poor law commissioners – he also sought further evidence from surveyors, builders, prison governors, police officers and factory inspectors who had first-hand knowledge of the living conditions of the poor. He himself edited the information received and then published it in *The Sanitary Conditions of the Labouring Classes in Britain in 1842*. The Report became the Stationery Office's most successful publication to date.

The conditions it revealed were horrifying. Typical was the evidence of a young doctor called Robert Baker on conditions in parts of Leeds.

> Of the 586 streets of Leeds, 68 only are paved by the town, i.e. by the local authorities; the remainder are either paved by owners, or are partly paved, or are totally unpaved, with the surfaces broken in every direction and ashes and filth of every description accumulated upon many of them. In the manufacturing towns of England, most of which have enlarged with great rapidity, the additions have been made without regard to either the personal comfort of the inhabitants or the necessities which congregation requires. To build the largest number of cottages on the smallest allowable space seems to have been the original view of the speculators, and the having the houses up and tenanted, the ne plus ultra of their desires. Thus neighbourhoods have arisen in which there is neither water nor out-offices, nor any conveniences for the absolute domestic wants of the occupiers. The courts and cul-de-sac exist everywhere. The building of houses back to back occasions this in a great measure. It is in fact part of the economy of buildings that are to pay a good percentage. In one cul-de-sac, in the town of Leeds, there are 34 houses, and in ordinary times there dwell in these houses 340 persons, or ten to every house – but as these houses are many of them receiving houses for itinerant labourers, during the periods of hay-time and harvest and the fairs at least twice that number are then here congregated.[2]

Another who gave evidence for the Sanitary Report was John Roe, surveyor of the Holborn and Finsbury district who was the inventor of the egg-shaped sewer. Roe had devised a system of flushing which reduced the cost of cleaning sewers very considerably. For short streets and courts he had reduced the size of drains from 4 ft 6 in. to 15 in. in diameter. Finding that the practice of joining sewers at angles, sometimes even right angles, caused eddies and deposits of sediment, he adopted curves of not less than 25 ft radius. Chadwick was greatly impressed and set Roe to

5

work on a series of experiments to ascertain for different discharges and gradients the most economical sizes of pipe, and the best materials for their construction. Chadwick, whose practical appreciation was remarkable, wrote

> As the old formulae, now in use, are founded on imperfect data and experiments, and not only give results so far above what experience shows to be the fact, but which, even if they were correct, would be of most limited application, they are obviously uncertain guides, and it is better to trust to our observations of what actually takes place. This, in fact, is experimenting on the largest and safest scale.[3]

When later the opposition to him grew, and he was questioned on the value of these experiments, he replied that drainage was a matter of gauging and experiment which, if carefully conducted, would eventually remove all grounds for differences of opinion. 'Great was gravitation – it would not be diverted by passion or ignorance, and would prevail.'[4]

Chadwick in his summary demonstrated the correlation between insanitary conditions, defective drainage and overcrowded housing on the one hand, and disease and low expectation of life on the other hand. In Manchester, for example, the life-expectancy of the labouring population was only 17 years, whereas in Rutland it was 38 years.[5] Characteristically he had no doubts as to the validity of his conclusions and he set out forcefully how matters could be improved.

> The primary and most important measures, and at the same time the most practicable, and within the recognized province of public administration, are drainage, the removal of all refuse of habitations, streets and roads, and the improvement of the supplies of water.

> That the chief obstacles to the immediate removal of decomposing refuse of towns and habitations have been the expense and annoyance of the hand labour and cartage requisite for the purpose.

> That this expense may be reduced to one-twentieth or to one-thirtieth, or rendered inconsiderable, by the use of water and self-acting means of removal by improved and cheaper sewers and drains.

> That refuse when thus held in suspension in water may be most cheaply and innoxiously conveyed to any distance out of towns, and also in the best form for productive use, and that the loss and injury by the pollution of natural streams may be avoided.

> That for all these purposes, as well as for domestic use, better supplies of water are absolutely necessary.

Figure 1.1 Sir Edwin Chadwick, James Simpson, James Leslie and J. Wignall Leather

That the expense of public drainage, of supplies of water laid on in houses, and of means of improved cleansing would be a pecuniary gain, by diminishing the existing charges attendant on sickness and premature mortality.

That for the protection of the labouring classes and of the ratepayers against inefficiency and waste in all new structural arrangements for the protection of the public health, and to ensure public confidence that the expenditure will be beneficial, securities should be taken that all new local public works are devised and conducted by responsible officers qualified by the possession of the science and skill of civil engineers.

That the oppressiveness and injustice of levies for the whole immediate outlay on such works upon persons who have only short interests in the benefits may be avoided by care in spreading the expense over periods coincident with the benefits.[6]

The effect which Chadwick's Report had on public opinion forced the Government to set up a Health of Towns Commission under the Duke of Buccleuch as Chairman and with Robert Stephenson and the distinguished canal and railway engineer W. (later Sir William) Cubitt, FRS as two of the thirteen members to explore the matter still further with a view to ultimate legislation. Chadwick acted as unofficial secretary to the Commission and dominated the proceedings.

One witness was Richard Kelsey, surveyor to the City Commission. He had a map of the sewers in his district but without levels shown on it, and he boasted that no-one except himself could tell which way the sewage flowed in the sewers. He declared that 'the maxim of the Commissioners is never to make any sewer so small as that a man cannot get into it easily', so that even in courts and alleys a sewer 3 ft by 2 ft 2 in., with brickwork 14 in. thick, was used. Sewers of this size, he admitted, presupposed accumulations. These brickwork caverns were rarely inspected or cleaned out and were sometimes put to strange uses, the beadle of one parish having been buried in a sewer.[7]

It was against this background of credulous ignorance and outdated tradition that Chadwick brought forward his own witnesses, one of whom was Dr Dyce Guthrie who, within a few years, became himself a fatality in the service of public health. In answer to one question Guthrie said:

The curved invert at the bottom of main sewers is indispensable to their perfect action and I admire most those which have the segment of a smaller circle at the bottom, that such an arrangement gives full action to the water at the time when it is most needed, viz. when the quantity is smallest. The shape I approve of is that in use in the Finsbury and Holborn commission.

In answer to another question he replied:

I am aware of the system of flushing in adoption in the Holborn and Finsbury district and I look upon this as a great improvement for I have had repeated opportunities of judging its beneficial effect but I hold every system of flushing to be imperfect which merely hurries along the contents of the principal or main sewers whilst the putrefying debris of inhabited tenements is left undisturbed in house drains.

He considered that the size of the latter ought to bear a direct proportion to the supply of water and suggested not more than 3–6 in. for an ordinary tenement.[8]

In the poorer urban districts water was either not supplied or only supplied intermittently from stand-pipes, and it was evidence such as that given by Guthrie which made Chadwick realize that to provide drains and sewers was not enough; there must also be a constant water supply available in every tenement.

Another witness was the Scottish pioneer, Robert Thom (1774–1847), who had designed for Greenock a combined scheme for both water power and town water supply, completed in 1827. In a preliminary report dated 1824 on this scheme, named Shaw's waterworks, Thom had written:

Here you would have no steam engines vomiting forth smoke and polluting the earth and air for miles around, but, on the contrary the pure 'stream of the mountain' flowing past in ceaseless profusion, carrying along with it freshness, health and vigour; whilst in its progress through the town, everything having a different tendency would be swept before it into that great reservoir of health and purifier of the elements – the ocean.[9]

Giving evidence on his water-supply system, Thom said:

In every case where the distributory basin can be placed high enough, the pipes in the streets ought to be kept constantly full so as to be always ready at a moment's notice to extinguish fires, and the distributory basin should be placed high enough to send the water over the top of the highest houses by merely putting the hose of a fire-engine on one of the fire-plugs which should be attached to the pipes at short distances through all the streets. The advantage is immense – and were it properly and generally practised, there would be little need for insurance from fire. Provision should also be made for cleaning the streets, lanes, sewers etc. by the water. When the cholera commenced at Greenock, the many dirty streets and lanes in the town were cleaned by a copious supply of water sent down from the Shaw's Water Aqueduct. Hence, in all probability, the few deaths which happened there, compared to those at Dundee, Dumfries, Musselburgh, and other places similarly low and dirty.

Asked whether his system was applicable to other towns he replied:

9

> By the gravitational system no additional expense is incurred; but where
> steam or other power is used to raise the water, the expense is very great.
> Hence the unwillingness of water companies, who have to maintain a
> mechanical power, to keep these pipes full at high pressure.[10]

The next two witnesses were Thomas Wicksteed, Engineer of the East London
Waterworks, and Thomas Hawksley, Engineer of the Trent Waterworks, Nottingham. Both engineers agreed that large masses of water could be raised comparatively cheaply by pumping, but the former raised many objections to the constant-
supply system whereas the latter supported it. Wicksteed argued that to supply
20 000 houses with ½ in. diameter lead pipes an aggregate area equal to $27\frac{1}{4}$ sq. ft.
requiring a 71 in. main would be required for constant supply, whereas only a 20 in.
main would be necessary for intermittent supply. Hawksley replied that this was
based on the false hypothesis of all the pipes discharging at the same time. Wicksteed also believed that if a separate supply was given to all the houses in a poor
district the lead piping would soon disappear. This had not happened at Nottingham, said Hawksley, and indeed water at high pressure acted as 'a police on the
pipe'.[11]

Thomas Cubitt, the builder, would have made illegal the renting of houses
without a water supply,[12] but the London Water Companies, represented by Wicksteed, were sufficiently strong to prevent the Commission from insisting on constant supply. Possibly, as Hawksley alleged, the London Water Companies kept
the population on short supply because only in that way could they spin out their
inadequate resources.[13] On the other hand the evils of intermittent supply were
clearly revealed in the Commission's reports. Water standing in uncovered
cisterns was badly polluted by dirt and refuse, and great inconvenience was caused
to those wanting clean water by the need to be on hand when the water did come
on, once in 24 or even 48 hours.[14]

Hawksley was asked his opinion on competition between private companies,
and he replied that it was usually injurious to both the shareholders and the general
public. He said:

> Two capitals became invested; two sources of wear and tear are created – two
> managements – and two complete sets of officers must be maintained; two
> causes of loss and leakage are established; for all which the public must and do
> ultimately pay as well as for the enormously expensive conflict to obtain the
> Act of Parliament, and for the rivalry and strife of several subsequent years. It
> may be mentioned that in some districts of London, three, four, or five
> companies have pipes, and are occupied in performing the service which
> might be quite as effectually rendered by one, and perhaps by that one, under
> proper supervision, at half the cost of the present supply. These companies

seldom continue in active competition for long periods. Finding the competition ruinous, they coalesce openly or enter into a private understanding, by which the public are deprived of the benefits of the supposed competition. The charges are either increased or remain fixed much above those at which a single company would willingly supply.[15]

Rather later in 1847 Chadwick was behind the scenes in securing a model Waterworks Clauses Act which limited the profits of a company to 10 per cent and ensured that it must comply with a reasonable demand for water, including a supply for cleansing sewers, watering streets and a constant supply of wholesome water for the inhabitants.

Liverpool was an example of a town supplied by two water companies with a private understanding between them that each had a monopoly in its own district to the prejudice of the public interest. One correspondent wrote:

> The complaints as to the scarcity of water . . . and also the price of that much needed commodity are both loud and general, but the companies . . . do not see fit to lower their price; and so long as *both* companies have a mutual understanding, they may advance the price, or make specific arrangements as favourable to themselves as they choose and I am not aware that anyone has redress. If you don't like the price, you need not take the water. But what are you to do? The supply of rainwater is so uncertain and so impregnated with soot that it is not fit to drink.[16]

The Corporation was concerned about the inability of the companies to deal with fires, and in 1847 they voted £100 000 to the Highways Board to make provision for this purpose. The Board appointed James Simpson, engineer to the Chelsea Water Company and then at the height of his career (see Chapter 5) as their engineer, and he proposed a scheme including a new well, a service reservoir and a steam engine for pumping water from the well to the reservoir; the head of water in the reservoir being used to keep a new and independent system of mains under full pressure for fire-fighting purposes.

Hawksley's evidence to the Health of Towns Commission on constant supply for both domestic and fire-fighting purposes had much impressed J. M. Whitty, the influential editor of the *Liverpool Post*, and he sent a copy of it to the Highways Board. As a result Simpson and three members of the Board visited Nottingham to see Hawksley's works there and the former wrote a report on the visit. The Board attempted to keep the report confidential but, goaded by Whitty,[17] they finally published it. On the extension of the constant supply to the inhabitants for all purposes, Simpson had written that it would be exorbitantly expensive and useless: 'what dependence can we place upon it? I answer, at once, little or none, because its

11

thousands of pipes and cocks in private places are not susceptible of hourly and im-mediate inspection and control.'[18] Whitty sent Hawksley an account published in his paper of a Board meeting at which it was claimed that the constant supply system was inapplicable for general use, to which Hawksley replied that what had been used successfully at Nottingham for 13 years could also be used at Liverpool.[19] Subsequently Whitty sent Chadwick and Hawksley a copy of Simpson's report which infuriated both of them.[20] Hawksley wrote a most intemperate attack on Simpson in the *Liverpool Post*, which the latter ignored and the controversy died down.[21] Simpson completed his water supply scheme for supplies for fire-fighting, watering streets, and other public purposes only.

As recorded elsewhere (Chapter 5, p. 78) Chadwick and Simpson met on neutral ground in February 1845 but they crossed swords at both Manchester and Sheffield. In a letter to Hawksley in May 1845, Chadwick wrote:

> The Mayor and Town Clerk of Salford came to tell me today that the Man-chester Waterworks Company had suddenly denounced the constant supply – had called upon Mr. Simpson who had stated to the Committee that it might do very well for a new district but that for an old district such as Manchester it would entail an additional expense of more than £100 000.[22]

In another letter 2 months later to Hawksley, Chadwick wrote: 'The Sheffield Waterworks bill was passed today. I was called upon to give evidence and did so, but it was unavailing in stopping it. The Committee took the practical evidence of Mr Simpson.'[23] Simpson, a professional engineer of the old school, and Chadwick remained antagonists.

From the evidence given before the Health of Towns Commission which in-cluded references to the value of sewage as manure, Chadwick developed his 'venous and arterial system' for towns which envisaged a constant water supply and the use of water closets in houses, the immediate discharge of both soil within the houses and refuse outside the houses into egg-shaped sewers, with the sewage flowing smoothly and rapidly to the fringes of towns to be there dispersed to manure the crops while the river from which the water supply was originally drawn remained pure and undiluted. Chadwick claimed that the many problems of public health would thereby be solved, and wrote: 'we complete the circle, and realise the Egyptian type of eternity by bringing as it were the serpent's tail into the serpent's mouth'.[24]

In 1851 Chadwick recommended that the nine water companies which shared the water supply of London should be bought out and consolidated under one ad-ministration serving the whole metropolis. The Government did not accept Chad-wick's recommendations but the Metropolitan Water Supply Act was passed through Parliament in 1852. Under this Bill, the companies were obliged to move the intakes from which they drew their water from the Thames to some place above Teddington weir (thus avoiding the daily agitation and re-agitation of the sewage of the capital by the tide) by 31 August, 1855; to filter all water intended for domestic use and cover all service reservoirs used for storing filtered water. The 1852 Act also stipulated that within 5 years a constant supply must be laid on by every company. It was not until 1899 – 3 years before the Companies were bought out and the Metropolitan Water Board was formed – that all Londoners were receiving the promised constant supply.

To observe the many factors affecting public health, and to draw conclusions from them, medical statistics were necessary. From 1838 these were brilliantly supplied by the Assistant Registrar General William Farr, FRS (1807–84) who raised the subject to a recognized science. In 1866 there was an outbreak of cholera in East London and Farr, studying the notifications of decease which came in daily to his office, was struck by the way in which the deaths were concentrated in a particular part of London. On 1 August, 1866 Farr published in *The Times*, along with the customary weekly return of mortality, an appeal for help for the sufferers of whom 1253 had already died; he also pointed out that the area attacked exactly coincided with that supplied by the East London Water Company. Wicksteed's successor, Greaves, replied in *The Times* that not a drop of unfiltered water had for several years past been supplied by the Company for any purpose, and flatly denied the accusation. However, a public enquiry, held after 6000 people had died, entirely vindicated Farr. The original intake on the river Lea had been superseded by a new intake further upstream. The open reservoirs at the old intake, however, still remained part of the domestic water distribution system and there was a direct connection between these reservoirs and the river Lea through a sluice which Greaves subsequently admitted was opened three times (in contravention of the 1852 Act) during 1865.[25]

The Health of Towns enquiry had revealed too many town councils completely oblivious of filth, with neither the desire nor the ability to introduce improvements. For his grand design of providing every town in Great Britain with the new arterial system, Chadwick despaired of using them as his instruments. On the assumption that profits could be made not only from water but also from manure, he therefore started sounding rich capitalists with a view to forming the first nationwide utility company. He received support from, among others, Sir John Easthorpe, the first Chairman of the London and Southampton Railway; Raikes Currie, the 'Nabob' who had brought an enormous fortune from India; Larpent, the millionaire; Morrison, the railway projector; Lewis Ricardo, nephew of the famous and wealthy David Ricardo.

In 1844 Thomas Hawksley was in partnership with a Mr Jalland. In June of that year Chadwick wrote to Hawksley inviting him to become one of the engineers of the Town Improvements Company, as it was called, and the subsequent fortunes of the company – also of their relations with each other – can be followed from the correspondence between them. Chadwick also mentioned in his letter that he was visiting Nottingham, and there is a letter from Hawksley signed 'Your very *eager* servant', expressing great disappointment at having missed him at Nottingham station, where he had gone at 8 a.m., and stating that he was very anxious to speak to him about the Towns Improvement Company, particularly as regards his remuneration.[26] From Chadwick's next letter it is evident that he called on Hawksley before leaving Nottingham and that the time already spent by Hawksley on giving evidence at the Health of Towns enquiry, apparently with little or no remuneration, was also discussed. Chadwick wrote:

> I shall be very much mistaken if in respect of the examination as to the water supplies your partner is not ultimately found to be wrong that the time has been misspent in a business point of view. I know you have no other motive than the public service but there is no reason that the evidence you give should be privately prejudicial. I shall be very happy to see you in town, the sooner the better. . . . Yours ever.[27]

Whilst no mention is made, in the letter, of any remuneration for services, Hawksley was astute enough to realize that he would make good business contacts and he agreed to become one of the engineers of the company. When and as the opportunity occurred, he also intended to promote his own private practice.

After giving evidence at the Health of Towns enquiry, Hawksley prepared a proof of his evidence and some statistics, which Chadwick received during June. Hawksley advocated infant mortality statistics to which Chadwick replied:

> Agreeing with you as to the very high value of the proposed returns of infant mortality, I think you go too far in recommending they should supersede all other returns. The public mind is in a barbarous condition in respect of infant mortality. It is really the least cared for and even thought well of. I think the returns of the adult mortality, in classes, in every way of the greatest importance. The public is not to be trusted to make inferences.[28]

He told Hawksley to leave out of his proof some 'laudatory epithet as regards myself'. Three days later Chadwick discussed corrections to Hawksley's proof and added 'Mr. Smith told me today that he has advised the people at Glasgow to consult you.' Smith of Deanston had proposed two alternative schemes for Glasgow's water supply[29] but neither was taken up; nor was Hawksley commissioned on this occasion.

The first report of the Health of Towns enquiry contained the evidence given by the medical and technical witnesses and the publication of this report in July 1844 had an immediate effect on Thomas Hawksley's reputation, raising him from the status of a little-known architect and surveyor, with some claim to also be an engineer, to that of an eminent engineer whose evidence was quoted as far afield as Bombay and Melbourne. The authorities responsible for water supply for Boston, Lincoln and Coventry soon approached him.

In July 1844 Chadwick wrote enthusiastically to Shaftesbury,[30] the Bishop of London and Lord Ebrington to draw their attention to the Health of Towns report just published and to some of the evidence given in it, in particular that given by Thomas Hawksley on water supply.[31]

In a letter to Dr Southwood Smith, also written in July, Chadwick declared:

> but in respect of that which is the key to all effective cleansing and sanitary operations, the supply of water, I think the evidence I have collected from Mr. Hawksley and others will revolutionise the whole of that branch of engineering, and place our towns on an entirely new footing. Until these conclusions had been established, I am convinced that the practice and position of the Water Companies formed an impenetrable barrier to all improvement.[32]

A statement made by Hawksley during the 1844 Health of Towns enquiry which has often been quoted is as follows:

> My own observations and inquiry convince me that the character and habits of a working family are more depressed and deteriorated by the defects of their habitations than by the greater pecuniary privations to which they are subject. The most cleanly and orderly female will invariably despond and relax her exertions under the influence of filth, damp and stench, and at length ceasing to make further effort, probably sink into a dirty, noisy, discontented, and perhaps gin-drinking drab – the wife of a man who has no comfort in his house, the parent of children whose home is the street or gaol. The moral and physical improvements certain to result from the introduction of water and water-closets into the houses of the working classes are far beyond the pecuniary advantages. . . .[33]

The most desperate conditions were found in the older towns where there was a greatly increased demand for labour but where there was no room for new cheap housing. The very poor had to live near their work but could not afford to pay high rents; the more precarious and wretched their employment, the more likely it was to be near the heart of the town, where the value of land was usually rising and the increase in commercial property was diminishing the space available for housing. At Nottingham this state of affairs was made even worse by the unwillingness of the freemen, who had rights deriving from feudal times, to allow the borough

15

fields surrounding the town to be enclosed. This had the effect of increasing competition for land inside the old town and preventing necessary improvements, including main drainage and sewerage, from being carried out.[34] The freemen's own poverty made them the more anxious to keep their grazing rights and the town became, in Hawksley's expressive pun, 'hide bound'.[35]

The Enclosure party, led by Hawksley, prepared a Bill for enclosing the Common land, and in February 1845 he arranged for 80 copies of the Bill to be sent by Hansard to Chadwick. He also wrote to Chadwick asking him to distribute the copies to influential persons including Shaftesbury and Sir Robert Peel. He added:

> You will hardly believe it, the Corporation of Nottingham are now actually seeking to throw out the Inclosure Bill because it contains clauses of sanitary regulation and provision etc. . . . The Corporation are tampering for Votes with a few of the 'Cowocracy' who style themselves the Freemans Rights Committee – an interest I am very sorry to say of the most ignorant corrupt and degraded kind – an interest which has been the curse of Nottingham as respects its Sanitary and Commercial prosperity for many years past. The gross political bribery and corruption of Nottingham obtains more from the debatable and obnoxious character of the Freemans rights and claims than any other cause – these debatable rights and claims the Corporation have always been anxious to keep alive as most excellent grounds for agitation at the proper periods. The result however has been a greater loss of life (by undue mortality) in 20 years than the entire loss of the British Army in killed and wounded at the Battle of Waterloo.[36]

The slum landlords, whose interest it was to maintain the *status quo*, were no doubt a powerful faction to contend with. At the 1844 Health of Towns enquiry, Hawksley said:

> It would be injurious to invest any local body with new powers of expenditure without the means of supervision and regulation by a competent superior authority to protect and promote the true interests of the community. It is impossible that common local authorities, subject to all local interests and influences, could conduct such an important business with any proper degree of efficiency, foresight and economy. There is already not only a mischievous division and petty hostility amongst local authorities, but strong and direct interest against improvements, to overlook which would be completely fatal to any plan of local remedies. In Nottingham, for instance, I had repeatedly heard the owners of the small houses in the most crowded, unhealthy and altogether worst conditioned districts, warmly object to the enclosure of the commonable or lammas lands, using such terms as these: 'If those lands are

enclosed and built upon, our houses will be emptied.' In other words, the working class of that town are compelled to submit to a positive diminution of life resulting from confinement in an unhealthy, uncomfortable and, in some respects demoralising situation for the supposed benefit of this class of proprietors, I say supposed, for a large amount of loss of rent as well as for an increased amount of local taxation falling on the owners and expended in relief is undoubtedly occasioned by the bad and crowded condition of the dwellings which the working class are thus under the necessity of occupying.[37]

In spite of the opposition of the freemen and the slum landlords, the Nottingham Inclosure Bill received the Royal Assent in 1846. At this time Hawksley and Chadwick were the best of friends but the former was later to become strongly opposed to centralized control.

Having had a request for advice from Berlin, Chadwick wrote in August to Hawksley: 'I am told I am a greater prophet in Germany than in England'[38] and enclosed with his letter for the latter's comments a draft prospectus for the proposed utility company which commenced as shown in Fig. 1.2.

So ambitious was Chadwick at this stage that the utility company was to be called 'The British, Colonial & Foreign Drainage, Water Supply & Towns Improvement Company' but when the company was finally registered the overseas references were dropped. Amongst the Provisional Directors, he included two of his lifelong friends: Dr Neil Arnot, who had rendered him such valuable assistance in his enquiries on public health; and the political economist, Nassau Senior. Another Provisional Director was the inventor of penny postage, Rowland Hill. Chadwick also included a team of technical consultants chosen by himself for their known sympathy for his advanced ideas in sanitary engineering: Hawksley, as already mentioned, and Chadwell Mylne for water supply; John Roe and Butler Williams for sewerage and drainage; and Smith of Deanston and Captain Vetch for sewage disposal. Chadwell Mylne was so heavily engaged on the Continent, in particular on a water supply for the city of Lyons, that the burden of giving advice on water supplies in Great Britain fell on Hawksley.

While the draft prospectus does not include Chadwick's name, in his letter to Hawksley he proposed himself as managing director.

Hawksley does not appear at this time to have made any comments on the draft prospectus. In September he wrote to Chadwick that Leicester was now ripe for waterworks and added: 'I do not like to stir myself unless you would oblige me by paving the way with a few letters to Mr. Hodson and others of your friends. Mr Paget and others strongly advise me to go and wish to accompany me but I am diffident on the subject.' Referring to the quarrel with Simpson he continued:

I think the Health of Towns Commission must crush Mr. Simpson and his

17

PROSPECTUS OF A PUBLIC COMPANY

TO BE CALLED

THE BRITISH, COLONIAL, & FOREIGN DRAINAGE, WATER SUPPLY, AND TOWNS IMPROVEMENT COMPANY.

Active Capital, £1,000,000.

To be extended as additional opportunities of beneficial Investment may be offered. In Shares of Fifty Pounds each.

Provisional Directors, *with power to add to their numbers.*

DR. N. ARNOTT.

JOHN CROSTHWAITE, ESQ., *of Liverpool.*

SIR JOHN EASTHOPE, BART. M.P.

LORD EBRINGTON.

RAIKES CURRIE, ESQ., M.P.

EARL FORTESCUE.

ROWLAND HILL, ESQ.

LIEUT.-COLONEL HUTCHINSON, F.R.S., *of the Bengal Engineers.*

SIR GEORGE H. DE LARPENT, BART.

JOHN MACGREGOR, ESQ.

JAMES MATHESON, ESQ., M.P.

JAMES MORRISON, ESQ., M.P.

CHARLES MORRISON, ESQ.

JOHN MOSS, ESQ., *of Liverpool.*

J. LEWIS RICARDO, ESQ., M.P.

NASSAU WILLIAM SENIOR, ESQ., *Master in Chancery.*

ROBERT AGLIONBY SLANEY, ESQ., *of Shrewsbury, one of Her Majesty's Commissioners for inquiring into the Health of Towns.*

Engineers.

JAMES SMITH, Esq., *of Deanston.*

CAPTAIN VETCH, *of the Royal Engineers.*

WILLIAM CHADWELL MYLNE, Esq., F.R.S., *Engineer to the New River Company.*

THOMAS HAWKSLEY, Esq., *Engineer to the Trent Water Works Company, and also to the Gas Company, Nottingham.*

J. ROE, Esq., Engineer to the Commissioners of Sewers for the Holborn and Finsbury division of the Metropolis.
BUTLER WILLIAMS, Esq., Civil Engineer, Late Professor of Geodesy to the College of Civil Engineers at Putney.
WILLIAM LINDLEY, Esq., Engineer for the Drainage Rebuilding, and Water Supply of Hamburgh.
HENRY AUSTIN, Esq., Architect and Engineer, Secretary to the Metropolitan Improvement Association.

Standing Counsel.—GEORGE COODE, Esq; and D. H. GAEL, Esq.

Solicitor.—SIR GEORGE STEPHEN, and B. W. HUTCHINSON, Esq.

Bankers.—MESSRS. CURRIE and CO., 22, Cornhill.

THE objects of the Company are, to supply water to towns; to effect their drainage and cleansing, and to apply their refuse to agricultural production; to supply gas, and carry out any connected or similar improvements, of towns either in the British empire or abroad, where adequate interest and security can be given for the capital invested.

The recent Government inquiries into the means of improving the health of the inhabitants of towns and populous districts, have established the facts, that the primary means are to be found in the adoption of improved systems of supplying water, especially in combination with improved modes of house and street drainage and public cleansing. The Commissioners, in their last report, set forth as two of their main recommendations, that the distributory apparatus for the supply of water within the houses,—that is to say, the extreme branches as well as the mains to which water supplies have heretofore been commonly limited by companies,—and the apparatus for house drainage, should, as far as practicable, be laid down and maintained under one establishment, for the sake of economy to the consumer as well as of more perfect efficiency. In the evidence collected by the Commissioners, it is shown, that if these improvements be properly carried out, they will, whilst yielding a fair return to the capitalists who undertake them, also effect reductions of existing money charges, as well as contribute in an eminent degree to the health, the personal comforts, and

Figure 1.2 Towns Improvement Company prospectus 1844

19

plans lest the fact of rejection of constant supply at Liverpool should prejudice the recommendations of the report. I believe a poke in the ribs from your pen would be annihilation to him! [He concluded] Pray present my apologies to Mrs. Chadwick for the many late hours I kept with you in Stanhope Street and believe me, My Dear Sir,

Yours most Obligedly[39]

Chadwick replied that he would send him an introduction to Mr Hodson in Leicester when he wished.[40] Unfortunately, in their final report the Health of Towns Commissioners did not come down firmly on the side of constant supply. Chadwick ignored the suggestion that he should make a direct attack on Simpson.

Having heard in October that Chadwick was not having much success in raising money for the Towns Improvement Company, Hawksley shrewdly enough wrote:

I am not of the opinion Northern & Western people afford you much effective assistance – they are all chiefly speculators and jobbers and therefore look at nothing but railways which offer far greater undercurrents to bulls and bears than your propositions. They do not and *will* not understand the proposed union of moral, social and pecuniary gains,[41]

Chadwick replied that Sir John Easthorpe had given his hearty concurrence and had declared his willingness to invest £50 000 or more in the Company.[42]

It was not long before others also thought on public utility lines, and Chadwick – writing in February 1845 – warned Hawksley that in the *Morning Chronicle* there was an advertisement announcing the formation of a British & Foreign Waterworks Company registered provisionally, capital £500 000 in 10 000 shares of £50 each, Thomas Wicksteed Engineer.... 'This must quicken our movements as to the formation of a Company.' Various people, including Sir John Easthorpe and Mr Currie, had agreed to meet Chadwick urgently and he asked Hawksley to let him have figures and business calculations with a provisional estimate of what would be wanted for Leicester, Lancaster and Bristol, the first places where he was trying to get work for the proposed company.[43] In his next letter Chadwick wrote that Lord Fortescue and his son, Lord Ebrington, were joining the company,[44] and in the next letter of significance from Chadwick to Hawksley, written in May, he referred to Bristol as follows:

I am afraid that the Mr. Morgan, the projector of the new Bristol Waterworks stands no chance of getting the money wanted there, that he is a man who has been bankrupt more than once and discreditably, and is such a person that the intended company could not act with, that his project will fail and must be opposed, and therefore you will most probably be required to oppose it, and ought not therefore now have anything to do with it.

In this same letter he also wrote:

> Mr. Tyrrel a very respected solicitor of great influence in Exeter . . . has consulted me on the drainage of that city; the application of the refuse: and the combination of the gas and water supply which he thinks may be most advantageously carried out by the proposed company. He wishes aid to prepare a scheme. I have chalked out a course for him one part of which is that you should very early visit Exeter, perhaps with Mr. Smith of Deanston, to take a view of the town and as much of the existing works as may be seen and prepare a report for the Company.[45]

Chadwick tried, apparently unsuccessfully, to arrange for Hawksley to meet Tyrell in his office. Seven weeks later Chadwick for the first time displayed some irritability in his correspondence with Hawksley and wrote:

> I received on Tuesday a letter dated Monday stating that you would write to me fully on that evening. Now neither yesterday Wednesday nor today Thursday have I received any full letter or any letter whatsoever. I mentioned to Mr. Smith that I expected to hear from you. He mentioned to me that he had written you and that you had promised to have breakfast with him but that you had neither come nor has he heard from you.

For the second Health of Towns report Hawksley had promised unwisely to supply tables for the discharge of sewers of different diameter and gradient which were long overdue, and referring to these tables Chadwick concluded: 'Now I beg of you in the most friendly way not to expose me as your friend to reproaches for being overtrustful or to derision when I say "Mr. Hawksley has promised." It is in many ways very inconvenient. I have delayed visiting to Bristol in the expectation of hearing from you.'[46]

To this letter Hawksley replied immediately, describing very distressing circumstances regarding the birth of a baby with a defective intestine and an unsuccessful operation on it: 'The poor child yet lingers on in hopeless misery agonising its mother and affecting me by its piteous cries.' He implied that he had already done a great deal for Chadwick, that he was too busy to do anything more for him at present and wrote: 'Lincoln and Boston and Coventry and Leicester must be attended to by a professional man even though the House of Parliament Commission may not have "for the love of God" all they could desire.'[47]

Although sympathizing with Hawksley on his domestic troubles, Chadwick was annoyed with him for giving priority to his fee-earning private practice over

21

outstanding unpaid work, in particular tables required urgently by the Government printer. He wrote:

> I have no doubt of the patriotic intentions with which you have given up your time to sanitary investigations and to your Nottingham enclosure act but whatever your intentions might be, and however great the present sacrifice may be, I have no doubt whatever, that you have made no ultimate sacrifice whatsoever, and that you have made a good and profitable business investment. And it is quite right and satisfactory that it should be so. It would have been perfectly justifiable had you come forward to vindicate your own claims to confidence. The evidence in the Sanitary report will secure you a leading and even European professional reputation. This will be extended further by your evidence on the Atmospheric Railway.[48] You must now confirm it by good conspicuous works to some of which I hope and indeed, I am confident, if you enable me to speak of you with perfect business confidence, I shall be enabled to put you in the way.[49]

In his next letter in July Chadwick wrote: 'I was glad to see your answers in the hands of Mr. Hobhouse [Secretary]. Whether used or not, it is important to be able to say that you have complied with your printed promise',[50] and he also refers to arrangements for himself, Smith and Hawksley to meet in Bristol from which it is evident that on both subjects Hawksley had responded quickly. The three men visited Bristol and this city continued to be the subject of correspondence between Chadwick and Hawksley until the beginning of November 1845 but, as recorded elsewhere, their potential clients, the Merchant Adventurers, were defeated in a Parliamentary contest by the Bristol Water Company and, with this defeat, all hopes of the Towns Improvement Company operating in Bristol were lost. No success was achieved with Exeter either.

Whilst this breach between Chadwick and Hawksley was temporarily healed, there were major differences of principle between them that were soon to come to the surface. For the time being, until the Towns Improvement Company was backed financially, Chadwick was unable to pay for Hawksley's services. Nevertheless he considered that for any potential client to which Hawksley had been introduced by Chadwick, he had first claim on Hawksley's services. Hawksley, on the other hand, held quite the opposite view and considered that he was free to accept commissions from anybody who was prepared to pay for his services.

Unless a proper sewerage system was also constructed the mere substitution of water closets for earth closets caused flooding of cesspools and the advantage of an improved water supply was offset by worsened sanitary conditions. For this and other reasons Chadwick insisted on combined systems of water supply and drainage; he regarded water as being not only a substance which one drank but also the motive force of his new arterial drainage system. Hawksley, on the other hand, was fully prepared to accept commissions for water supply only, with no regard as to the possible need for sewers.

Chadwick had written that he was unwilling 'to ask the gentlemen who have given their names as directors to put their hands in their pockets for money before the Company is constituted or before shares begin to be taken'[51] to which Hawksley replied: 'I am persuaded that you are not quite right in your views with respect to the company. *Money* is wanted before you can gather the required amount of information and must be found in this as in the preliminary stages of other undertakings.'[52] Two days later, on 7 August, 1845, the company was at last registered.

Chadwick had for some time been taking an interest in Lancaster and had already stayed there with his family. Early in August he had planned to make another visit to Lancaster, but because he could not get away he wrote to Hawksley asking him 'to run over to have a look at the town'. Later the same month Chadwick himself visited Lancaster and Preston, where he found to his dismay that Hawksley had been engaged by a lawyer acting on behalf of a group of speculators to assist in the setting up of a new waterworks company in competition with an existing one. Hawksley's letter is missing but it can be inferred that he wrote to Chadwick accusing him of going to Preston because he had learnt that he (Hawksley) had gained a commission there.

Chadwick's main object was the drainage of Preston and he replied:

> As respects Preston, I must set you right as to the facts. Your statement to me of your retainer there has nothing to do with me going there. . . . I never conceived that there would be room for new capital for the water supply. . . . You have communicated to me neither many nor any particulars that might not have been communicated to perfect strangers. . . .

After making some scathing remarks about the group with which Hawksley proposed to associate himself, Chadwick continued:

> I pray you to guard your judgement against being misled by the retainers and misrepresentations of such men. Public opinion is setting against the lawyer-craft which does this. Consider how . . . your advocacy of the new Company would square with your public examination and condemnation of the intrusion of second capitals in the same field? Why it were a scene which would rejoice the Simpsons and the Wicksteeds exceedingly, but at which I and your best friends must be sorely grieved. . . . Projects for carrying out singly and separately what appears to be the most promising of immediate profit, in the face of the evidence that such project ought not to be carried out separately seekless of future inconvenience, are hardly respectable and bespeak the mere

23

commonplace jobbers. [He concluded] Be firm to comprehensive and lasting principles, extricate yourself from the Preston attorney's hands and be of good cheer. Yours ever.[53]

No further mention of Preston is made in the correspondence.

Early in September 1845 Chadwick wrote to Hawksley to enquire when he could visit Lancaster and Clitheroe.[54] After meeting a deputation from Bolton who also wished to carry out improvements to the water supply, drainage and cleansing of their native town, Chadwick wrote again a few days later about Bolton and continued:

> Will you let me know as soon as possible how soon you can visit Bolton and make the examination required. . . . I shall assume you will be enabled to make imediate arrangements for going there, and have sent herein the plans alluded to . . . and would be glad if you would put yourself in communication with Mr. Winder the solicitor and inform him as well as myself. I will, as early as I can, send you further instructions.

In a postscript Chadwick added: 'If your engagements will not permit you to give immediate attention to the work pray return the plans by train'.[55] Indicating that in future he expected to be engaged directly and not through Chadwick, Hawksley replied: 'Obliged to return from Boston on pressing professional business but have heard nothing from Bolton, Clitheroe or Lancaster – I wrote to Bolton for an appointment. I have an order to *execute* the Coventry works *immediately*.'[56] On receiving this letter, Chadwick wrote:

> I hope that tomorrow's post may bring a less ambiguous and more satisfactory letter than the one I have received today from you. You told me that you would be ready after Tuesday or at all events in the middle of the week to go to Lancaster and Clitheroe and I have considered you engaged for these places and eventually for Bolton on the termination of your engagement with the so-called Lancashire Water Company. Both at Lancaster and Clitheroe I had led, upon your promises, parties interested to expect that they would be visited in the course of the week.[57]

Hawksley, who in one year had built up a thriving private practice, was no longer hungry for work and at the end of September he replied:

> I am sorry that an unexpected *detention* in Town should have prevented the receipt of your letter till last evening – this, however, is too common an occurrence with engineers who indeed can scarcely be said to have a habitat to excite your surprise.

With respect to the Towns you mention I assure you I do not consider myself *engaged*, as no responsible party has as yet communicated with me on the subject and time is now too precious to be expended on *uncertain* attempts to do even good. If you knew the half of the time and money I have wasted and lost by the acceptance of indefinite employments, you would I am fully persuaded coincide with me in thinking that I ought no longer to continue in the same course of professional negligence.

With respect to the formation of your company, I fear you are losing invaluable opportunities in the endeavour to obtain the sanction of a name – five days at the present time are worth five hundred five weeks hence as you will assuredly find, notwithstanding your anticipations to the contrary, when you attempt to proceed with any of your more important projects. You may also calculate upon a damp in the money market in consequence of a revulsion arising out of the rash speculation in Railways.

I am prepared on all sides to accept engagements of a profitable and reputable character and I have at the present time several works (besides projects) in operation and formation. I cannot therefore with any prudence keep myself any longer out of the field and I am sure you will on reflection be of the same opinion. – You may however fully rely upon my disposition to do all I can in conjunction with you provided I am for the future regularly and professionally employed.[58]

Whilst Hawksley was no longer the eager servant, and declined to become involved on a speculative basis in Lancaster, Clitheroe and Bolton, he continued on a somewhat ambiguous basis to serve Chadwick at Leicester.

Referring to Leicester, Chadwick wrote to his Chairman, Lord Francis Egerton, that 'an attorney is pushing for a water supply separately and in support of which he had unluckily retained our proposed engineer Hawksley who holds himself bound by his retainer'.[59] As a consequence, a curious situation arose in which Hawksley, whose name remained on the Towns Improvement Company's prospectus, was apparently acting both for the London company and for a Leicester group interested primarily in water supply. At a meeting in Leicester on 19 August, 1845, at which Hawksley was also present, Chadwick addressed the group and explained his proposals, as a result of which a resolution was passed that a Report setting forth the plan proposed by the Towns Improvement Company should be presented.

With the intention of making it serve as a precedent for other places, Chadwick put a great deal of time and effort into writing a full explanatory report which was printed and on which Hawksley commented:

The report proceeds upon the supposition that the London proprietary are to supersede the Leicester proprietary – whereas the undertaking at the meeting was this; that the Leicester proprietary were to form a Company and obtain an Act, accepting if they thought fit, upon a due consideration of Mr. Chadwick's report, the whole or any portion of the London proprietary as Joint Share-holders in the undertaking. I am fully convinced that the Leicester gentlemen have never contemplated that the Water Works would be taken out of their hands and have therefore no hesitation in recommending that the Report be corrected accordingly.[60]

In spite of Chadwick's reluctance to accept this advice, negotiations continued to a stage at which Parliamentary plans were being considered.

In September 1845 Chadwick wrote to the Company's banker, Raikes Currie, that the Leicester people threaten to go for water supply only 'if we are not ready with the money loan'[61] but a month later Chadwick was able to inform Hawksley that the London Committee members by individual subscriptions totalling £100 000 had agreed to take up two-thirds of the Leicester shares provided the other third were taken up at Leicester.[62]

In October Hawksley informed Chadwick: 'I have found a very suitable site for the supply of Leicester with excellent water from a natural head distant 9 miles – This will please.'[63]

One of the consequences of the railway mania was that practically all the survey-ors were engaged on railway plans and were demanding very high fees for their services. Hawksley reported great difficulties in the preparation of plans due to lack of surveyors,[64] and added:

> I have thought a great deal with reference to the Irrigation and am quite decided in the opinion that permissive powers only should be applied for – This will remove the proceedings from the 2nd to the 1st class bill list, save the risk of opposition, and enable us to dispense with elaborate and extensive plans of all the country adjacent to Leicester which we must otherwise deposit on the 30th November. I do not apprehend that compulsory powers are necessary but if difficulties should arise in carrying out the scheme, it may then be overcome by an Act to enlarge the powers of the former Act.[65]

Being suspicious as to Hawksley's intentions, Chadwick replied: 'All prudent measures for retaining ground I shall be the first to promote, as I should oppose anything that would give complete measures the go by.'[66]

Evidently the plans for a Parliamentary Bill were not completed by 30 November and the last letter on Leicester is one in January 1846 from Hawksley who writes to Chadwick: 'Permit me to express my opinion that any attempt to obtain the univer-sal powers now proposed would make the project most unpopular in Leicester and would be fatal in Parliament.'[67] Soon after the date of this letter negotiations broke down, and Chadwick took no further part in the affairs of Leicester. Hawksley became consulting engineer to the Leicester Water Company. Between 1852 and 1854 he planned and constructed the Thornton reservoir, and in 1868 he made large extensions called the Bradgate Works.[68]

During all this time that Chadwick was trying to get his Company airborne, railway speculation was going on. As Hawksley remarked, the return Chadwick was able to offer to speculators could not compare with the returns claimed by railway promoters, and this made it very difficult to persuade people to invest money in his company. In November 1844 Chadwick wrote from Manchester to Hawksley:

> I found all the leading people at Liverpool, to whom I had access . . . so full of
> railway arrangements, the Alliances in Treaty between the old companies,
> and the formation of new lines, the new Birkenhead Dock speculations in
> which they are deeply embarked, that the time appeared to be peculiarly un-
> favourable either for getting money or attention to new measures. . . . I
> returned last night to see what might be done in Manchester. There trade is at
> present so unusually active and so profitable that capital is about to be
> embarked in the extension of new mills. I cannot at present see much prospect
> of large adventures from hence. On the whole the best prospect seems to be
> with the unemployed capital in London to which I shall return on Sunday or
> Monday.[69]

Chadwick was no more successful in London. Almost a year later, whilst he was again in Manchester, he wrote to Hawksley: 'None of the people here express doubts of our getting whatsoever money we want in time – but the difficulty of getting attention during the railway mania is very great.'[70]

In November 1845 Chadwick wrote to Egerton that money was not coming in on account of the railway mania, that very few shares in the Towns Improvement Company had been applied for, and that another difficulty encountered in the money market was the impression that the Company was a philanthropic rather than a commercial one. 'This objection had been very early raised and one of our Capitalists had objected to *me* as tending to taint the list [of directors] with benevol- ence and philanthropy!'[71]

On Sunday 30 November, 1845, the last day that year on which railway plans for consideration in the next session of Parliament could be deposited at the Board of Trade, there were fantastic scenes.

> Riots between groups of rival speculators broke out in Preston and Mansfield;
> roads and railways leading to London were blocked with coaches and special
> trains as 800 groups of eager promoters joined the race to Whitehall. Robert
> Stephenson's office in Great George Street was described as resembling a

27

levee of a Minister of State as hordes of railway promoters endeavoured to obtain his blessing on their schemes. In vain would tempting bribes be offered, for the association of the name of Stephenson with any project was enough to set its shares at a premium.[72]

The publication of the Second Report of the Health of Towns Commission in 1845 also led to a stampede of a different sort. In that Report public control of water supplies at some future date was foreshadowed, and this led to groups of specu-lators who had formed embryo water companies and existing Water Companies rushing to grab the most eligible sources of supply for the towns. In 1846 the number of schemes for water supply and drainage before Parliament was 46 – twice the normal number – with Bristol, Manchester, Liverpool and Edinburgh each having two competing Water Bills. Chadwick was alarmed on two fronts: one being that just when legislation was under consideration for combining water supply on the constant supply system and drainage in every town, water companies of the old school with intermittent supplies would establish themselves in positions of advantage, thus presenting serious obstacles to the new principles; and the other being that if the Towns Improvement Company was denied control of the water supply it would lose 'the commercial force, which is so salutary in over-coming the vis inertiae of the towns themselves'.[73] Investors knew there were divi-dends in water but they were not so easily persuaded that this was also the case with drainage.

After Chadwick received notice from Hawksley at the end of September that his services were no longer available on a speculative basis for new work, the close re-lationship between them ceased. Chadwick did not complain and they might have remained friends if, at this critical junction in Chadwick's affairs, Hawksley had not tried to persuade Chadwick to bring about an amalgamation of the Towns Im-provement Company with one of his own clients. Like Andrew Undershaft, who considered that the true faith of an armourer was 'To give arms to all men who offer an honest price for them without respect of persons or principles,'[74] Hawksley allowed anyone to engage him who would pay him a fee; this led to a serious rift between him and Chadwick.

In October 1845 Hawksley wrote to Chadwick:

> I have been to Bolton, Manchester etc., and have made a minute survey and estimate in relation to the really magnificent project of the Lancashire Water-works Company. The whole scheme is such as I can entirely commend – The water is most abundant and beautifully soft, the elevation very great so that the supply can be afforded to Manchester & Salford above the upper floors of the highest buildings – an extensive reservoir already exists and the facilities for filtration are almost unequalled. Moreover the difficulties with the Mill

Owners will be few and the Compensations taking all circumstances into account moderate.

As Hawksley was employed by the millowners themselves, it is not surprising that difficulties with them were few! Hawksley continued:

> Now this being the case do you not think it would be advisable for the London Company to try to effect an amalgamation with the Lancashire Company . . . and that too without loss of time especially as the surveys are going on and the notices must be very shortly given. I think so and should be most happy to contribute my aid but you must, of course, consider this suggestion as quite confidential and as arising entirely out of my own position with respect to yourself and the London Company. . . . You have not a moment to lose.[75]

There was an existing water supply company in Manchester and, as Hawksley well knew, Chadwick was in the middle of negotiations for this company to be purchased by the Towns Improvement Company. One can only surmise at Hawksley's motives in making this proposal but he was probably afraid that, unless he could get Chadwick's support, the chances of the Lancashire Water Company getting their Bill would be small.

The proposal cannot have appealed to Chadwick because it embraced only water supply and did not include drainage; it departed as regards Manchester from one of his principles, in introducing a second rival water company where one already existed; and he was suspicious of the motives of the promoters. Probably hoping to persuade the Lancashire Water Company to also undertake drainage, however, he temporized, and Hawksley in his next letter wrote that, as Chadwick wished, he had told the Lancashire Water Company that the London Company were ready to amalgamate with them. He added:

> I have ventured to suggest that they should place themselves in official communication with the London Company without loss of time. You will find them to be keen sensible and active minded men, well looked up to and wealthy withal and influential. They are moreover men who will see their way clearly before they embark in a speculation. I therefore recommend you not to complicate the water supply *in this instance* with sewage (which the London Company may if it pleases take up on its own account under a separate bill) but rather accomplish the improvement of the Water supply of Manchester before anything further is proposed. You will also find it desirable to offer liberal terms in relation to the local Management and direction.[76]

Chadwick in reply referred to a recent meeting of the committee of the Towns Improvement Company and wrote:

> I was not in a position to bring the subject of the amalgamation . . . before the Committee. You have not supplied me with a single figure on which men of business could act . . . what extreme nonsense it is to talk of an *immediate* decision to join, we know not what upon, a loose dictum. . . . This hurrying and grabbing of water sources must not be allowed, it is most improvident and unbusinesslike and mark me, it will not succeed.[77]

Chadwick was already suffering from the great disappointment of no longer being able to employ Hawksley except on a basis for which he had no funds, and he must now have come to the conclusion that Hawksley lacked firm principles. This appears to have been the last personal letter that he wrote to him.

In a letter to Chadwick's secretary, Holland, written in February 1846, Hawksley attempted to gain a reconciliation and wrote in conclusion: 'allow me to assure you that I have the highest opinion of Mr. Chadwick whom indeed I regard as one of the most eminent men of the day and I therefore much regret . . . our views should be so dissimilar.'[78] No reconciliation took place.

The Manchester Corporation, which later sponsored the successful and cheaper Longdendale scheme for Manchester and Salford's water supply, opposed the Lancashire Water Company and the latter abandoned their Bill. Bateman's comments written in 1884 on Hawksley's scheme were:

> The quantity of water which the Company would have been able to bring to Manchester would not have exceeded six or seven million gallons a day, and the lowest price at which it could have been sold there would have been 2½d per 1,000 gallons, or about £22 000 per annum for six millions daily – an excessive price compared with what it would have been obtained for elsewhere. The quantity was not sufficient for the two boroughs of Manchester & Salford; and what the rest of Lancashire, with its million of inhabitants, must have done for its share of the supply from the 'Lancashire Waterworks', it would have been difficult to say.[79]

At the end of 1845 five competent engineering reports remained the extent of the Towns Improvement Company's achievements. In January 1846 Chadwick wrote to Egerton: 'The Money panic has revived. Our solicitors fear that the political storms will prevent attention being given to any private business this session.'[80] A year later he wrote: 'The Railway demands for money and other causes of pressure on the money market continue to defer our prospects of meeting demands for assistance from the Company',[81] and finally 3 years later, having abandoned the enterprise, he wrote: 'The expositions promulgated by the Towns Improvement Company did great good in paving the way and it is much to be regretted that the money market has never so recovered as to enable it to be carried forward. It is now greatly wanted.'[82]

30

2   The rise and fall of the Board of Health

In 1847 Lord Morpeth, an ally of Chadwick, introduced a Bill which would have required town councils and town commissioners to supply water to every house, and either to construct the necessary waterworks or to make contracts with water companies (Fig. 2.1). Drainage, sewerage and street paving were also to be undertaken. The Act which in 1848 finally reached the Statute Book hardly fulfilled Morpeth's hopes but it established a Central Board of Health with permissive powers (except in extreme cases). The members of the Central Board were Morpeth, who was also a junior Minister in the Government, Shaftesbury, Chadwick and later Southwood Smith as a medical commissioner.

The Central Board employed inspectors, and for the cost of a survey undertaken by an inspector a district could obtain all the powers for which a costly local Act would otherwise be required. Through its engineering inspectors the Board achieved valuable results. These inspectors were chosen by Chadwick and were informed that the principles already established for future operations 'will render inapplicable much of the experience that has been formed in the execution of existing works of house, street and land drainage, water supply and general cleansing'. Applicants were required to submit a paper on how they would remedy the defective drainage of some imaginary town. In this way Chadwick built up a team of adherents to tubular glazed pipes, constant water supply and arterial drainage. His inspectors included Robert Rawlinson, the subject of Chapter 10; William Ranger, a former lecturer at the College of Civil Engineering at Putney, who had gained experience in the Fens and on Pevensey level; and William Lee, whose antecedents are not known. Chadwick chose Henry Austin, another engineer and a brother-in-law of Dickens, as the Secretary. The inspectors were all of them possessed of enthusiasm for the new principles of public health engineering, and they were often the first to give serious competent consideration to the framing of comprehensive schemes for water supply, sewerage and drainage.

The inspector could be summoned by a petition signed by one-tenth of the ratepayers; alternatively the Board could hold an enquiry into the sanitary condition of any place if the death-rate exceeded 23 per 1000 without the consent of the inhabitants but, in practice, the Board did not use this authority unless they were assured of substantial local co-operation, and in most cases a local Board was formed. The Board exercised considerable tact and withdrew with admirable caution when the opposition seemed predominant.

For those places applying to the Board for help, and which were visited by an inspector, under a set of written instructions made by Chadwick the inspector was required to consider:

(1) how water, pure and wholesome, from springs or rivers or upland gathering grounds, could be brought to the population;
(2) how it could be carried away again after use bearing human wastes with it; and
(3) how the products of the sewers could be utilized to manure the neighbouring farmland.

As regards the third item, land treatment of sewage, which was practical for small communities (and was the only form of sewage disposal known at that time which is still recognized under favourable circumstances as a possible form of treatment today), was very beneficial in preventing or reducing the pollution of streams and rivers. It is questionable, however, whether the sewage was of much value as manure. Peruvian guana, some six to ten times as concentrated as liquid sewage manure, was soon to be imported on a vast scale and J. B. Lawes was starting to manufacture superphosphates, and in due course other artificial manures, devised for specific crops. Between them these developments reduced the value of sewage manure to a negligible quantity.

The Central Board of Health sanctioned mortgages to the extent of about one million pounds and its achievements by the end of 1853 can be summarized as follows:

Number of requests for intervention received	284 towns
Number examined and reported on by inspectors	243 towns
Number brought under 1848 Health Act	182 towns
Number in which surveys were completed or in progress	126 towns
Number with completed new combined water supply, sewerage and drainage schemes	13 towns
Number with approved plans for new combined water supply, sewerage and drainage schemes	18 towns
Number with approved plans for new sewers, for water supply extensions or other improvements contemplated under the Act	39 towns

Towns with a total population of about 2 million, including Gloucester, Salisbury,

SANATORY MEASURES.

LORD MORPETH THROWING PEARLS BEFORE ———— ALDERMEN.

Figure 2.1   Introduction of the Public Health Bill by Lord Morpeth (*Punch*, 3 June, 1848)

Ely, Dover, Preston, Lancaster, Penzance, Wigan and Chelmsford with approved plans, and Rugby, Tottenham, Alnwick, Morpeth, Hitchin, Ormskirk, Barnard Castle, Ottery St Mary, Ashby-de-la-Zouche, Launceston, Croydon and St Thomas's Exeter, with completed works in operation, had been brought under the Act. Of the latter, only the works at Croydon were not working satisfactorily. Seven or eight of the larger towns such as Manchester, Liverpool, Leeds, Birkenhead, Nottingham and Newcastle, obtained their own Parliamentary Acts and did not come under the General Board of Health.

Very different were Chadwick's relations with the senior members of the engineering profession. In the 1840s their main interest was railways but, though of lesser importance as it seemed to them, they were quite prepared to give weighty opinions on water supply, sewerage and drainage.

The most versatile of them all was the great Brunel who achieved fame in

33

railways, tunnels, bridges and ships but whose ideas on town drainage were, curiously enough, very conservative and weak. When he, William Cubitt (not to be confused with the builder, Thomas Cubitt) and J. Walker were asked for advice by the Corporation of the City of London, they wrote:

> On the subject of the shape of the sewers, our own observation from the specimens we have seen, confirmed by that of our assistants, leads us to conclude, that the particular shape has very little indeed to do with the clearing away of the deposit; certainly very much less than is supposed or alleged by the respective advocates of the several shapes proposed. We think, that the clearing is regulated in a small degree by the size; but more by the positive quantity of water, and the inclination of the drain. But although in strict theory the velocity of a given quantity of water running in the bottom of a sewer of the same height, width, and elevation, will be greater in the narrow-bottomed or egg-shaped than in the circular, it does not follow as a necessary consequence, that this greater velocity or greater depth of water will more effectually carry with it grit and sand that collect in the bottom. Practically the wear of the flatter sewer will be more uniform – and as we have observed, experience has proved the flatter shape has advantages. So much are we impressed with this opinion, that in place of advising an invert more pointed and contracted than the semicircle, we should recommend the trial of a flat bottom of stone or other hard material, 14 inches broad, for a sewer of 3 feet in width at the springing of the arch, and 5 feet high, as more likely to keep itself clear, less subject to unequal wear, and certainly very much more convenient for being cleansed.
>
> That the form of sewers has practically very little to do with the general question of their keeping clear of deposit, this depending very much upon their fall and the quantity of water; but that no fall or quantity of water is likely to be obtained, even in the city sewers, sufficient to keep them clear of obstructions, without the occasional aid of men in the sewer to remove hard deposit.[1]

In their conclusions they wrote:

> To remove and abolish all cesspools is a recommendation which, as applicable to all present houses, we believe to be impracticable without enormous expense, and to an extent of interference with private property that would hardly be submitted to, and at the same time, we believe that such a general disturbance of the substances to be removed would be unnecessary and often highly dangerous.[2]

Chadwick pointed out that in the First Report of the Health of Towns Commission William Cubitt was one of the commissioners who, in 1844, had signed a statement in approval of the testimony of medical witnesses which said:

The report has brought before us facts in support of their strongly urged and unanimous opinion that no population can be healthy which lives amidst cess-pools. . . . They state the necessity of preventing all accumulations of stag-nant refuse in or near houses, and of substituting a system of house-drainage and cleansing aided by the introduction of better supplies of water into the houses.[3]

Consistency was evidently not one of Cubitt's virtues!

The progressive stages in the drainage of courts in the Tower Hamlets District, shown on Fig. 2.2, illustrates the advantages in economy of Chadwick's rational approach compared with the extravagant and unsalubrious systems of the time. As was to be expected, however, there were teething troubles in introducing the new

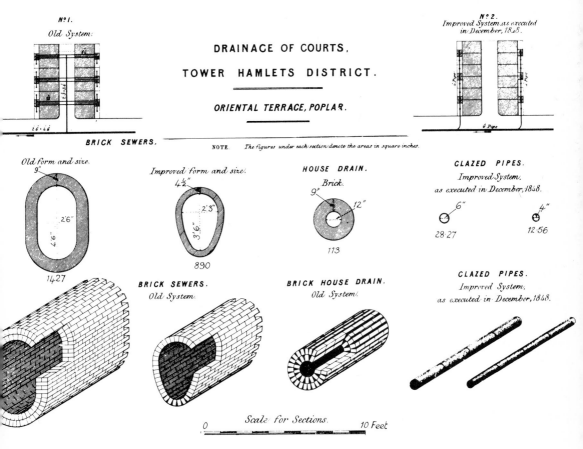

Figure 2.2   Drainage of courts – Tower Hamlets district 1844

35

self-cleansing system and William Cubitt, J. M. Rendel and Robert Stephenson, the three engineer members of the Metropolitan Commission of Sewers, together with a protegé of Brunel, John (later Sir John) Bazalgette, who became the Commission's Superintending Engineer, were quick to seize upon them. There was what to modern eyes seems a most extraordinary opposition to the new system, and the dispute was allowed to develop into one of prestige instead of economic values. Rendel was heard to refer to Chadwick's ideas as 'Sanitary Humbug' and to declare that it was quite sufficient for the Commissioners to carry sewers down the main streets leaving the owners to drain into them or not as they thought fit.[4] 'As to pipes he would not touch one' Stephenson declared. 'He hated the very name of them, and felt inclined never to mention the word again.'[5]

Bazalgette proposed to spend £2 million on laying down 1000 miles of brick sewers when for one-third of this amount self-cleansing pipes could be installed. Whilst Bazalgette was to redeem his reputation years later by designing and constructing the first effective main drainage system for London, completed in 1874, it has to be recorded with regret that the evidence he gave in 1852–54 against glazed pipe sewers was biased and distorted. Chadwick summed up the situation as follows:

> Observations of the laws of moving waters, or the condition under which water in slow motion deposits matter in suspension, or, with increased motion, lifts and removes first fine sand, then, with accelerated motion, coarser sand, then pebbles, then large stones, and lastly boulders and vast masses, and consideration of the inclinations by which velocities might be regulated, should have prevented such noxious as well as expensive errors as are displayed in the sewerage arrangements for the relief of towns. Much of the practice of those engineers who have given evidence in favour of large sewers of deposit ought to have taught them better. Where, to cleanse a harbour, dock, or basin, the scouring power of water is resorted to, sand, mud, solidified, and shingle are carried out by a narrow and confined jet of water being gradually brought to bear upon the broad accumulation. But, it has been noticed that Mr. Rendel proposed to preserve deep water up to the gates of the Birkenhead Dock, by letting out a thin sheet of water, at a depth of 20 ft. over the whole area of the entrance, which would give one uniform and continuous scour out into deep water in the river. The practice of intermittent scouring may have led these engineers away from the consideration of the continued action so necessary in sewers and drains, and so easily attainable where the outlet is free.[6]

There were two sets of tables extant for the discharging capacity of sewers; one prepared by Thomas Hawksley for the Health of Towns Commission, to which reference has already been made, and the other by John Roe, the surveyor of the Finsbury Sewers Commission. Both tables showed that the existing sewers and drains were far too large in spite of the tradition behind them, but Hawksley's tables proposed larger sewers than Roe's. Hawksley received a letter written on behalf of Chadwick raising some questions about his tables, to which Hawksley, being still anxious to make his peace with Chadwick, replied offering to call on Chadwick and to explain to him personally the principles on which his tables were based.[7] This offer was probably ignored and, being always biased towards the more economical solution, Chadwick came down in favour of Roe's tables.

That Chadwick in reaching towards the twentieth-century would step on many corns was inevitable; that he should also stamp on them is regrettable. In an official Government report published in 1850, he opened hostilities with his former colleague by writing:

> Calculations for the capacity of sewers where they have been made at all have proceeded on the assumption that it is necessary to provide under all circumstances and in all positions for the contingency of rain floods almost incredible. Mr. Hawksley's tables are estimated for the enormous fall of 2 ins. depth of rain in an hour . . . it requires merely a glance at the streets of a town built on sloping ground, like Liverpool, during even a moderate heavy rain, to be convinced that a greater part of the rain drained directly by the surface of the street into the river and never enters the sewers.[8]

From that time onwards Hawksley, whose fury was like that of a woman scorned, became Chadwick's most bitter enemy. 'Heav'n hath no rage like love to hatred turn'd'.[9]

The powers of the Central Board of Health in relation to those local authorities applying under the 1848 Act have already been described, initially the application of the Act worked well but there was a growing body of opposition to the overriding control of the Central Board. For example, in November 1850 the *Sheffield & Rotherham Independent* published an attack on centralization and Government control with the Board of Health as its principal target, and referred in laudatory terms to the proposal of a Mr H. M. Griffiths of Birmingham calling for funds to combat the Acts of Parliament which it was feared the Board would promote to extend their powers.[10]

In the matter of engineering practice the Central Board could and did exert very real influence. The local Boards were made to submit their plans and estimates in the greatest detail to a Superintendent Inspector, and a loan was not sanctioned until he had certified them. This was intended by Chadwick to ensure that the new principles would be applied with economy in expenditure. 'No one was to be clean except with Chadwick's patent soap.'[11] It was not surprising, therefore, that many Boards concluded that the quickest way to get the Central Board's sanction was to approach the Board's engineers themselves. The Inspectors were paid by the day and were free, once they had completed an engagement for the Board, to undertake private commissions.

After an examination of plans prepared by Hawksley for the improvement of Durham, Lee, in his capacity as one of the Board's inspectors, reported that he could not see why works estimated by Hawksley to cost £6000 could not be done for £4300. May, who was in partnership with Hawksley, wrote to enquire by what authority the Board required engineers to submit details of their plans and estimates to other engineers, perhaps much their junior, who were their direct competitors, a practice 'subversive of honourable competition and degrading in its character, as creating a repugnance in the mind of those best able to serve the public to such supervision'.[12] Chadwick, recollecting that Hawksley had recently argued before a Parliamentary Committee that water supply and drainage should not be united under one body ('In the one case it is a supply of . . . goods . . . and in the other simply removal of a nuisance!'[13]) replied to May that, despite his experience as a waterworks engineer, Hawksley had never drained a town in his life and had always maintained that drainage was a separate branch of practice, with the consequence that 'the junior inspector has had far more practice in town drainage but more particularly improved *town* drainage than you both put together or any one of the engineers the most eminent you have named'.[14] Until there were a sufficient number of completed examples of arterial drainage on the new principles, Chadwick regarded the competition of his engineering inspectors with the professional engineers as being essential, and he wrote to the Dean of Durham that 'All this means as it seems that Mr Hawksley objects to any examination of his plans or to such examinations only as he likes or by whom he likes. . . . I do not understand how professional engineers could get on if they are never to act, except when they are clear of rivalry.'[15]

During one of his attendances before a Select Committee of the House of Commons, Hawksley made various complaints against Chadwick, and allegations against one of the inspectors named Ranger, which he was asked to put in writing and he published them in April 1853 as a pamphlet.[16] After describing the powers which, in his opinion, had been wrongfully given to the Board he wrote:

> Works cannot, however, be executed without funds, an application to the General Board, therefore, becomes necessary and is made. The General Board, however, instead of limiting its inquiry, as is done by the Treasury and other departments of Government, to the necessity of the work upon which the money is proposed to be expended and the consequent general propriety of such expenditure, demands plans, surveys, detailed estimates, and other minute details of the work itself. Having obtained these they are placed in the hands of some one of the Board's Superintending Inspectors, to inquire, to

examine, and report upon. But it so happens that Mr. Chadwick (who in fact, though not in law, is the Board) entertains most peculiar views in favour of diminutive 'tubular pipe drains', 'combined back drainage', 'impermeable sewers', 'drainage water supplies', 'soil pans fed direct from water mains', 'distribution of sewage water by pumping over adjacent lands', 'large scale surveys' etc., in not one of which he is countenanced by the most eminent and most practical men of the profession.

'Combined back drainage' was a system whereby the house drains were taken from the back of the house (where the water closet was situated) and led into a branch sewer immediately behind the back of the house, this branch sewer being common to all the houses in the row (Fig. 2.2). This was very much cheaper than the earlier system which gave each house a separate drain but led it from the water closet all the way under the house, from back to front, to the middle of the street where it discharged into a large brick sewer.

It is surprising that Hawksley included 'large scale surveys' among Chadwick's peculiarities as he had frequently complained of their absence when working for the Towns Improvement Company and none knew better than him how essential they were to any sound engineering plans. Probably he was referring in particular to the large scale survey which Chadwick had ordered from the Board of Ordnance for London which caused a lot of prejudiced and ill-informed controversy at the time but which Bazalgette was subsequently able to use as the basis for his main drainage scheme for the metropolis.

That Hawksley could regard as Chadwick's eccentricities all those matters (with the exception of drainage water supplies and distribution of sewage water over land when attempted on too large a scale) which one could describe as being his successful achievements shows how much his judgement was warped by his intense hatred of Chadwick.

Hawksley continued:

> And it further happens that the five Inspectors selected by the Board not only do adopt Mr. Chadwick's peculiar views, but are also permitted, and by Mr. Chadwick directly encouraged, to obtain from Local Boards, as private engineers and for their own emolument, the execution of as many as possible of the works proposed by local authorities. . . . The result of the operation of this system has been most mischievous. The grossest jobbing prevails. Difficulties are thrown in the way of improvement. One system of construction, and that undoubtedly of a most erroneous and even pernicious character, is insisted upon, and must be extended over the whole kingdom. Able professional men are wrongfully injured, both in reputation and pocket, for the gain of the Government Inspectors. Confidence in the integrity of public men is utterly

destroyed. Provincial towns are deprived of the advantages of self-government, and the hitherto supposed supremacy of Parliament, absolutely negatived.

After complaining about the way in which Lee had conducted the inquiry at Durham, he went on to make very serious allegations against Ranger whom he accused of having reproduced word for word, as his own work at Barnard Castle and Southampton, specifications obtained from an examination of Hawksley's plans for the Darlington waterworks. He added: 'In the case of Croydon, Mr. Ranger rejected two plans successively submitted, and immediately accepted the appointment of an engineer to the Local Board. In the case of Coventry, where I acted for the Corporation, Mr. Ranger, who inspected, also became the engineer!'

Hawksley also alleged that Chadwick had suggested that inspectors should supersede Hawksley himself at Leamington and Rendel at Great Grimsby and he had objected personally to the employment of Wicksteed by the Leicester Local Board. Hawksley concluded:

> And in the whole there were, as early as February of the present year, no fewer than 44 cases (as appears by an admission of Mr. Chadwick) in which public Inspectors in the pay of Government had become private engineers in reference to works over which the General Board assume an irregular and certainly unauthorised control.

For the reasons already explained, Chadwick had, in fact, encouraged the inspectors to accept these commissions but by the middle of 1853 a number of examples of the new works were in operation and Chadwick agreed that the time had come for them to be full-time employees on an annual salary. This protected them from the suspicion that self-interest dictated their attitude to the drainage schemes they examined, and relieved them of the invidious duty of passing judgement on the plans of professional rivals. It also set them free to devote all their time and abilities to their public functions.

In 1852 the Central Board issued its 'Minutes on House Drainage' as a manual for local boards, being a developed account of the arterial system, which received the most vehement opposition from engineers in private practice. 'Their experiments so indifferent, results so anomalous and conclusions so worthless had been republished after they were known to be worthless', screamed Hawksley.[17] The Minutes were so bitterly attacked because they demonstrated to local authorities the cheapness of the new system whereby a town could be sewered and drained at one-third of the former cost. A long argument followed, but with more than 1000 miles of pipes laid in 1854 it became 'as useless to persuade the public that pipe sewerage was a failure as to make a Manchester man believe that calico was an unfit article for clothing'.[18]

Unfortunately after succeeding his father (as Lord Carlisle) in 1850 Morpeth left active politics. His successor Lord George Seymour seems, with the encouragement of the Treasury, to have actively thwarted the Board of which he was a member and, although its activities and achievements were welcomed during the great cholera epidemic of 1848, its unpopularity with vested interests grew.

During 1852, Shaftesbury was confiding to his diary:

> *The Times* has taken up the note of the undertakers, the water companies, the Parliamentary agents and the whole tribe of jobbers who live on the misery of mankind and are hunting the Board of Health through brake and briar and to be 'in at the death'! Be it so. If we fail not a body will be left to shout 'unclean, unclean' and form and guide and impel public opinion. Matters will become worse and worse. I tremble for the issue. . . . The Board of Health is to be destroyed; its sin is its unpardonable activity. . . . And will this endeavour be blest at last or will our enemies succeed in destroying the only institution that stands for the physical and social improvement of the people? Our foes are numerous and I dread their success; it will vex me beyond expression to see Chadwick and Southwood Smith given the right-about, and the Board which, under God, has done and has conceived so many good things broken up.[19]

The 'unpardonable activity' of the Board brought it into unavoidable collision with a wide range of powerful interests which Shaftesbury listed in his diary as follows:

> The parliamentary agents are our sworn enemies because we have reduced expenses and consequently their fees within reasonable limits. The civil engineers also because we have selected able men who have carried into effect new principles and at a less salary. The College of Physicians and all its dependencies because of our independent action and singular success in dealing with the cholera when we maintained and proved that many a Poor Law medical officer knew more than all the flash and fashionable doctors of London.
>
> All the Board of Guardians: for we exposed their selfishness, their cruelty, their reluctance to meet and to relieve the suffering poor, in the days of the epidemic.
>
> The Treasury besides; (for the Subalterns there hated Chadwick; it was an ancient grudge and paid when occasion served.)
>
> Then came the Water Companies whom we laid bare and devised a method of supply which altogether superseded them. The Commissioners of Sewers for our plans and principles were the reverse of theirs; they hated us with a perfect hatred.[20]

Almost needless to say, amongst the civil engineers who lobbied against the

Board and took a very active part in bringing about its fall was Thomas Hawksley. A society calling itself the 'Private Enterprise Society' of which the chief working members were Hawksley and Simpson, put out pamphlets of the most vehement kind with titles such as 'The privileges of Parliament endangered and the Rights of the People violated'. So successful was Hawksley in propagating this distorted propaganda that even 40 years later he was praised for his part in bringing down the Board, as follows: 'He opposed very strongly certain views and plans put forward by a public body called the General Board of Health, and exposed with great force the fallacies they were promulgating and the mischief they would do. In April 1853 he addressed a letter to the Marquis of Chandos on this subject.'[21]

In 1854 Shaftesbury, Chadwick and Southwood Smith were all forced to resign, and at a farewell dinner Shaftesbury, quoting from St Paul's Second Epistle to the Corinthians, gave his colleagues a final benediction; 'We are troubled on every side, yet not distressed; we are perplexed, but not in despair; persecuted but not forsaken; cast down but not destroyed.'[22]

After these resignations of the first Commissioners, the Board itself only lasted a few more years. Its work was farmed out among other government departments until 1871 when it was reborn as the Local Government Board, the ancestor of the Ministry of Health. What Chadwick struggled for, and what Hawksley fought against so bitterly, has now come to pass. Today it is accepted as a matter of course that central government working through local government is responsible for Public Health.

After Chadwick was forced to resign in 1854, he never again held public office though he lived on writing and arguing for his ideas for another 36 years. He had been made a CB at the Prince Consort's instigation in 1848; he was made a knight only the year before he died in 1890. Being a man of very strong principles and great strength of character, he was staunch enough to be able to face up to much opposition and ridicule. He was a poor public speaker and, to many of his acquaintances, he was a bore. As one who knew him said '. . . he babbled too much not of green fields, but of sewage. I remember Lord Farrar when president [of the Political Economy Club] calling Mr Chadwick to order and in tones of thunder saying, "the subject is taxation not drainage".'[23] Nevertheless he was held in very high esteem by a close circle of friends. John Stuart Mill said of him:

> I may say in brief that he is one of the contriving and organising minds of the age; a class of mind of which there are very few and still fewer who apply those qualities to the practical business of government. He is, however, one of the few men I have known who have a passion for the public good; and nearly the whole of his time is devoted to it in one way or another.[24]

The Nation owes an immense debt to him.

42

The Leathers and the Leeds Water Supply Company

Not all sanitary reform stemmed from the work of Chadwick; in Leeds, for example, the credit is due to Robert Baker, to whom reference has already been made in Chapter 1, and other members of the medical profession who, after the outbreak of cholera in the town in 1832, formed themselves into a local Board of Health. A Report written by Baker with an accompanying map led the doctors to believe that

> the streets in which malignant cholera prevailed most severely were those in which the drains were most imperfect, and that the general health of the inhabitants would be greatly improved, and the probability of a further visitation from such malignant epidemics diminished by a general and efficient system of drainage, sewerage, and paving, and the enforcement of better regulations as to the cleanliness of the streets.[1]

The Report was sent to the Home Secretary but appears to have been pigeonholed in Whitehall. Baker's interest in environmental health led in 1838/9 to a house-to-house survey and map of Leeds[2] printed in part by the Statistical Society.[3] This emphasized even more clearly how it was in the undrained streets and slums of the town that epidemic diseases were most prevalent. The Leeds Improvement Act of 1842 did give the Corporation power to sewer and drain streets and construct common sewers. The first main drainage scheme was constructed during the 1850s.[4]

For Chadwick's Sanitary Report Baker again produced a map and Chadwick wrote:

> By the inspection of the map of Leeds which Mr Baker has prepared at my request to show the localities of epidemic diseases, it will be perceived that they . . . fall on the uncleansed and close streets and wards occupied by the labouring classes and that the track of the cholera is nearly identical with the

track of the fever. It will also be observed that in the badly cleansed and badly drained wards to the right of the map, the proportional mortality is nearly double that which prevails in the better conditioned districts to the left.[5]

The main impetus in getting the 1842 Improvement Act accepted had been Robert Baker, but immediately after this accomplishment he became the victim of the first of those periodic bouts of nervousness over expense that were to occur from time to time after each major extension of municipal government, and in December 1842 he was turned out of the council by his own ward because he wished to drain their locality at a cost of £30 000.[6] Baker played no further part in the local government of Leeds and in 1858 he became the Factory Inspector for the Midland district. He was made a CB and he died at Leamington in 1880 at the age of 76.[7]

Various suggestions for a new water supply were put forward but made no progress either through disagreement between the engineers or because of disagreement about the financial arrangements.[8] A suggestion to levy a rate was objected to, since it would mean a tax on a few for the benefit of all.[9] Eventually it was decided to form a joint stock company and £10 000 in shares was quickly subscribed, one subscriber of £500 being a civil engineer named George Leather junior (1787–1870) who, with his eldest son, John Wignall Leather, had an office in Leeds, the title of the firm being George Leather and Son.[10]

The Leeds Waterworks Company in 1837 engaged George Leather and Son to be their consulting engineers. At that time George Leather, at the age of 50, was one of the most outstanding engineers in the country. As a boy he had assisted his father George Leather senior (1748–1818), who was the resident engineer on the construction of the Surrey Iron railway,[11] on the setting out of this railway; later he had been the resident engineer on the 9½-mile-long Pocklington canal, completed in 1818, and since 1820 he had been consulting engineer to the Aire and Calder Navigation Authority. For this Authority he had been responsible for vast improvements to the navigation including the Knottingly Goole Canal and the establishment of the port and town of Goole.[12] George Leather's achievements on bridges were no less impressive; he had constructed the Monk, Hunslet and Astley bridges across the Aire and the Dunham bridge with four spans, each 120 ft long, across the Trent. The 112 ft span Monk suspension bridge had cast-iron ribs and wrought-iron suspension rods. The 152 ft span Hunslet suspension bridge was of similar design but also incorporated hinges at the abutments, thus making it the prototype of the two-pin arch. The Astley and Dunham cast-iron bridges were of a unique double-arch hinged design. None of these bridges still exists, but it was as recently as 1976 that Dunham bridge was demolished. Leather returned to the arched suspension type for his greatest iron bridge, Stanley Ferry aqueduct, commenced in 1837 and completed 2 years later. This remarkable structure, in principal similar in design to the Sydney Harbour and Newcastle-on-Tyne bridges, still carries the Aire and Calder canal over the river Calder on a single span of 155 ft. The Crown Point cast-iron bridge at Leeds, which still exists, was completed in 1840 and was also designed by Leather. This is a straightforward single span of 120 ft. [13]

The Leathers had not previously been involved in the professional disagreements between rival engineers but their appointment reopened disputation. Supporters of Fowler, who had prepared the Parliamentary plans for the Eccup scheme, cast grave doubts on the competence of the Leathers to deal with waterworks, and innuendoes circulated about money lost by the North Midland Railway and the Goole Steam Company through their mistakes. These were ably rebutted by J. Wignall Leather who had previously been overshadowed by his gifted father but who now emerged as a personality to be reckoned with in his own right. [14]

Leeds was one of the first provincial towns to be able to boast of a house-to-house piped supply which had been built by George Sorocold in 1694. [15] The supply was taken from the river Aire and it served the wealthier inhabitants of the town. When the Leathers arrived on the scene, in 1837, there had not been much improvement since Sorocold's time and the source of supply was still the river Aire which had become very polluted.

The Eccup scheme as proposed by Fowler consisted of a main storage reservoir 5 miles north of the centre of Leeds on the Eccup Beck, a tunnel 1½ miles long under Adel Moor to a site known from a structure built by the Leathers as Seven Arches (Fig. 3.1) and a conduit 3 miles long from Seven Arches to a service reservoir with three storage reservoirs feeding into the conduit and one storage reservoir on the conduit itself at mid-point. One of George Leather's first actions on being appointed was to modify Fowler's scheme by having in addition to the Eccup main reservoir, only one storage reservoir at Westwood. He also moved the service reservoir ½ mile closer to the town from which a pipeline connected to the town mains.

Under the scheme, the water from various springs was to be collected in the Eccup reservoir and the landowners and millowners affected by the loss of spring water were to be compensated with money. Commencement of the work was considerably delayed by the task of gauging the streams to establish the amount of compensation to be paid to each riparian owner, and by negotiations for purchasing the necessary land; but by the summer of 1840 it was possible to make a start on constructing the works.

The project was divided into six contracts and the only one to encounter major difficulties was the one for the tunnel. To speed the work six shafts were sunk, but they encountered hard rock and were frequently flooded with the consequence that the first contractor went bankrupt. A second contractor completed the tunnel, which was brick-lined and egg-shaped over two-thirds of its length, in the summer of 1842. Water encountered during construction of the tunnel was used as a temporary supply from August 1841, after which date the grossly polluted river Aire

Figure 3.1 Severn Arches aqueduct

was no longer used. By May 1843 some 47 miles of pipeline had been laid in Leeds and the townships of Hunslet and Holbeck.

Initially a constant supply was provided, but as early as February 1845 the supply had to be restricted to 3 days a week for 3 months. A scheme was therefore prepared to tap some springs from the Bramhope tunnel constructed by the Leeds and Thirsk Railway Company and an Act authorizing this scheme was obtained in 1847. However, the works authorized by this Act were not constructed. Instead arrangements were made with Lord Harewood to take water from the Stub House Beck, a little to the north of Eccup, to Eccup reservoir. This enabled the Water Company to deliver 1.3 mgd to Leeds. During 1850, the embankment of the reservoir was raised 4 ft and the reservoir capacity was increased from 217 million gallons to 263 million gallons. However in 1850 there was a drought and a repetition of the experiences of 1845. By the autumn of 1850 the springs and streams were lower than they had been since 1826. The difficulties the Water Company had in maintaining the water supply were increased by the phenomenal rise in demand. Between 1842 and 1852 the number of houses supplied with piped water increased from 3000 to 22 732, and between 1841 and 1851 consumption rose from 36 million gallons to 362 million gallons per annum.

Wignall Leather was instructed to explore and to report on the best means of increasing the Water Company's resources. He investigated and reported on two alternative pumping schemes on the river Wharfe and a scheme for exploiting the springs from 25 000 acres in the Washburn valley by gravity. For the Washburn scheme he estimated that the demands of the existing millowners could be adequately met by the construction of a compensation water reservoir at Frewston (Fig. 7.1) about 14 miles NNE of the centre of Leeds. He proposed that a pipeline should be laid from a certain stream 2½ miles up the valley from Frewston to the Stub House conduit, the water from many other streams being taken into the conduit as it went down the valley. Whilst the estimated initial costs for both the pumping schemes were lower than for the gravity scheme in his report dated 6 October, 1851 Wignall Leather pointed out the superiority of the Washburn springs as regards water quality and he recommended this scheme as being the best and the most economical in the long run. In addition the negotiations for major land purchases would be conveniently confined to three prominent landowners.

Unfortunately on 5 February, 1852, only 4 months after Wignall Leather had submitted his report, the Bilberry dam designed by his father failed, and this disaster, which is described in the next chapter, must have greatly influenced the directors against any scheme involving a dam. J.F. Bateman, who at that time was engaged on the Longdendale Waterworks for Manchester, was asked to give a second opinion and he fully supported Wignall Leather's Washburn scheme. He stated in his report that the Bilberry embankment was 'badly constructed at first and totally neglected afterwards, being allowed to remain in a dangerous condition for years' and he regarded the collapse as an isolated example. However, he was not able to persuade the directors to adopt the Washburn scheme; instead, in consultation with the town council which was shortly to take over responsibility for water supply from the Company, the directors decided in favour of pumping from the river Wharfe.

In 1866 this supply was described as being 'much contaminated with the sewage and refuse of various towns'[16] but shortly afterwards the 1867 Leeds Water Act enabled the Corporation to exploit the Washburn catchment area and again to discontinue abstracting water from the river Aire.

4   George Leather (1787–1870) and the collapse of the Bilberry dam

The range of hills running north and south on the border of Lancashire and Yorkshire form a portion of what is called 'the backbone of England'. They abound in narrow valleys which during winter are abundantly supplied with water from the heights. This water power has tempted manufacturers to build mills in most of the valleys and, as one of these establishments paved the way for the construction of others, manufacturing villages have grown up by which the eye of the traveller is pleasantly arrested as he passes eastward from Manchester across the elevated chain alluded to. On the western side cotton prevails; in the hollows and dales opening eastward woollen manufacturers; but both have a similar character and have been attracted to those nooks and picturesque retreats among the hills by the supply of a cheap motive power which a moist climate secures to them. In summer however the streams run low and the mills being always on the increase the formation of large reservoirs becomes requisite.[1]

One such valley as *The Times* writer in 1852 described above is the Holme Valley, a few miles south of Huddersfield, which terminates in the high lands known as Holme Moss on the west and Black Moss and Ramsden Edge on the south – a distance of 3 miles above the small town of Holmfirth. Streams flowing into a small river called the Holme afforded every facility for water power. Mills were erected for the manufacture of fancy woollens, which had for many years been woven in the valley by the 'master clothiers' as they were then called.

Often these master clothiers were five, six or seven persons, originally workmen, who had saved a little money by great industry and who had clubbed together to take a mill between them. When there was excessive flooding in the valley or very low flows in the stream they were amongst those who suffered most.

Late in the year 1836 a group of these master clothiers and other interested manufacturers held a meeting at which their common problem of shortage of water to operate their waterwheels in summer was discussed. They resolved to construct

49

eight reservoirs to regulate the flow of the rivers Holme and Colne and to seek the necessary powers from Parliament.

By the end of December 1836 promises of subscriptions to a total of £20 150 had been obtained from 47 local people. The security of these subscriptions was to be guaranteed by mortgages on the charges to those whose mills benefited from the regular water supply, and in June 1837 the Act setting up the Holme Reservoirs Commission received Royal Assent. The Commissioners were to be millowners or owners or occupiers of falls of water to the value of not less than £100 per annum. Powers were given to raise £40 000 by subscription.[2]

At a time when there were only seven dams in the United Kingdom more than 60 ft high the first three of the eight proposed dams were to exceed this height. This extraordinarily ambitious project was as remarkable for the North of England at that time as the creation of the North of Scotland Hydroelectric Board was to be for Scotland 100 years later, but with the most unfortunate differences that the former was undertaken by a group of technically ignorant and inexperienced men with limited financial resources.

Such outstanding enterprise deserved success but no projects were begun under less auspicious circumstances. As compared with steam power, which was beginning to take over, the projects may not have been economically viable. Nevertheless, some success might have been achieved if both the financial backing behind them and the means of recovering the expenditure, which later was to cause a lot of acrimonious disputes, had not both been very weak; financial stringency, which was felt from the very beginning, was ultimately to lead to disaster.

Whilst the Commissioners appointed committees to negotiate with landowners, to engage an engineer, and to control releases from the reservoirs, they did not delegate authority to a committee to take charge of the construction of the works. The Act apparently only provided for a committee of management to control releases from the reservoirs after they were built. Authority was subsequently delegated on 12 May, 1843, to a general committee to carry out repairs but by then it was too late. Unfortunately, through ignorance and lack of practical experience, one of the directions in which the Commissioners sought to save money was in fees paid for engineering services and no engineer was engaged by the promoters to advise them on the siting of these dams. The sites were presumably chosen from topographical considerations without any exploratory test pits or trenches by the surveyor who prepared the parliamentary plans. Since 1792 Parliament had required that for any Bill for public works, plans must be deposited with the text. The extent to which the alignments for these dams could subsequently be changed would also be restricted by limits of deviation.

A committee to negotiate with the landowners was appointed in August 1837, and it was not until 8 months later, by which time the dam centre lines must have already been firmly fixed in the minds of the Commissioners and the landowners, that the same Committee was authorized by the Commissioners 'to engage a competent engineer upon such terms as shall seem to them proper'.

Whilst in civil engineering today the difficulties that can arise with divided responsibility and the need for unambiguous terms of engagement between an authority and a consulting engineer are both fully recognized, this was not the case during the first half of the nineteenth century. The Committee evidently decided that a consulting engineer was needed to prepare the designs for the dams on the alignments that had already been chosen, and for the preparation of the specifications and contract documents so that tenders could be invited from contractors, but that they could economize on his services for supervising.

Accordingly it was not until a year after the Act had been passed that George Leather received a letter dated 18 June, 1838 from William Stephenson, acting clerk to the Holme Reservoirs Commissioners, in the following terms:

> We are directed by the Commissioners to enquire whether you would undertake the management of making these reservoirs. The Commissioners would employ a surveyor under you, namely Jonathan Crowther, or some other gentleman, to attend to the works, so that you would only be required to come over now and then as circumstances might require. If you can make it convenient to give your attention to these reservoirs, you will be so obliging as to favour us with your terms, in order that we may lay them before the Commissioners without delay, as they are extremely anxious to proceed.

In his reply accepting the appointment and specifying his terms George Leather recommended the Commissioners to have plans and specifications prepared and the work properly laid out, and then to employ practical men to be constantly on the spot. Crowther appears to have been the surveyor who prepared the parliamentary plans but, perhaps because Leather did not consider that he had the necessary practical experience, no agreement was concluded with him to undertake the supervision of the works.

As the crow flies, Leeds is 18 miles from Holmfirth, but there was no rail communication between Leeds and Holmfirth nor with Huddersfield at that time and a visit to the dam sites probably meant for George Leather an absence of not less than 3 days from Leeds.

Evidently the Commissioners did not wish to incur the expense of frequent site visits by Leather such as were, in fact, essential if Leather was to supervise the construction of the works properly. He, for his part, may erroneously have felt relieved not to have the responsibility of making uncomfortable horsedrawn, or horseback, journeys often at a time when he was very busy on other projects. He failed completely to realize how much more difficult and dangerous major earth dams were than any of his previous undertakings. Instead of taking every possible precaution

51

and supervising their construction himself, he treated them like mill-dams. Over the Bilberry dam in particular George Leather's sound judgement deserted him with disastrous consequences.

To make matters worse, no authority to pay Leather his fees was delegated to the Committee who negotiated with him, and it required a full meeting of the Commissioners, who frequently disagreed amongst themselves, to authorize expenditure for any visits to be made by him. When later it became urgently necessary for Leather himself to visit the works, no official resolution requesting him to do so appears to have been approved. In the Commissioners' Order Book there is one occasion in March 1840 when the Clerk is instructed to write 'to Mr. Leather to send a competent person over to examine and measure the work done at Bilberry Reservoir and the state of the works there with as little delay as possible', but there is no record that Leather ever received an official request to visit the works himself.

He seems also to have decided that, as someone else was being appointed to attend to the works, the supervision of construction, including ensuring that the works were carried out in accordance with his drawings and specifications, was not his responsibility. During the first 2 years after the contract was let, which was the critical period, he appears never to have visited the Bilberry dam site. Whatever the legal interpretation of George Leather's responsibility was, this was his fatal mistake which a decade later was to blight his brilliant career. When later he started visiting the works without official requests to do so, it was too late.

Without entering into any formal contract with George Leather, or even recording that they were engaging his services in their Order Book, the Commissioners employed him on the basis of this exchange of letters. The ambiguity in Stephenson's letter as regards responsibility for supervision was to cause a great deal of trouble later.

The Commissioners decided to proceed first with the Bilberry, Holme Stye and Boshaw Whams embankments. Presumably making use of the parliamentary plans as the basis for his contract drawings George Leather prepared the specifications and contract documents for these three embankments, and sent them to the Clerk on 3 October, 1833 – only 3½ months after being appointed by the exchange of letters. It is inconceivable that in so short a time any extensive exploration by trial pits at the dam sites could have been undertaken.

Leather's estimate for constructing Bilberry dam was £13 000. On 26 October, 1838, after being allowed barely more than a fortnight to prepare their bid, the tender of Messrs Sharp for constructing the Bilberry dam for £9324 was accepted in spite of a warning from Leather that it was too low. Tenders from other contractors for the other two embankments were accepted at the same time.

Thus only 4 months after Leather had been appointed Consulting Engineer, the Commissioners had awarded contracts for all three embankments. No doubt a great deal of the trouble which developed later was due to the haste with which the

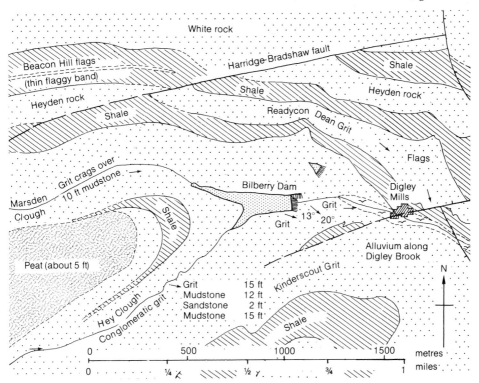

Figure 4.1   Geological map of Bilberry reservoir (after Bromehead, 1926–27)

contract documents had been prepared, the lack of any proper site investigation, and the very inadequate time given to contractors to prepare their tenders.

The Bilberry reservoir area is in millstone grit (Fig. 4.1). At the dam site, the dam centre line is due north and south with the reservoir on the western side and with the strata dipping at 13° to 20° in a south-easterly direction with no evidence of faulting.[3] The only Quaternary deposits in the immediate vicinity of the dam are peat on Wessenden Head Moor and colluvium in the Digley valley, the nearest boulder clay being on the western flanks of the Pennines at least 8 km (5 miles) from the embankment. It is most probable that materials of local derivation, such as weathered shale for puddle clay, were used for construction but the sources are not known.

The main features of Leather's designs for the Bilberry embankment are shown (Fig. 4.4). The dam had a maximum height above streambed level of approximately 67 ft. It had a puddle clay corewall 8 ft wide at the top and 16 ft at ground level which extended below ground level as a clay-filled cut-off trench. For the removal of surplus water during floods the designs included a spillway or waste pit in the form of a circular chimney with an internal diameter of 15 ft which communicated with a culvert beneath the dam. Its height from the bed of the reservoir was 59 ft and was originally 8 ft lower than the top of the embankment. The normal method of releasing water from the reservoir was through two patent trap-doors, or shuttles, at the bottom of the chimney.

> These traps or shuttles were placed the one inside, the other outside of the east wall of the chimney and were worked by perpendicular rods, raised by a common screw on a platform at the top of the chimney. In the event of the trap-door being insufficient to carry the surplus water away during extraordinary supplies, the water, on rising to the level of the chimney or bye wash, would meet with a source of escape presumed to be adequate to all contingencies![4]

On the recommendation of George Leather a stonemason, John Tait, was appointed as inspector, not only for the Bilberry embankment but also for the other two embankments. There was also an overseer under Tait named Chieseman, who may have devoted his attention solely to the Bilberry embankment. By today's standards, both in education and in numbers such a supervisory staff would be considered woefully inadequate for a major dam such as the Bilberry embankment.

George Leather's assistant was James Falshaw who was born in Leeds in 1810, his father being a wool merchant of that town. After leaving school, Falshaw at the age of 14 was articled for a term of 7 years to an architect and surveyor of Leeds. When his apprenticeship expired the great boom in railway construction had just started, and Messrs Hamar and Pratt, railway contractors, employed him first as agent on a section of the Leeds and Selby line and afterwards in the multiple capacity of agent, engineer, book-keeper and cashier on the Whitby and Pickering railway.

He joined Leather's staff in 1836 and remained with him for 7 years. Subsequently Falshaw was to have a brilliant career as a railway contractor in Scotland and he also became Lord Provost of Edinburgh and a baronet but, at the time of which we are speaking, he was a young man under 30 years of age with no experience in waterworks construction.[5]

Early in 1839 the first contractor, Messrs Sharp, started work on the Bilberry embankment and brought it up to its full height, but it leaked very badly. After attempts had been made to cure the leakage a dispute arose with him about continuing the necessary repairs and his contract was terminated in 1843. During the years 1843–45 a second contractor, Messrs Porter, made unsuccessful attempts to repair the embankment. On 5 February, 1852, shortly before 1 a.m., some 7 years after Messrs Porter had left the site, the dam failed (Fig 4.2). The horror of this disaster was well captured by a contemporary artist (Fig 4.3).

The flood wave resulting from the collapse of the embankment killed 81 people and caused a lot of destruction in the Digley Valley and at Holmfirth. It completely destroyed 4 mills, 10 dyehouses, 27 cottages, 7 tradesmen's houses, 7 bridges and 18 barns. Perhaps the worst hit was the Digley Mill, 60 yd long and 4 storeys high, containing 34 power-looms which had extensive outbuildings including dye works, two residential houses and 7 cottages; as can be seen from the drawing (Fig 4.3), only the chimney remained after the catastrophe. The flood also caused serious damage to 17 mills, 5 dyehouses, 44 large shops, 139 cottages, 11 public houses, 3 churches, 6 bridges and 2 iron foundries. With most of the mills out of commission, the disaster caused widespread unemployment amongst the local population, a total of 7128 comprising 4986 adults and 2142 children.[6] Great interest and sympathy was aroused throughout the country, the wants of the homeless and destitute were attended to at once, there was a very good response to public appeals and a sum of £31 345 was distributed amongst the sufferers. In addition, £7000 was allocated for the repair of the Bilberry reservoir.

An inquest was held after the disaster during which evidence under oath was given on 18, 19 and 27 February, 1852 and contemporary supposedly verbatim accounts of this evidence are available. The evidence quoted is as recorded in the *Leeds Mercury* dated 21 and 28 February, 1852. The Order Books of the Holme Reservoirs Commissioners for the years 1838 to 1852 are also available and assist in unravelling events. As was only to be expected when referring to the past, particularly the work done under the first contract more than 10 years previously,

Figure 4.2 Bilberry reservoir – breach as seen from the inside

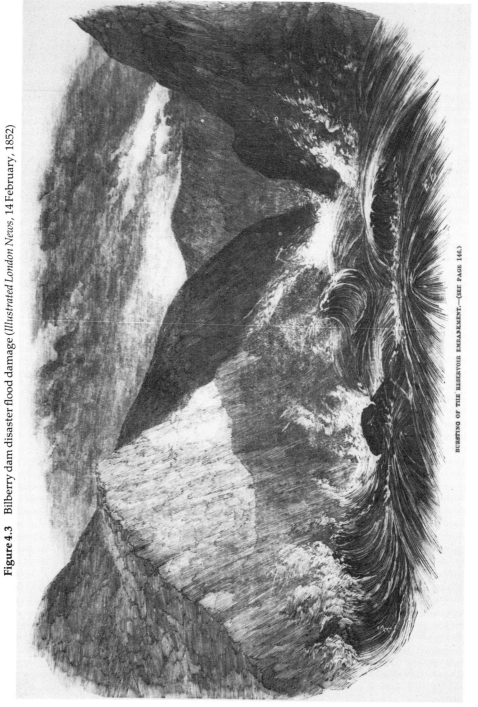

Figure 4.3 Bilberry dam disaster flood damage (*Illustrated London News*, 14 February, 1852)

BURSTING OF THE RESERVOIR EMBANKMENT.—(SEE PAGE 146.)

REMAINS OF HOLME BRIDGE.

BROADHEAD'S MILL.

REMAINS OF DIGLEY MILL.

there were some contradictions between the statements made by various witnesses and it has been necessary in interpreting them to use a certain amount of subjective judgement; nevertheless the main stream of the evidence is clear.

Instead of directing that the culvert with its forebay should be constructed first, and that the stream should be diverted through it before the commencement of the excavation of the cut-off trench – as would be normal practice today – Leather made the great mistake of allowing both to proceed at the same time. Reliance for stream diversion was placed on inadequate troughs across the cut-off trench with the consequence that the cut-off trench was flooded from time to time. This must have been very bad for the puddle clay, particularly in the critical contact zones between the clay and the rock, and no doubt was one of the major causes of the leaks which appeared later.

At the beginning of 1839 excavation of the cut-off trench was put in hand by Messrs Sharp, and soon afterwards a spring was encountered in the bottom of the trench near the centre of the dam site. In the expectation that the weight of the puddle clay would push the water back into its own course, clay puddling proceeded without any action being taken to isolate and divert the spring; but after the puddle wall had reached a certain height, the water forced itself out on the lower side of the embankment. What happened next was described by Joseph Sharp, surviving son of one of the contractors:

> By somebody's order, I don't know whose, we then took out a piece of the embankment to the solid, outside the trench, and a circular piece of puddle was put in joined up to the old puddle wall. We never saw any more of the spring during the time we were there.

According to the evidence given by Tait, the puddle trench was constructed in a crescent shape in accordance with instructions from Falshaw who visited the works at the time.

He said that, on the supposition that Falshaw and Leather were in communication with each other, he took orders from Falshaw as if they came from Leather. He also said that he had informed Leather in one of his periodic reports to him about the spring but Leather, who repeatedly declared that he knew nothing about it, denied this and to support his contention he read to the Coroner the report he had received from Tait for the period 21 June to 26 July, 1839:

> They began setting the masonry at the culvert on Monday last, they have got 30 feet of the first course set. There is not much difference in any other part of the works since Mr. Falshaw was here; the puddle trench is just in the same state, and likely to be so, without there comes two or three weeks of fine weather, or they adopt some other method from the one they are at present following.

They worked at it up to last Friday night and had got it cleared out to within a foot or so of the bottom, when it began to rain very heavy, and continued to rain all night and by Saturday morning the place was again completely filled with water and a great deal of dirt washed in again.

The rest of the report described recommendations Tait had given to the contractor on the construction of a stank to keep water out of the puddle trench and the contractor's reluctance to do this on account of the expense.

Having read this report to the Coroner, Leather then declared that it was the last report he ever received on the puddle trench from Tait, and that from it he inferred that the water referred to was not from a spring but was what came through the debris of the valley from the stream above.

Leather concluded his evidence by stating:

I never met with a spring in a puddle trench which I did not take steps to remove (i.e. take it away by solid masonry),[7] as I considered its presence there very dangerous. Mr. Falshaw was my clerk and he occasionally came over to measure the work done by the contractor. I again say I never received any communication about a spring of water.

It appears that Falshaw, who later in life was noted for his decisiveness and self-reliance, took more responsibility on his shoulders than had been delegated to him and gave instructions which he did not report to his chief, or that Tait had been acting on his own initiative and took the opportunity of Falshaw's absence to shield himself behind him. Unfortunately Falshaw, who was in Scotland, was not called upon to give evidence at the inquest.

Tait, a stonemason, was probably too inexperienced to appreciate at the time the dangers of the spring and, presumably for that reason, made no mention of it in his report. So far as can be determined from the Order Book, the Commissioners did not send any request to Leather to visit the site nor instructions to deal with the spring. They were probably ignorant of the dangers of the spring and the essential need for Leather himself to attend to it. Leather did not visit the site whilst the cut-off trench was being excavated.

Masonry culverts constructed during Victorian times as reservoir outlets were very liable to give trouble, particularly where they crossed puddle trenches,[8] and the Bilberry culvert was no exception. Whilst the details of the design of this culvert and its crossing of the cut-off trench are not known, it was a source of great trouble and anxiety; it was evidently badly fractured. Leather was much more concerned about leakage from the culvert than from elsewhere and, while the spring was to have a devastating effect on the embankment later, leakage from this source was evidently not conspicuous during the time that Messrs Sharp were working on the site.

The first defect was reported to Leather in May 1841 and he inspected it on 2 June, 1841. He is recorded as having said:

> There was a head of water which was muddy (but it came principally through the culvert) showing that the water was acting on the puddle. It was stated by some of the men that part of the masonry was bad and we sunk down and found it so. We sunk a pit down and replaced the masonry belonging to the culvert, making it solid but it did not remedy the defect, the leakage was not stopped.

After this unsuccessful attempt to cure the leak, Messrs Sharp stopped work and demanded payment. Because the leakage was not cured Leather, however, refused to certify satisfactory completion of the works and the contractors were not paid. Eventually the contract was terminated.

Some time during the spring of 1843 the leakage became worse and the water burst through the culvert. There was a meeting of the Commissioners on 12 May, 1843 and: 'The General Committee empowered to take such steps as necessary to repair the breach in the dam so as to make it secure. Two Commissioners to wait on Mr. Leather to consult him on repair.'

In August 1843 Leather who, according to the Order Book, had been paid £150 on account of his services 5 months previously, prepared a contract and specification 'for a portion of the embankment to be taken away and replaced and for the culvert to be rebuilt', and this was awarded to Messrs Porter; a new inspector, Jonathan Thorpe – also a stonemason – was appointed to supervise the work.

At the time when Messrs Porter started work, leakage through the culvert was still Leather's principal concern. With the object of diverting the leakage into a prepared channel so as to facilitate repairs to the culvert, Leather gave instructions that after part of the embankment had been removed, a drift which was presumably partly in trench and partly in tunnel was to be excavated parallel to the culvert in the shale from the downstream side to near the centre line of the dam. At the end of the drift a masonry culvert 10 ft long and 6 ft square, with an aperture in the middle to take the water, was to be constructed. A crater on the upstream side of the cut-off trench became noticeable and some consideration was given to extending the drift to it. The contractor, David Porter, gave evidence:

> In 1843 I was employed by the Commissioners to pull down a part of Bilberry embankment and make it good and also a culvert which we had to pull down and build up again. We had a drift to drive near the byeworks to take away the water which might come in contact with us. . . . We received instructions to extend the drift to a hollow place in the embankment and to the inside of the reservoir. I believe these were Mr. Leather's instructions but they were given to us by Mr. Jonathan Thorpe, the inspector of works. But we did not do it as

the inspector after telling us to do it stopped us again. The water, after this, got through between the shale and the mason's work instead of through the aperture. When we came to fill up between the masonry and the puddle, there was so much water in the place that it would not fill up. They fetched nine of the Commissioners who employed my men to fill it up. I told them it would give way; it would not stand. Instead of a stiff puddle, it was all sludge and the men worked up to their knees in it. In about a week after Mr. Leather was fetched. I saw him at the reservoir. He said they were very foolish to send for him so often as Littlewood was the engineer and not him, they did not work to his order. I never saw him before that at the reservoir nor since either.

Littlewood was an architect appointed in 1843 to measure the work done by Messrs Porter. According to Leather himself he made four visits to the works during 1844 and it appears to have been during his first visit that he ordered the drift. After he had made a second visit to the site and the attempt to divert the leakage at the culvert had failed, Leather evidently came to the conclusion that the dam could not be made to hold water without a puddle lining.

I described that to some of the Commissioners who were present and how it ought to be done, in which they seemed to acquiesce and I gave orders to the overlooker to have the water got out at the bottom of the reservoir. When I went again in September, I found nothing had been done and the overlooker told me my orders had been countermanded. Jonathan Thorpe was the overlooker. I understood that Mr. Littlewood had countermanded my orders and I considered I had no further connection with the works.

Porter made no mention of any instructions to empty the reservoir having been passed on to him, and it would appear that his only meeting with Leather was during his last visit in September. According to Littlewood: 'All Mr. Leather ordered was done except the work at the bottom of the reservoir which was found impossible to do, as they could not pump out the water.'

Whatever the truth of the matter, Leather took great umbrage and stated at the inquest 'I ceased to superintend that work'. Nevertheless, Leather did assist the Commissioners again when later there was a proposal to go to Parliament.

With a rate of settlement on the crest above the culvert that can only have continued for a short period, Porter concluded his evidence as follows:

The embankment settled two or three inches every morning. At the end of the masonry the puddle was very thin from the run. The sinking of the embankment was from the puddle being too weak from having too much water and it was washing away daily. This place was at the end of the masonry. The run came out nearly level with the byewash and we had to make it good. If they had not stopped up the water course between the shale and masonry we could have made it good. . . . If the directions of Mr. Leather to carry on the drift had been carried out, the embankment would have been safe; and that it was not carried out in consequence of the nine commissioners mentioned.

Whilst many of the commissioners had lost all confidence in their engineer, the contractor evidently still had some confidence in him.

A Bill had been prepared, the objects of which were to repeal the existing Act, to alter the method of rating which had caused a great deal of acrimony and to authorize the borrowing of a further sum of money to repair the existing reservoirs, in particular the embankment of the Bilberry reservoir. J. F. Bateman and George Leather were each asked for their estimate for the cost of the necessary remedial works for the Bilberry dam, and gave sums of £2900 and £7800 respectively. In his estimate Bateman appears to have allowed only for a puddle clay lining on the upstream slope of the embankment whereas Leather evidently also allowed for other work including probably repairs to the culvert.

Perhaps by this time the leakage from the spring was sufficiently strong for Leather to become aware of it, also of the need to do something about it, and he may also have included drainage works for it. The Bill was then deposited but, at a subsequent meeting of the Commissioners held on 29 December, 1846, the conclusion was reached that it was 'unexpedient to proceed with such a Bill and no further proceedings were taken therein'.

After this final blow George Leather appears to have given up entirely and, except for an unsuccessful attempt to obtain from the Commissioners settlement of his outstanding accounts amounting to £250, nothing more is recorded of him until scarcely more than 5 years later the dam failed and he was called upon to give evidence at the inquest.

A workman named Charles Batty, who was referred to as 'the drawer of the reservoir', was responsible for controlling releases from the reservoir in accordance with directions given to him from time to time. As part of his evidence he is reported to have said:

> The height of the embankment was higher than the waste pit when I was first appointed in February, 1846, the embankment has settled since. There is a settlement opposite and near to the waste pit which is the same now as it was then. There is another settlement near the opposite side. There was no settlement near the middle when I was appointed. Subsequently to that another settlement took place near the middle. It was about two or three years since that took place and since my appointment that puddle bank has settled about 10 feet.

An interesting observation made by another witness, which was corroborated by two other witnesses, was that 'there was another leakage in the centre of the slope and when the reservoir was pretty well filled it was very strong. At the time of the high flood six years ago [1846] I noticed this leakage and also ever since.' The puddle corewall being damaged, the hydraulic gradient in one location evidently emerged above the surface of the relatively steep downstream slope when the reservoir water level was high enough.

After Messrs Porter left, the Commissioners' funds were exhausted and there was no money available for maintaining the embankment, but at least they could have removed the top stones of the waste pit from time to time so as to keep the level of the top of the chimney well below the level of the deepest depression in the crest of the embankment. However, there was strong opposition to any reduction in the storage capacity and, as a body, they lacked the determination to make the safety of the dam their paramount consideration. At one meeting of the Commissioners, Littlewood recommended that an opening should be made in the side of the waste pit so that the reservoir should not fill higher than 35 ft. Littlewood was requested to see it done and he delegated the task to Thorpe. Shortly afterwards Thorpe informed Littlewood that when he started erecting the scaffolding for making the opening, he met some of the Commissioners who told him not to make the opening and that any attempt to do so would be resisted by force. Littlewood then let the matter drop. Thus the Commissioners' commercial interests were allowed to overcome prudence and their duty to the general public.

'During the last two weeks of January and the early days of February, 1852 there was heavy rainfall and on Wednesday, the 4th, the reservoir water level was rising at a rate of 18 inches an hour.'[9] During the night of 4 February there was a full moon, the rain had ceased, and what happened shortly before and after midnight that night was described by an eyewitness as follows:

> The water began to run into the hollow or sunken part of the embankment [said by another witness to have been 6 ft deep] about eleven o'clock but I am not certain as to the exact time. In half an hour, or rather more after that, the water began to flow over the embankment, I remained there about an hour after that on the embankment: as soon as the water began to run over, it began to wash away the outer embankment in small quantities. It ran over very slowly at first. Afterwards the embankment came down in larger quantities. After the stream had run over some time, a stream burst out at the bottom of the embankment, I did not stay until it burst, I saw it heave a large quantity of water from the bottom, and then I ran off.

The last person called to give evidence was the Commanding Royal Engineer at Newcastle-upon-Tyne, Captain R. C. Moody,[10] who had been sent by the

Government to inspect and report on the breached Bilberry embankment. After having said that the 'waste pit was designed to carry off the waste or flood water, but the top of the embankment having sunk below the top of the pit, and suffered to remain so, the flood waters had no proper or sufficient escape, but went over the dam, which, as a necessary consequence, gave way', he made some very sound recommendations on the selection and distribution of fill material:

> The length of the dam is 310 feet, and was carried up to 98 feet [*sic*] high,[11] according to the original design. This mass, or rather that part of it on the outside including the puddle, acts by its weight, which should rather more than counterbalance the pressure or weight of water acting against it. The object of the puddle wall is simply to prevent the water getting through to the outer portion. It is to keep the whole water-tight, and is not to be considered as having any strength in itself. Such a dam answers extremely well, if the materials are carefully selected and the whole work well executed.
>
> The heaviest portion of the materials (the heavier the better, stones, etc.) should be placed on the outside, and the more binding materials on the inside. Close also to the puddle dam or wall; on both sides, the material should be very binding in its quality and well rammed; the nearer it approaches in effect to puddle the better.

This distribution in itself mitigated the effect of differential settlement between the clay of the corewall and the material in the shoulders but if, nevertheless, cracking of the clay core still occurred, it had the further advantage of reducing the hydraulic gradient through the clay core and providing, to some extent, filters with a good chance that any leakage which did occur would be clean and, therefore, not dangerous. In addition, the distribution tended to increase the stability of the downstream slope by making the outer layer of it free-draining. It required a second dam failure 12 years later before Moody's recommendations became more or less standard practice and they have been responsible, in no small measure, for the remarkably good performance record of earth dams with clay cores, none having failed since 1864 and many of them being over a hundred years old.

Moody added:

> In the construction of the Bilberry dam this careful selection has not been made. The material is similar on both sides, and loose in its nature. The inner portion is permeable throughout, and instead of the part next to the puddle dam being closely rammed and almost puddle in its character, a dry, open puddle wall or backing appears to be carried up from the bottom, on both sides of the puddle dam, inviting the water, as it were, to act on the whole inner surface of the puddle, and to escape with greater ease at any leaks or fissures arising from settlement or bad execution of work.

64

Moody's description was subsequently endorsed by J. F. Bateman who, referring to the puddle clay corewall, said 'everything in the shape of stone was objected to, and the stones from the puddle were piled on each side so as to form rubble drains or walls'.[12]

Moody continued:

> In flowing over the top of the dam (which it ought not, if the waste pit was in a position to act) the water would flow down through this dry rubble to the very bottom and, acting on any cavities or porous or weak portions at that part of the embankment, would act with immense hydraulic pressure – in fact, on the principle of an hydraulic ram. In the case before us you have it in evidence that the water, before passing over the outer surface of the dam, did pour down for half an hour, and also acting on the water which was forcing its way through leaks and a spring at the bottom, almost simultaneously with breaking away in masses from the top. It was thus the whole dam gave way, and the volume of water in the reservoir burst forth at once.
>
> It appears in evidence that the spring at the bottom of the puddle trench was not led away by any of the usual modes. I think it proper to observe that the expense of doing this would have had to be borne by the contractors. It, however, was not done, but very objectionable plans resorted to in the hope of choking it up, or 'weighting it down' to use the words of the eyewitness. But it was not to be 'weighted down': it rose as the work rose, materially injuring the lower portion of the puddle, making it weak and bad, of a nature easily to be worked away with the water of the spring, as the latter forced itself through the outer part of the embankment like a little rill of water issuing from the foot. At times this rill was clear, and at times muddy, and yellow. The muddiness varied with the head of water in the reservoir. To the weak nature of the puddle at the base, and the washing away from time to time by the continuous run of water from the spring under the bottom of it, the great settlement of the puddle dam in the centre is to be attributed, a settlement which continued to go on during the construction and after the dam had been raised to the height required by the specification.

Moody was an acute observer and referring to the two pits or craters along the crest of the embankment still remaining after the collapse of the dam he said:

> The lowest point of the pits now remaining are exactly at the edge of the puddle dam and immediately over the dry rubble backing described before. In one instance the lowest point is at the inner edge and in the other at the outer edge of the puddle dam. Both are shown in the plans and sections before you [Fig. 4.4]. The top of the dam, nearer the centre but close to this little crater or pit, has

sunk bodily all across, and in the sunken part is a large crater formed, I conceive, at the same time as the higher one. This sunken part is over the culvert and is no doubt due to the washing away of the bad puddling over and above the culvert where it passes through the puddle wall below.[13]

Whilst there cannot be any certainty, the formation of the third and largest crater near the centre of the dam, which was washed away, admits of speculation as to its

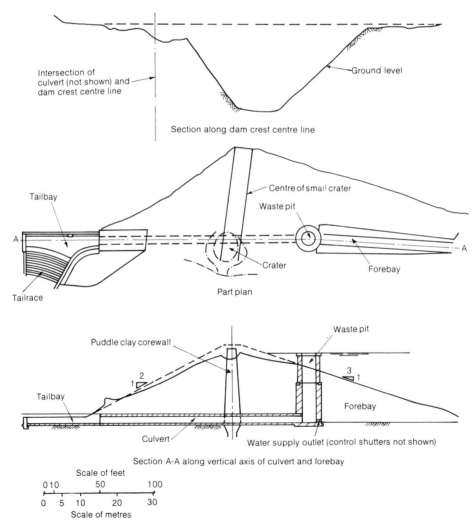

Figure 4.4   Part plan and sections of first Bilberry dam after collapse on 5 February, 1852

cause. Craters on the upstream side of the embankment crest were observed at the Balderhead dam[14] and the Upper Roddlesworth dam,[15] in both cases due to swallow holes rising from below. At the inquest Leather said: 'The embankment was formed of the debris of the valley. I gave them instructions to mix the small and large together. The puddle is the main thing; the other material is merely to give weight to the embankment.' Both Moody and Bateman described the material on both sides of the clay corewall as being rubble. Prior to the reservoir becoming full or nearly full for the first time in 1846, the leakage through the corewall adjacent to the spring appears to have been relatively small, but under the increased head when the reservoir water level rose, it no doubt increased and, by removing material, it probably formed a cavity on the upstream side of the corewall as illustrated in Fig. 4.5. During the next few years the cavity gradually migrated upwards until in 1849 or 1850 it appeared on the crest of the embankment. After the cavity emerged on the surface, erosion continued and lowered the crest of the dam more than 8 ft, so that it fell below the top of the waste pit with the result that when the reservoir became full in 1852, the embankment was overtopped with disastrous consequences.

The jury returned a verdict as follows:

> We find that Eliza Marsden came to her death by drowning, caused by the bursting of the Bilberry reservoir. We also find that the Bilberry reservoir was defective in its original construction, and that the Commissioners, engineer, and overlooker, were culpable in not seeing to the proper regulation of the works: and we also find that the Commissioners, in permitting the Bilberry reservoir to remain for several years in a dangerous state, with the full knowledge thereof, and not lowering the waste pit, have been guilty of gross and culpable negligence; and we regret that the reservoir, being under the management of a corporation, prevents us bringing in a verdict of man-slaughter, as we are convinced that the gross and culpable negligence of the Commissioners would have subjected them to such a verdict had they been in the position of a private individual or firm. We also hope that the legislature will take into its most serious consideration the propriety of making provision for the protection of the lives and properties of Her Majesty's subjects exposed to danger from reservoirs placed by corporations in situations similar to those under the charge of the Holme Reservoir Commissioners.

Whilst by an Act passed in 1863 any person who wished to complain about the safety of a reservoir could do so to a magistrate it was not until 67 years later that an effective instrument for ensuring with reasonable probability the safety of dams, namely the Reservoirs (Safety Provisions) Act 1930, came on the statute book.

The Coroner's verdict at the inquest on the failure of the Bilberry dam and,

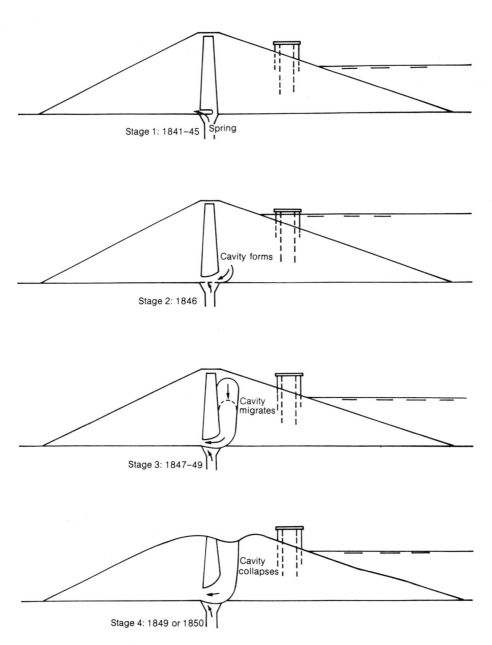

Stage 1: 1841–45 | Spring

Cavity forms
Stage 2: 1846

Cavity migrates
Stage 3: 1847–49

Cavity collapses
Stage 4: 1849 or 1850

Figure 4.5 First Bilberry dam – postulated sequence of events leading to formation of large crater

perhaps even more, Captain Moody's condemnation, were great blows to the reputation of George Leather and he retired from business 3 years later. When, on 2 April, 1870, he died in his 84th year, a brief announcement appeared in the *Leeds Mercury* with no mention of his great achievements on the Aire and Calder, nor his fine bridges. Thus a brilliant career came to a tragic end in obscurity. His nephew John Towlerton Leather, the subject of Chapter 13, was responsible for the design of the Dale Dyke dam which collapsed in 1864, but he was more fortunate in escaping the censure of his contemporaries.

What were the reasons that made George Leather stay away from the works during 1839, the critical year when the cut-off trench was being excavated and backfilled with puddle clay? The ambiguous terms of engagement have already been discussed and, at the inquest, Leather denied any responsibility for seeing that his specification was carried out. His firm had been engaged for waterworks by both the Leeds Water Company and the Bradford Corporation; the Stockton and Hartlepool railway, for which he had prepared the plans in 1837, was under construction with Mr (later Sir John) Fowler as resident engineer, and he must have been a very busy man. In a letter written to his son, John Wignall, in 1826 when George Leather was 39 years old, he complained of being taken so ill as to be unable to attend to business and being obliged to stay principally in bed for several days. Perhaps, as Leather grew older, these attacks of ill health became more frequent and increased his reluctance to take long and uncomfortable journeys. It was not until December 1845 that it was possible to travel by train from Leeds to Dunford Bridge 5 miles from Holmfirth, and a direct link between Leeds and Holmfirth via Huddersfield did not become available until July 1850. While, at the inquest, Leather did not complain of not being paid his fees during the first few years, he probably anticipated difficulties in obtaining payment for unrequested visits and this may also have deterred him. The true reasons for George Leather's inaction in so far as the Bilberry dam was concerned at this critical time will never be known.

5 James Simpson (1799–1869)

(a) THE CHELSEA AND LAMBETH WATERWORKS COMPANIES AND THE NEWCASTLE WATERWORKS

The Chelsea Waterworks Company dated from the year 1722 when an Act was passed for supplying the city and liberties of Westminster and parts adjacent with water from the Thames. A Charter[1] was also granted to the Company.

The water was to be raised into convenient reservoirs between Oliver's Mount and Hyde Park. In 1726 the Company was authorized to convert two ponds in St James's Park into reservoirs, and in 1727 to construct a reservoir in Hyde Park. The Company supplied water to the Round Pond in Kensington Gardens and was granted the privilege of taking the overflow from the Serpentine in Hyde Park. The original motive force for the pumping was a tide mill. At that time the extent of low-lying land at Pimlico that could be filled by canals or cuts was very considerable. The canals were filled at high tide, the sluices shut, the sediment allowed to settle during slack tide, and part of the water was then released to drive an undershot waterwheel, the remainder being pumped to the reservoirs at St James's Park and Hyde Park. For the reservoir in Hyde Park, the static head was about 70 ft above the Thames at high water and the length of wooden pumping main was approximately 1830 yd. During the early 1740s two atmospheric engines were erected as the main pumping plant but the tide mill waterwheel with its pumping apparatus was still in use as a supplementary source as late as 1775.

The atmospheric engines were replaced by two Watt engines, the first one in 1778 and the second in 1803. The horsepower of the latter, which was a self-acting engine, was 43.2 and it delivered 175 cu. ft of water per minute into the reservoir in Hyde Park, consumption being 7.3 lb of coal per horsepower per hour. It remained substantially unaltered during the following 35 years.[2]

During the early years of the nineteenth century Thomas Simpson, who had come to London from Cumberland as a practical millwright in 1778, raised himself to the position of Engineer to both the Chelsea and Lambeth waterworks companies. His fourth son James, who had been born in his father's residence on the Chelsea waterworks, learnt his engineering from his father and when his father died in 1823 he succeeded him as engineer to both the waterworks companies. James Simpson's work for the Lambeth Water Company will be referred to later.

For these first river pumping stations at Chelsea and elsewhere, the water was drawn raw from the river, the only precaution adopted being screening to intercept the grosser kinds of rubbish. Especially in time of flood, the water was turbid and unpalatable and many complaints were received including some from the Royal Palaces. Sir Frances Burdett, in a petition presented to the House of Commons in 1827 stated

> that the water taken from the river Thames at Chelsea, for the use of the inhabi-
> tants of the western portion of the Metropolis, being charged with the contents
> of the great common sewers, the drainings from dunghills, and laystalls, the
> refuse of hospitals, slaughter-houses, colour, lead and soap works, drug mills
> and manufactories, and with all sorts of decomposed animal and vegetable
> substances, rendering the said water offensive and destructive to health,
> ought no longer to be taken up by any of the water companies.

It was in response to the great need to improve the quality of the water supply that James Simpson developed the slow sand filter for which he is justly famous. At the time when Simpson turned his mind to filtration, some filters had already been built, but in most cases the processes used for cleaning the filter sand after use inter-fered with the efficient operation of the filter by disturbing the surface of the sand too much and they were generally overloaded. Robert Thom, for example, had de-veloped an ingenious system whereby the filter sand was cleaned by reversing the flow of water through the filters, but it was not until the use of chemicals for water treatment had been developed during the twentieth century that the standard of bacteriological purification obtained by this method, known today as the rapid gravity filtration process, could in any way approach that achieved by the slow sand filter. While Simpson was unable to use bacterial analysis as a yardstick, because at the time bacteriology as a science did not exist, his intuition nevertheless served him equally well. On the basis of his observations on other filter plants in 'Glasgow and a few dyeworks in the manufacturing districts',[3] also his own experi-ments on a small-scale plant, he constructed in 1828 for the Chelsea Water Company over about one acre of land his first large slow sand filter bed, the form of which has not been materially improved up to the present day.

According to a contemporary account the filter beds were undulating and

> are constructed by laying down over earthenware drain-pipes pierced with
> holes, first, a layer of coarse gravel, obtained by dredging the river – of pebbles,

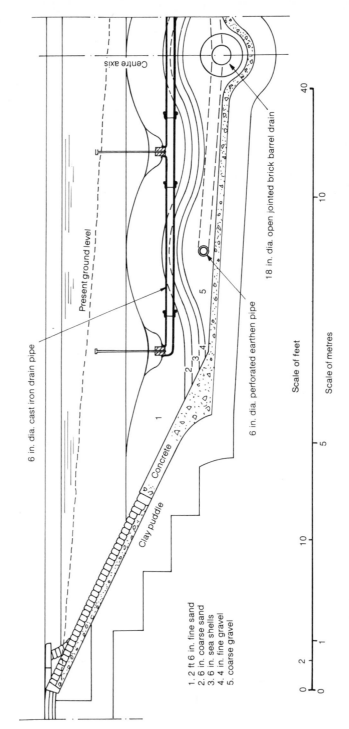

6 in. dia. cast iron drain pipe

Present ground level

Centre axis

Concrete

Clay puddle

1. 2 ft 6 in. fine sand
2. 6 in. coarse sand
3. 6 in. sea shells
4. 4 in. fine gravel
5. coarse gravel

6 in. dia. perforated earthen pipe

18 in. dia. open jointed brick barrel drain

Scale of feet

Scale of metres

Figure 5.1 Filter bed at Acomb Landing near York, 1847 (redrawn from contract drawing dated 1847 signed James Simpson)

in fact; secondly, a layer of fine gravel; thirdly, a layer of seashells imported from Harwich; fourthly, a layer of coarse sand; and fifthly one of fine sand. The shells overlapping prevent the sand from sinking into the pipes [Fig. 5.1]. After draining through the five layers, which effectively clear the water of every impurity held in suspension, it flows into a well. . . .[4a]

from which the water was pumped into the distribution system.

It was found that the bulk of the sediment resting on top of the sand formed a slime layer and that it was only necessary to remove periodically the top ½ in. or so of sand, wash it, and replace it to restore the filter bed to practically its original efficiency. The secret of success lay in the slime layer, which removed not only most of the odour, flavour and discoloration of the water but also bacteria.

Simpson was also responsible for improvements to pumping engines. Thomas Wicksteed, after visiting Cornwall, had promoted the use of Cornish pumping engines in his own and other waterworks and for more than 30 years this type of engine was the backbone of the water industry. The engine was developed to very large sizes. Thus a Cornish engine having a cylinder 112 in. diameter and a pump plunger 50 in. diameter, both with a stroke of 10 ft, was erected by the Southwark and Vauxhall Water Company in 1852. However, the practical limit of expansive working with a single cylinder was at length attained, and engineers turned their attention again to the compound engine conceived and patented by Arthur Woolf in 1803 but not exploited by him. 'James Simpson . . . after due consideration of the problem, about 1845 brought out the double-acting beam rotative compound engine, with flywheel to take control. . . . Simpson started works at Grosvenor Road Pimlico to make these engines and they had a considerable success',[4b] coal consumption per unit of work being about two-thirds that required for a Cornish engine. He further developed this type by arranging them in pairs with the flywheel in between the cranks at right angles. A typical Simpson engine is that built in 1856 for Green Lanes, Stoke Newington (Fig. 5.2).

Simpson

> constructed waterworks for the supply of Windsor Castle during the reign of George IV and in succeeding years he was more or less constantly engaged in designing or conducting water supplies to the royal palaces, as well as being consulted on various sanitary works in connection therewith, and he was thus to the period of his decease engaged in the service of the department of works, either as a civil engineer designing works, or giving advice, or as a manufacturing engineer, constructing machinery for the Board of Works at his extensive works at Pimlico.[5]

Largely as the outcome of the recommendations of the Health of Towns Commission published in 1844 and 1845 the drainage of London, hitherto based on the cesspool system, began to be superseded by water-borne sewerage. Although this was beneficial in some respects, one very unfortunate consequence was that more sewage than before found its way into the Thames, which became even more offensive than previously. The Lambeth Water Company drew its water from a worse spot than the other companies. While not admitting publicly the deterioration in the quality of the river water, Simpson realized the need for improvement, and in his report dated November 1848 to the Directors of the Lambeth Water Company he wrote:

> Notwithstanding that every effort has been made to keep pace with the constantly increasing demand for water, by enlarging and extending the Works, it has become obvious that this demand is augmenting in so great a ratio, that the capabilities of the present pumping machinery, even if urged to the utmost, would soon become insufficient, and that some additions and alterations of a comprehensive nature must ere long be determined on. The wants of the districts have been very much influenced, of late years, by the favourable changes in the habits and feelings of the inhabitants in regard to their domestic arrangements, and their desire to avail themselves of the more abundant and convenient supplies of water afforded by Companies, instead of rain water polluted by soot, or the scanty, precarious, and often objectionable supplies obtained from pumps, draw-wells, ponds, and other such sources. An idea of the increase of the demand may be formed from the fact, that the number of houses supplied by the Company has increased at an average rate of four hundred per annum in the present district alone. It is also important to observe that the demand for water is now increasing at a still higher rate than heretofore; for not only are buildings extending in every direction, particularly in the suburban districts south of the Thames, but the late sanitary movements have given such an impetus to the progress of cleanliness, that it is become little short of compulsory upon all classes to provide themselves with abundant supplies of pure wholesome water, as one of the most essential elements, not only of private comfort, but of public health.[6]

Particularly as Simpson was far from sympathetic towards Chadwick, it is interesting to read the change in public opinion only 6 years after the publication of the latter's report. After referring to his previous reports, Simpson continued:

> I made a careful survey of the River and adjacent country, and found that from a point at Long Ditton, about one mile and a half above Kingston, or twenty-three miles above London Bridge, a line only ten miles long could be drawn to the Brixton reservoirs, avoiding all hilly land, and presenting a most favourable direction for an aqueduct or main-pipe. This point, therefore, from its many advantages, is the position I have chosen for the new Works of supply; it

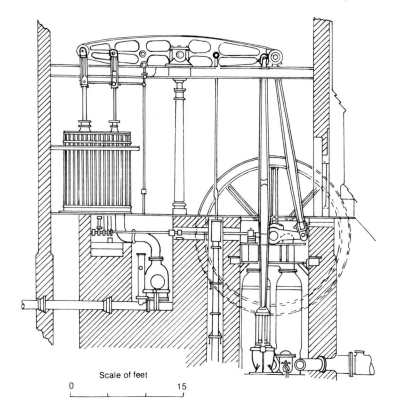

Figure 5.2 Pair of James Simpson's rotative beam engines at
Green Lanes, 1856 (reproduced from Fig. 32 of reference 2)

is three miles above the highest range of the tide at Teddington Lock, and is
sufficiently remote from the influence of disturbing causes to ensure the pure
quality of the water.

It is therefore intended to abandon altogether the present source of supply,
and to erect steam-engines at Ditton to propel the water along a cast-iron aqueduct or main-pipe, of ten miles in length, to the present reservoirs at Brixton
and Streatham, from whence it will be distributed through the existing works
and pipes, precisely as heretofore.

The water at Ditton, being usually very clear, will be passed at once from the
river by conduit-pipes to the filters, from them to the wells of the pumping-
engines, and thence through the aqueduct or main-pipe to the reservoirs. The
filtering apparatus will be erected on such a principle, that the water must of
necessity pass at all times through the filtering medium before it can reach the
pump-well of the steam-engines.[7]

His recommendations were accepted and, after the necessary Parliamentary powers had been obtained, the new works at Long Ditton were completed in 1852.

The first edition of Dr Snow's book *On the mode of Communication of Cholera* appeared in 1849 and the second edition in 1855. In the second edition he drew attention to what had happened during the cholera epidemic between July and October 1854 in a part of south London which was served both by the Southwark and Vauxhall Company and by the Lambeth Company, the former still drawing its supplies from the Thames at Battersea and the latter from the new site at Long Ditton.

> The pipes of each Company go down all the streets and into nearly all the courts and alleys [wrote Snow]. In many cases a single house has a supply different from that on either side. . . . No fewer than three hundred thousand people of both sexes, of every age and occupation, and of every rank and station, from gentlefolks down to the very poor, were divided into two groups without their knowledge; one group being supplied with water containing the sewage of London and, amongst it, whatever might come from the cholera patients, the other having water quite free from such impurity. [Snow declared] No experiment could have been devised which would more thoroughly test the effect of water supply on the progress of cholera . . .

and all that was necessary to turn it to account was to make house-to-house enquiries which revealed that whereas 5 out of every 10 000 persons served by the Lambeth Company died, as many as 71 persons out of every 10 000 persons served by the Southwark and Vauxhall Company died, thus giving further proof that the disease was water-borne.

By their action in moving their intake to Long Ditton the directors of the Lambeth Water Company anticipated the decision of Parliament in 1852 in the Metropolis Water Supply Act (15 & 15 Vict., C. 84) that no water company after 31 August, 1855 should take its supply from the Thames below Teddington Lock. Under powers exercised by the Corporation of London (later transferred to the Thames Conservancy Board in 1857), the amount of water each Company could extract from the river, including the Chelsea and Lambeth Water Companies, was limited to 20 mgd. Experience taught the Lambeth Water Company that Ditton was not the best intake site, as the river when in flood was found to be discoloured by the discharge of the rivers Mole and Emmet close by, and in 1871 powers were obtained to move the intake works 3 miles further upstream to West Molesey.[8]

Initially the town of Newcastle depended upon springs for water supply.[9] As the region developed it abstracted water from the Tyne in the later years of the seventeenth century, but after the turn of the century the river was discontinued as a source in favour of further springs in Gateshead. Fires were frequent, and being desirous of having in its own power the means of extinguishing them, the Newcastle Fire Office, one of the local fire insurance companies, took over these early undertakings in 1797 and was able to supply water principally from underground sources except when emergencies led to the river again being used. Unfortunately one such emergency use of the river as a source happened to coincide with the arrival on Tyneside of the country's first cholera epidemic, the disease having been notified in Sunderland in October 1831, and there were more than 500 deaths in Newcastle and Gateshead. Besides complaints about the quality of the water it was alleged that, by not giving adequate supplies to fires at properties insured by rival companies, the Fire Office used its monopoly to encourage householders to insure with it. The Fire Office (in turn) was purchased in 1836 by the Newcastle Subscription Water Company formed 4 years earlier and, abstracting water from the river Tyne which was passed through filters, it was able to supply both domestic and industrial users, the latter including tanneries, breweries, railways and glassworks.

As stated elsewhere (Chapter 1, p. 8), a Health of Towns Commission was set up in 1843 and the Commissioners entrusted the task of reporting on Tyneside to Dr Reid who described appalling sanitary conditions, and wrote on the water supply of the two towns: 'In Newcastle a supply of very indifferent quality, costly to the poor, and not sufficient in quantity for the wants of the population has rendered this subject one of much local discussion.'

A native of Tyneside who was to have a big impact on the water supply and on the prosperity of Newcastle was William George Armstrong (1810–1900). He studied law and became a partner in a legal firm but he also displayed great gifts as an inventor in hydraulic machinery and weapons. He was elected a Fellow of the Royal Society in 1846 and, after serving as President of the Institution of Civil Engineers in 1882, he was raised to the peerage in 1887. As a manufacturer of munitions he was the model of Bernard Shaw's Mr Undershaft.

The most important landowners in the county were the Dukes of Northumberland, and an important developer of Newcastle was the architect, Richard Grainger, (1798–1861). On 23 December, 1844, Armstrong in his capacity as a solicitor wrote to the agent of the 3rd Duke:

> Mr. Richard Grainger, the eminent improver of the town of Newcastle upon Tyne has recently projected a Plan for supplying that Town and its vicinity with Water, and Notices have been advertised, at his insistence, of an intended application to Parliament in the ensuing Session, for the necessary powers to incorporate a Company for the purpose of carrying his project into effect.
>
> The leading features of his plan may be described as follows: In the first place it is proposed to construct a capacious reservoir in the bed of a stream at Whittle Dean . . . capable of containing upwards of a years supply . . . the quality of the Whittle Dean Water is peculiarly suitable for the use of a Town and from the

circumstances of the supply being obtainable from so high a level, the expensive operation of pumping will be entirely avoided.

The reply received was that 'His Grace is very favourable to a plan which bids fair, if ever carried out, to supply the large populations of Newcastle and Gateshead with an abundant supply of excellent water. . . .'

The movement for sanitary reform initiated by Chadwick's 1842 report was beginning to have its effect, and in order to obtain the good will of the Town Council and the general public it was decided that the new water-supply scheme should be designed on the principles of constant supply. On 26 February, 1845, Chadwick wrote to Hawksley:

> I have had today Mr. Armstrong the solicitor from Newcastle with their engineer, Mr. Simpson, here to help and advise as to a system of constant supply. I advised them to get powers for carrying water on and carrying it off the premises and to commute the first outlay for a rental, to lay down plugs for washing the streets and the prevention of fire and for these to seek a rate. I send you their prospectus. I should be glad to be aided with any points of criticism on Mr. Simpson's plan. His outlay seems to me very large, lead pipes too at Newcastle the seat of the pottery and glassworks.[10]

Although Simpson was not responsible for the conception of the project, the reference to his 'plan' indicates that he was now preparing the plans and estimates for steering the necessary Bill through Parliament. The scheme included a 24 in. diameter iron main 12 miles long from the Whittle Dean reservoirs to a service reservoir in Newcastle. Simpson, Grainger and Armstrong all gave evidence to a Select Committee and the Whittle Dean Bill received the Royal Assent on 30 June, 1845. In the same year the new water company purchased and took over the assets of the Subscription Water Company including an intake and pumping station on the river Tyne. The Whitte Dean works for which Simpson was responsible were completed in 1848. In his capacity as a manufacturer, Simpson supplied a press for testing the pipes used on the pipeline; he also supplied some of the valves.

The original intention was that after the Whittle Dean Works were completed abstraction from the river Tyne should cease, but such was the growth of population and water consumption that to maintain the supply the company by 1853 found itself again obliged to use the river as a supplementary source. Even before the Whittle Dean works were completed, the directors had started thinking about additional upland sources and it is recorded that in September 1849 the directors and Simpson visited the Pont stream 'during the present long drought and it was found to be yielding a considerable supply of water'. In 1850 the Company began negotiations in earnest with the millowners on the Pont to obtain rights to exploit it, but

without success, and the adamant refusal of one of the millowners even to negotiate had very tragic consequences. During the 1849 cholera epidemic Newcastle
and Gateshead had remained almost unscathed but during the 1853 epidemic
more than 1500 people died. As part of his evidence exposing cholera as a water-
borne disease Dr Snow wrote: 'All the three epidemics which Newcastle and Gateshead have suffered have borne a close relationship inversely to the purity and
abundance of the water supply.' Simpson was called upon to advise what should
be done, and in October 1853 he submitted a report prepared jointly with the
Company's own engineer in which he recommended a scheme for diversion from
the Pont, an additional impounding reservoir at Whittle Dean and, for emergency
use, a pumping station on the river Tyne further upstream than the existing river
intake where advantage could be taken of gravel and sand beds for natural filtration.

The first of Armstrong's industrial developments was initiated by his invention
of the hydraulic crane and his letter dated 24 November, 1845, to the Finance Committee in which he wrote:

> I beg to draw your attention to a plan I have matured for applying the pressure
> of the water in the streets' pipes in the lower parts of Newcastle to the working
> of cranes upon the quay with the view of increasing the rapidity and lessening
> the expense of the operation of delivering ships. It will readily be perceived
> that whatever has a tendency to accelerate the unloading of ships at the quay
> must not only be highly advantageous to the shipowners and merchants in the
> port but must also have the effect of increasing the accommodation to shipping
> which the quay is now capable of affording.

By 1847 Armstrong had resigned from the secretaryship and, with his partners, he
founded the Newcastle Cranage Company for the manufacture of hydraulic
machinery. With the establishment by Stephenson and Hawthorn also of works on
the Tyne, this created an unforeseen increase in employment and population on
Tyneside which enormously increased the demand for water and water consumption. Simpson was again called upon in 1853 to support a Bill in parliament for supplementary works. Although still Engineer to the Company, Rennison states that
the evidence Simpson gave did not relate closely to the proposed works but was
concerned mainly with comparisons with other towns. Hawksley, by now on good
terms with Simpson, also gave evidence in support of the Bill which received the
Royal Assent on 9 May, 1853. Simpson does not seem to have been concerned with
the execution of these works. The revenue of the water company increased rapidly.

> The rental of the Waterworks in 1845 was about £4500; this rental has rapidly
> and steadily increased since the introduction of the improved supply and it

now [1855] amounts to upwards of £16 000 per annum, whilst there is every prospect that the water rental will go on increasing as it has done in other places where works of the kind have been established.[11]

Armstrong became Chairman of the Whittle Dean Water Company (afterwards in 1863 to become the Newcastle and Gateshead Water Company) from 1855 to 1867. In 1861 he and his fellow directors were again having problems with water shortages, and the views of Simpson, Bateman and Hawksley were sought on what should be done. At a Special General Meeting of Shareholders held in January 1862 it was stated that Bateman replied first but apparently no record now exists to show that Simpson or Hawksley ever replied. After this meeting Simpson's connection with the Company ceased, and for a time Bateman became the Company's engineer.

(b) THE BRISTOL AND YORK WATERWORKS COMPANIES

In medieval times there were many springs and wells in Bristol, the majority of them being the property of religious foundations, and at least two churches – St Nicholas and Christ Church – had wells within their walls. Nearly every street had a water supply, usually discharged into a wooden trough, presented by a nearby priory. However, with the break-up of the monastic institutions during the sixteenth century the upkeep of these water supplies, including the maintenance of the conduits, devolved upon the several parishes; with the growth of population they became over-exploited and they began to become polluted.

A brave attempt to increase the water supply of the city was made when the first Bristol Waterworks Company was constituted in 1695. This initial undertaking proposed to take water at the extreme limits of the Corporation's jurisdiction at Hanham Mills and to carry it in pipes of hollow elm into the city. 'The scheme was completed in 1698 but never being well-managed and lacking an adequate controlling body, functioned only by "fits and starts" . . . for close on a century when borne down by debt and finding the corporation disinclined to accept the undertaking even as a gift', it went bankrupt in 1782.[12]

During the years 1804–09 William Jessop carried out some very remarkable improvements to the dock facilities at Bristol referred to as the Floating Harbour which very considerably increased trade and, with the demand for filling water tanks of ships, this made the need for an abundant source of pure and wholesome water greater than ever.[13]

The next water-supply project conceived was the construction of a canal from the Kennet and Avon near Bath to Bristol. It was intended that this canal should be used both for merchandise between Bath and Bristol and for water supply. Without restrictions being placed to prevent the canal from being used as a sewer by factories and dwellings, which were apparently not envisaged, it would soon have become as polluted as the river Frome and it is probably fortunate that, apparently through lack of sufficient funds, the Act of 1811 authorizing this ambitious project became a dead letter.[14]

In 1844 the Commission appointed to enquire into the state of large towns reported:

> Viewed as a sanitary question, there are few if any large towns in England in which the supply of water is so inadequate as at Bristol. The labour and consequent expense attached to the system of obtaining a supply of water from the draw-wells or pumps engenders filthy habits directly acting upon the health, and indirectly on the morals of the people. . . . The water of the pumps is generally hard and unfit for washing. . . . The labour of fetching water leads to a very sparing use of it.[15]

In the spring of 1845 there were two rival groups for supplying Bristol with water, one being the Merchant Venturers Company which proposed to extend a projected Clifton water supply scheme to supply Bristol, and the other being a group, later known as the Bristol Water Company, which proposed to bring water from the Mendips and other springs in Somerset to the town. The Merchant Adventurers, who had retained I. K. Brunel as their engineer, had previously proposed in 1842, without success, a scheme to supply Clifton and its environs from two springs on the banks of the Avon. Chadwick and Hawksley tried unsuccessfully to get them to adopt a combined drainage and water supply scheme.[16] The other group had a meeting on 20 June, 1845, at the Board Room of the Bristol Corn Exchange at which the selection of a consulting engineer was discussed[17] and minuted as follows:

> The inconvenience of not having an Engineer resident in London, easily accessible at all times, and especially during the preparations for Parliament, and while the Bill is in progress, are so obvious, that we did not consider it practicable to look on these Gentlemen as within the chance of your selection.
>
> We nevertheless made some enquiries respecting Mr. Hawksley and ascertained that his celebrity is limited to the Trent Works at Nottingham, which presented no peculiar Engineering difficulties, and that although a man of talent he has not been regularly brought up as an Engineer but was professionally educated as a Surveyor and Architect.
>
> Our report respecting the other Gentlemen is as follows. Mr. Mylne[18] is well acquainted with Bristol and was the Engineer who advised and carried into effect the culvert under the Frome – With regard to all engineering questions connected with Water Works, his experience and talent render his judgement

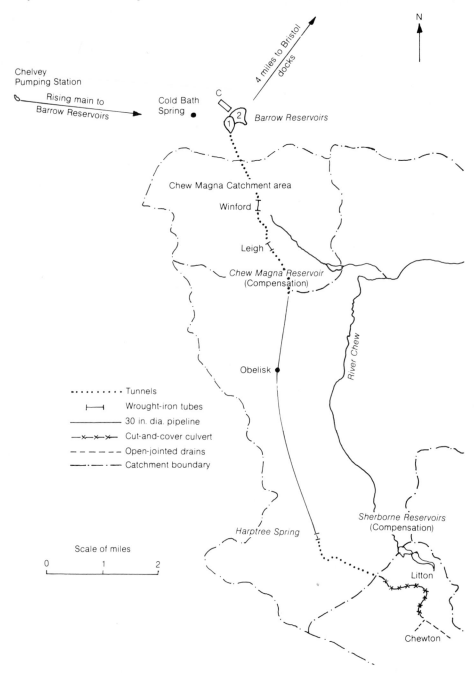

Figure 5.3   Works for Bristol's water supply authorized by the 1846, 1862 and 1865 Acts

to devise and execute everything necessary for a large City quite undoubted. His manner and appearance are calculated to create very favourable impressions.

Mr. Wicksteed[19] is a man of obviously considerable attainments and gave us much valuable information but he intimated that he disliked parliamentary business and found it inconsistent with his other engagements and he is not therefore open to a retainer from this Company.

Mr. Simpson appears to have been more extensively engaged in Water Works for large provincial cities than either of the other Gentlemen, or indeed than any of the eminent Engineers of the present day – He has conducted or is now managing Water Works at Edinburgh, Carlisle, Liverpool, Manchester and Salford, Newcastle and other places of minor importance and he is employed at Windsor Castle as to the domestic architectural arrangements, especially in relation to the supply of Water. His Father was Engineer to the Chelsea Works and the Lambeth Works and he succeeded his father after being educated from childhood in reference to his present profession of a Water Works Engineer.

The next meeting of the Board, on 7 July, 1845, confirmed the appointment of James Simpson as Engineer.

The Parliamentary contest between the two rival groups was won by the Bristol Water Company which was incorporated by an Act dated 16 July, 1846, and the first General Meeting of the Proprietors of the Company was held 3 months later on 15 October, 1846.

Simpson's Plan (Fig. 5.3) was to exploit the Cold Bath Spring 4 miles south-west of the Bristol docks and various springs in the Mendip valleys near Harptree, Litton and Chewton 10–12 miles south of the Bristol docks.

The Mendip hills are formed in the main of massive carboniferous limestone into which the rain, averaging about 41 inches annually over the hills and adjoining valleys forming the Company's catchment area of nearly 50 square miles, readily percolates. The limestone, with its innumerable fissures and caves, affords an underground reservoir, the outlets from which break out in springs that are seen emerging at Cheddar and many other places.[20]

Under the Act the Company was required to supply compensation water in the Valley of the Chew River by means of three reservoirs, one at Chew Magna and two at Sherborne (Litton) all three of which were constructed.

An aqueduct (Fig. 5.3), known as the 'Line of Works', which was approximately 11 miles long, was constructed on the eastern side of the Mendip Hills from Chewton and Litton to Barrow where it terminated in a reservoir of about 25 acres in extent formed in a natural dell or depression. 'The springs at Chewton and Litton were at an elevation of about 400 feet above the level of the docks at Bristol and were united below the ground level by means of collecting tanks, open-jointed drains and culverts';[21] the water was then conveyed by the several branches to the principal egg-shaped masonry culvert which for a distance of 2¼ miles was built in cut and cover and followed the contour of the hillside until it reached the entrance to the first tunnel. This was 1¼ miles long, driven nearly all the way through solid magnesium limestone conglomerate. Proceeding onwards from the first tunnel the line crossed Harptree ravine and 'was there joined by the branch aqueduct conveying into the main line a considerable feeder from the springs and waters of that romantic and picturesque gorge of the Mendip Hills.'[22] The aqueduct was continued across this ravine by means of the first of three oval-riveted wrought-iron tubes, further details of which are given below, supported on piers at 50 ft centres, the length of the crossing in this case being 350 ft and the height of the piers nearly 60 ft. The remainder of the aqueduct consisted of 4¼ miles of undulating 30 in. diameter cast-iron pipeline with an average gradient of 10 ft per mile, three tunnels with a total length of 2¾ miles and the crossing of two more ravines by oval-riveted wrought-iron tubes supported on piers, the length in both these cases being 825 ft. As compared with aqueducts on the continent, the design of which had changed little since Roman times, Simpson's tubular aqueducts were revolutionary in their lightness, efficiency and greatly reduced cost per unit length.

The internal dimensions of the tubes accorded with those of the tunnels which were lined with stone. The wrought-iron tubes were egg-shaped in cross-section measuring 4 ft 7½ in. vertically by 3 ft 6 in. at the widest point, the dimensions having been in some degree determined by the area in which men could work. The ends of the tube

> were connected with the tunnels by means of stone tanks and collars of clay puddling, 10 feet in thickness, in which the ends were embedded, so as to allow for any expansion or contraction, and to prevent leakage. The tube rested on cast iron saddles, fixed to the piers and abutments and provision was made in the saddles, by means of friction balls [Figure 5.4] to allow of the tube expanding and contracting with the variations of temperature each way from the centre saddle which rested on a pier of equilibrium. The balls of the centre saddle admitted of slight motion laterally but prevented the tube from moving endways in either direction.[23]

The wrought-iron plates used for the construction of the elevated tubular aqueducts were ⅜ in. thick at the bottom and ⁷⁄₁₆ in. at the top, and after more than 130 years service these tubes are still in constant use.

The stone-lined tunnels and tubes had a gradient of 5 ft in 1 mile and were capable of discharging 20 mgd. Simpson estimated that the 30 in. diameter pipeline would not be able to discharge more than 8 mgd, but the land purchased for the pipe track was wide enough to enable another line of pipes to be laid at a later date if required.

> The pipeline was so laid that the escape of air from the pipes whilst they were being charged with water took place at each extremity and at a high point on the pipeline where an open upright tube or standpipe was placed at a sufficient elevation to prevent any overflow of water. This standpipe was screened by being placed within a stone obelisk 50 feet high.'[24]

The obelisk is still standing to this day.

Three service reservoirs to maintain a constant supply were built at Cotham, Durdham Down and Bedminster Down. The Cotham reservoir in Clifton was supplied by gravity from Barrow No. 1 reservoir, the Durdham Down reservoir beyond the then limits of the city was supplied by pumping from the Cotham reservoir and the Bedminster Down reservoir, which served the area south of the docks, was supplied by gravity from the Cold Bath spring.

Figure 5.4   Detail of wrought-iron tube on 'Line of works' aqueduct 1850

These works were completed in 1851; the supply was to have been 4 million gallons a day but that in dry years this was not practical was recognised in 1860 and in 1862 the Company obtained an Act of Parliament enabling them to construct an additional storage reservoir (Barrow No. 2) but, before this was completed, the absence of rain in the winters of 1861, 1862 and 1863 so seriously affected the yield of the springs that early in 1864 recourse had to be taken to all available springs and other sources round Bristol and, notwithstanding the temporary pumping, the supplies were exhausted and the springs did not yield more than 350 000 gallons per day[25]

Under the 1862 Act the Company was also obliged to construct a compensation reservoir (marked with a C on Fig. 5.3) at Barrow.

An Act (the Bristol Waterworks Amendments Act 1865) was next obtained by the Company in 1865 which gave them powers to exploit the Chelvey and Midgel Springs 7 miles WSW from the Bristol docks and to pump the water from these springs to the storage reservoirs at Barrow. With a view to also exploiting underground water at a later date, Simpson selected a site for the Chelvey pumping station which was also a suitable site for sinking wells into the red sandstone.

With the completion, in about 1866, of Barrow No. 2 reservoir the total storage capacity, exclusive of mill compensation, was increased to 350 million gallons, equivalent to 88 days supply at 4 mgd. Simpson reckoned that, in conjunction with the springs to be tapped and the potential yield of the proposed wells at the Chelvey pumping station, this system would be able to maintain a constant yield of 4 mgd. In the first stage of development, aqueducts and works to carry the water from the Chelvey and Midgel Springs to the pumping station were constructed and two 60 hp engines with a total pumping capacity of 1⅓ mgd were installed. Pumping began intermittently in May 1867 and regularly in July 1868. It was not until after Simpson's death in 1869 that the well-sinking which he envisaged began, but that the works completed in his lifetime were already acclaimed may be judged by the comment quoted by the medical critic Stewart in 1867: 'Abundance of excellent water supplied by a private company from the Mendip Hills.'[26]

Well-sinking and drilling at the Chelvey pumping station began in 1870 and during the following decades many wells and boreholes were sunk. More powerful pumps were also installed, the ultimate pumping capacity with steam being 6 mgd. The 60 hp engines installed by Simpson were sold as scrap in 1937.

The Bristol Waterworks Company have in their archives the specification and Contract Document dated 31 July, 1847, for the construction of the two service reservoirs at Cotham and Durdham Down prepared by Simpson. This document was accompanied by six contract drawings. Two of the original drawings, and a third one issued on 4 September, 1847, still exist. The two reservoirs were of similar design and most of the specification clauses are common to both. The specification, which is about 4000 words long, is very comprehensive. The contract clauses, including a schedule of prices, are very thorough and account for another 2000 words.

Basically the service reservoirs were four-sided embankments with both the floors of the reservoirs and the centre cores of the embankments made watertight with puddled clay:

> The Floor Puddle is to be founded on the solid earth and all loose or unsound places in the Foundations are to be excavated and filled up solid with hard dry and suitable material pounded in regular courses, – the upright Puddles are to be founded on the Floor Puddle and the whole is to be properly tempered and worked with a sufficient quantity of Water to ensure it being perfectly watertight.

Under 'Materials' it is specified that: 'The Clay for the Puddling and Pounding is to be of a good tenacious quality and mixed in the proportion of 3 parts of Clay to one part of clean sharp gravel or broken stone passed through screens with one and one half inch meshes, the whole to be properly mixed and tempered.' The clay puddle is 'to be worked in regular and level courses not exceeding 6 inches each course in thickness'. Level courses with a limit of 6 in. is also specified for the earthwork in the embankments, and 'the whole is to be rammed solid as the works proceed'. Other clauses deal with stone pitching, retaining walls, footpaths, masonry structures, culverts, fences, etc., all described carefully in detail. Except for a reference to a mortar pugmill, which was probably hand-operated, there is no reference to machinery in the specification.

Space, and, no doubt, the reader's patience, will not permit more than a brief reference to the contract clauses but the subjects fully covered can be judged from some of the clause headings, i.e. Alterations and deviations, Extra Work, Materials and Workmanship, Power to Inspect Materials, Contractor to attend to Engineer's orders and directions, Imperfections or Insufficient Workmanship, Accidents and Damages, Notices to the Contractor, Period of Completion, Power to delay works in case of frost, Disputes to be settled by Arbitration, etc. Under the Arbitration clause there are two arbitrators, one being the Company's engineer and the other an engineer named in the Contract by the contractor and 'in case of their not being able to agree a third party to be named as Arbitrator by such two engineers the decision of any two so nominated being final and binding on both parties'. When one recollects that the specification for the Glencorse dam written 28 years earlier by Telford and Jardine was only some 300 words long, Simpson's specification is very professional and a forerunner of modern specifications. The contract clauses are also such as might be written today.

Many of the contract drawings prepared by Simpson for 'The Line of Works', the

Cotham and Durdham Down service reservoirs, the first Barrow reservoir and the Chew Magna and Sherborne compensation reservoirs authorized by the 1846 Act are still carefully preserved by the Bristol Waterworks Company. They display the same careful attention to detail and a high standard of draughtsmanship.

After the passing of the 1862 Act Simpson was called upon to prepare contracts for Barrow No. 2 reservoir, also for a compensation reservoir at Barrow. Whilst the specification for Barrow No. 1 reservoir no longer exists, the Bristol Water Company have the specification and contract drawings for Barrow No. 2 reservoir and it is interesting to compare this specification, dated 7 May, 1864, with Simpson's earlier specification for the service reservoirs dated 31 July, 1847.

Except where it abutted against the embankment of Barrow No. 1 reservoir the Barrow No. 2 embankment had outer slopes of 2½ to 1 and inner slopes of 3 to 1 with a central clay-filled cut-off trench and clay corewall, the maximum height being 30 ft.

Whereas almost no reference was made to machinery in the earlier specification, the Contractor is now required at the commencement of the works or within 14 days thereof to supply various items including:

> 1 Mortar Mill with tub shaft knives and gearing adapted to be worked by steam power.
> 1 Clay mill with combined rollers and pug mill capable of turning out 7½ tons per hour as made by Bradley and Craven of Wakefield.

The specification also states: 'An 8 horse portable Steam Engine has been purchased by the Company and will be put at the disposal of the Contractor for use on the Works in working the Clay and Mortar Mills.' Under Materials the specification for Puddle is almost the same as before but with the addition that 'the whole of the Clay is to be passed through the Clay Mill hereinbefore specified to be provided and properly mixed and tempered cut cross cut and trod and well worked in 6 inch courses throughout.' With his experience as a manufacturer of pumps and other machinery, it was to be expected that Simpson would be in the forefront in making use of machinery.

Another interesting innovation in the specification is the permission given to the contractor to use railways and railway waggons for excavation but, by implication, not for the construction of the embankment for which 'The earth and material is to be worked in regular horizontal courses not exceeding 9 inches each in thickness and every course is to be levelled and pounded or carted over to render the whole solid as the work proceeds and every means taken to consolidate the Bank.'

The date of the specification and contract, 7 May, 1864, is significant in that it is 8 weeks after the collapse of the Dale Dyke embankment on 11 March, 1864. Simpson was one of the engineers who investigated the cause of the collapse on behalf of the

Sheffield Waterworks Company (see Chapter 13) and it may well have been as a result of what he observed at Dale Dyke that he included in his specification the following:

> The earth and materials composing the embankments for a width of 20 feet on each side of the puddle walls are to be well broken and free from stones clods indurated earth and all hard lumpy material in order that the puddle walls may be fairly and equally supported on both sides . . . the puddle walls must be kept level and all step puddling avoided to the utmost possible extent.

Whilst leakage from Barrow No. 1 reservoir was a continuous source of trouble, and leaks through the embankment had frequently to be plugged, Barrow No. 2 reservoir was relatively watertight.

For his outlet works, Simpson used on both Barrow No. 1 and Barrow No. 2 reservoirs what he called a 'Grating Tank' as shown on Fig. 5.5. The whole structure is founded on concrete. Its main elements are a well built in masonry sited just upstream of the clay corewall and cut-off trench and two parallel masonry sidewalls shaped to accord with the inner slope of the embankment and terminating in the reservoir with oblong piers, the thrust on the walls being taken by 'sustaining bars' supplied to the contractor by the Water Company. Three grooves are formed in the sidewalls, two for screens 3 in. wide and one for stop planks 6 in. wide and 6 in. deep. The entry of water into the well is controlled through three draw-off sluices with pipes built into the wall of the well at different levels, the sluice spindles being operated from a platform at the top. The sluices being at different levels enables the water to be withdrawn from the optimum level from a water quality viewpoint. Water entering the well escapes through a 24 in. diameter cast-iron supply pipe laid apparently without any particular precautions across the puddle trench but embedded in concrete below original ground level beneath the downstream slope of Barrow No. 2 embankment.

In many respects Simpson's grating tanks, which he had also used on one of the Whittle Dean reservoirs, were an improvement on pipes not able to be controlled upstream laid below embankments and on masonry culverts (*see* pp. 59 and 125–129). The fact that water admitted to the 24 in. cast-iron supply main could be shut off when necessary was a substantial improvement, but nevertheless one might have expected that where the main crossed the puddle trench a crack due to differential settlement would occur. The fact that no such trouble seems to have arisen at Barrow can perhaps be attributed to the relatively modest height of the embankments and the particular geology at the site.

Not being concerned with the quality of the water released, and presumably also for reasons of economy, Simpson adopted simpler outlet works for the 40 ft high compensation reservoir embankment at Barrow with a well upstream of the clay

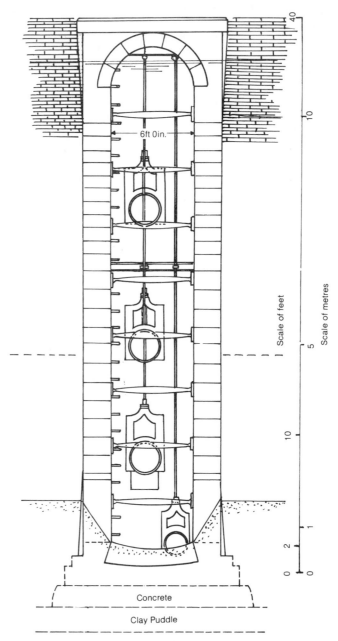

Figure 5.5   Outlet works (grating tank) at Barrow No. 1 reservoir, 1850
(redrawn from contract drawing dated 11 April 1850 and signed James Simpson)

corewall as before, but with the well connected to the reservoir by means of an 18 in. diameter cast-iron main buried beneath the upstream slope, the discharge of compensation water from this main being controlled by sluice valves on it inside the well. Water escaped from the well through a similar main laid across the cut-off trench and beneath the downstream slope. In this case Simpson had a 2 to 1 gradient on the inner slope and a 3 to 1 gradient on the outer slope. The drawings for this embankment are dated 30 October, 1862, and it was presumably required to be completed before work could start on Barrow No. 2 reservoir. Simpson died in 1869 and a contract drawing dated 21 July, 1870, signed by his former assistant, John Taylor – who succeeded him – shows reconstruction with the assistance of a deep timbered trench of the clay corewall and cut-off trench to greater depths than previously, indicating that, as originally constructed, the embankment was not watertight. This reservoir was abandoned in 1882.

The catchment area of the Chew Magna compensation reservoir is about 4300 acres, part of which is quite steep. The reservoir when full covers 9.4 acres. For this reservoir Simpson constructed a very small spillway discharging into a byewash with a slight gradient at first followed by a steep run down. In 1936 the Bristol Water Company lengthened the cill of the spillway and raised the crest level of the embankment a foot or two to provide 5 ft freeboard.

On 10 July, 1968, the heaviest rainfall in the Chew Valley in living memory occurred. The centre of the depression was over the Chew Magna catchment area where some 6.8 in. of rain fell in approximately 6½ hours. Starting at 18.30 hours, most of the rain fell between 20.00 hours and 24.00 hours. No-one saw what happened at the embankment but by morning the flood at Chew Magna had subsided. The bottom end of the byewash had disappeared and a hole some 13 ft. deep excavated where it had been. The sidewall of the byewash had been jumped where it narrowed and the jet of water had excavated a gash virtually clear of the slope of the bank.

There were many 9 in. diameter short logs (firewood) of elm or oak lodged on the crest of the embankment showing that it had been overtopped, but except for two small holes surmised to have been caused by heavy stones subsequently swept away and no longer visible, no damage whatever was done to the embankment and the grass was all the better for a wash. Two factors probably helped to save the embankment: one being that the crest was nearly level, thus avoiding concentration of flow in any one area, and the other being that it was of earth into which broken stone had been pounded when the 1936 work was in hand. 'Standing for 120 years means nothing in the context of floods. Dame Nature is only biding her time.'[27]

The York Waterworks Company, with antecedents going back to 1674, is the oldest Incorporated Waterworks in England. The celebrated Smeaton was at one time a proprietor and he installed a pump, adapted by him from a Newcomen

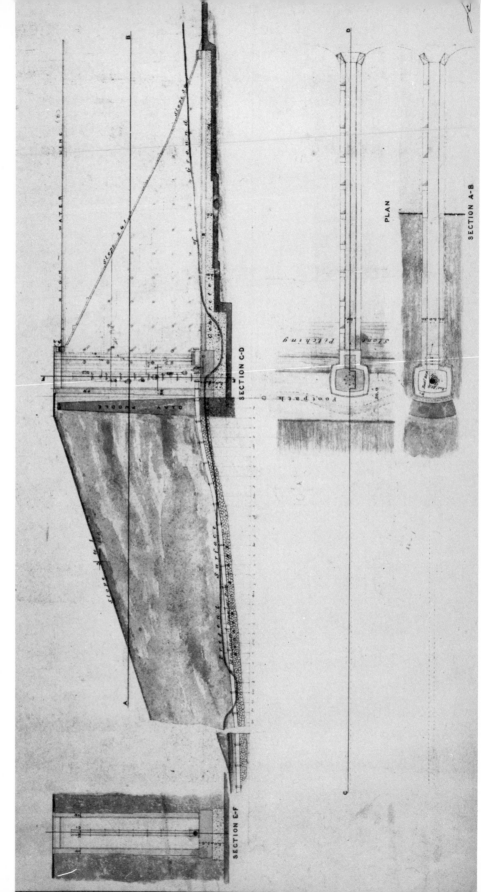

Figure 5.6 Outlet works (draw-off tank) at Horse Coppice reservoir, 1864

engine, for the waterworks. With the exception of the medieval Lendal tower used as an elevated water storage tank, however, all traces of these earlier waterworks have now disappeared. The origins of the present works date from 1846 when a company was formed to establish new works for meeting the increased demands and to provide a plentiful supply of pure and wholesome water. An Act of Parliament was obtained, the old works purchased and, on the advice of Thomas Hawksley, a site secured for the new works at Acomb Landing where the water of the Ouse was free from any of the contaminations by which it was then affected nearer the city. A site for a service reservoir was also acquired at Severus Hill, said to have been constructed by the Romans to perpetuate the memory of their Emperor Septimus Severus who died in York and whose body was burnt on the site, his ashes afterwards being conveyed to Rome for burial.[28]

James Simpson was next engaged. He arranged the installation of steam pumping plant and prepared a contract complete with a specification and drawings for three filter beds (Fig. 5.1) and two settling tanks at Acomb Landing and a service reservoir of 2 million gallons capacity at Severus Hill. Tenders appear to have been invited in July 1846 and a contract was awarded in December 1846. The conditions of contract are even more detailed than those for the Bristol waterworks and run to about 10 000 words. The specification is about 4000 words long.[29] In all respects except size, the filter beds were the same as those Simpson had so successfully constructed at Chelsea. One of these filter beds still exists and is still used to this day (1980).

(c) OTHER WORKS

Following the success of a well, referred to in Chapter 1, which Simpson sank in the red sandstone of Liverpool, during the 1840s he also sank a well in the same formation for Manchester but without achieving the same degree of success.[30]

On 15 October, 1845, a meeting of leading citizens in Newport was held at which it was agreed that the existing contaminated water supplies from wells could no longer be tolerated and a committee of six was appointed to bring forward a scheme. The committee lost no time in deciding that the country round Ynysyfto could supply sufficient water. On 30 October the committee decided to proceed with a scheme, engaged James Simpson to prepare the plans and instructed solicitors to obtain Parliamentary Powers. Capital was fixed at £20 000 and Parliamentary sanction was obtained on 16 July, 1846, only 9 months after the first meeting! Only 2 years later a reservoir with a storage capacity of 70 million gallons, and with a dam 42 ft high, had been built. One has to admire the vitality of the age.[31]

For the Stockport District Waterworks, Simpson designed the 60 ft high Horse Coppice dam including an outlet structure which he called a 'draw-off tank' (Fig. 5.6). It is somewhat similar to his grating tanks but in place of the well he substituted a standpipe, the top of which was several feet below top water level. Where the draw-off main crossed the cut-off trench it was supported on concrete. Untroubled by the possible consequences of rapid drawdown, which were to worry later designers, Simpson put a steep 2 to 1 slope on the reservoir side and a 3 to 1 slope on the downstream side of the embankment. Completed in 1864, the Horse Coppice reservoir remained in continuous use until 1948 when the reservoir was emptied to investigate leakage. A fracture was found in the outlet main which was repaired, and some of the draw-off valves were blanked off. During 1955–59 a 'dry' valve shaft was constructed to replace the 'wet' standpipe and a discharge tunnel was constructed to accommodate the outlet mains previously buried beneath the downstream slope of the embankment.[32]

In 1855 Simpson reported on a water supply of 6 mgd to be obtained by gravity through a 24 mile long pipeline from Cairnton on the river Dee for Aberdeen. Easton Gibb,[33] at the early age of 23, was awarded the contract in 1864 and the works were carried out under Simpson's supervision. Other towns where he constructed or improved waterworks were Cardiff, Reading, Cambridge, Carlisle, Exeter, Folkestone and Gravesend. He was also consulted, about the year 1856, as to gas and waterworks at Copenhagen, which he afterwards designed and carried out.[34] In association with two others he also reported in 1857 on proposals prepared by the Metropolitan Board of Works for the main drainage of London.[35]

In 1854 and 1855 James Simpson was elected president of the Institution of Civil Engineers. According to one source 'he was not brilliant as a witness nor as a speaker but his advocacy generally carried great weight with it and his opinions were held in high esteem not alone because of the soundness of his views but of his known and admitted honesty and uprightness of character!'[36] Simpson was one of the most influential waterworks engineers in the kingdom, particularly during the 1840s; he set very high standards in engineering practice and design and whilst he was ambivalent in his attitude towards constant supply, accepting it for Bristol and Edinburgh but rejecting it for London and Sheffield,[37] by his example in constructing, after thorough investigation, slow sand filters at Chelsea, he made a major contribution to the quality and safety of water supplies at a time when it was most needed.[38]

6 *James Leslie (1801–89)*

(a) THE EDINBURGH WATERWORKS

The original water supply for the City of Edinburgh was from wells and local sources, e.g. the Nor Loch, and the first public supply which came from outside the City was from springs at Comiston. Water from here was conveyed by means of a 3 in. lead pipe laid in 1676. Additional springs were later brought in from the same source, and between 1704 and 1720 the 3 in. pipe was replaced in stages by a 5 in. lead pipe. This pipe was in turn replaced by a 5 in. iron pipe in 1820.[1]

In 1760 the supply was increased from springs near Swanston in the Pentland Hills and wooden pipes were laid to carry water to the City. These wooden pipes were replaced by 7 in. iron pipes about 1790. During the Napoleonic wars nothing further was done and the population, which was rising fast in the city, was frequently 'thirsty and unwashed'.[2]

Very few people at that time enjoyed the luxury of a piped supply in their dwelling.

Those who were not so favoured were supplied by a class of water porters, male and female, called 'caddies', who traded under a licence and badge from the Magistrates, and supplied their customers at the rate of one penny per barrel, of from five to six gallons. The male portion of this set of persons were generally pensioners; the females were of the very lowest class; and as the licence and badge gave them a right of priority at the public wells, the multitudes of men, women, and children who attended at these wells for supplies were exposed to a description of Scotch Billingsgate in which these female 'caddies' excelled, and in which, fortunately, they have no representatives in our day. It fared ill with such poor persons as dared to complain of being hustled out of their turn by a member of this privileged body; and as during dry weather water could only be obtained at the wells once in four or five days, not unfrequently after midnight, there might be seen rows of vessels extending from 50 to 100 yards, each watched over by such members of the family as chose to surrender the hours which should have been appropriated to sleep, in order to obtain such a driblet of this necessary of life as could be carried off by hand. The weariness and fatigue of this watching were probably the least part of the evil. The quarrels, oaths, and bad language indulged in, and the consequent ruin to the morals of many young persons who were thus driven to congregate, were such that it was not surprising the inhabitants would no longer submit to the miserable supply which heretofore had been doled out to them, nor to the distress and misery of every kind attendant on that mode of obtaining it.[3]

A well-attended meeting of the inhabitants presided over by Frances Jeffrey, editor of the *Edinburgh Review*, was held in the Royal Exchange. The meeting declared that they were desirous of forwarding 'every measure lending to remove the evils from which the inhabitants have long suffered from the supply of water being extremely deficient both in quantity and quality',[4] and to carry out their objects they appointed a committee of which the two well-known authors, Henry MacKenzie and Henry Cockburn, were members. The result of that meeting was the formation of the Water Company which obtained an Act in July 1819. Under this Act the Company was empowered to carry out a scheme which had been proposed by Telford in 1811 which was to bring the Crawley spring situated in the Pentlands about 6 miles from Edinburgh and such quantity of water from the Glencorse Burn as might be deemed expedient, also to construct the Glencorse reservoir for the purpose of affording compensation to the millowners on the River Esk.[5]

The first Engineer of the Edinburgh Water Company was James Jardine (1776–1858) who had built the Union Canal and was the first person to determine the mean level of the sea. He undertook the construction of a pipeline, necessarily taking a circuitous route, which was 8½ miles long and which varied in diameter from 20 in. to 15 in., from the Crawley springs to the city. With Telford as chief designer he was also responsible for the execution of the Glencorse dam.[6] When the new works for bringing water from the Crawley springs were completed in August 1823 the supply amounted to 1–1½ mgd.

Matters now went on without complaint until the year 1842 when less than 12 in. of rain fell during the 7 months ending 31 October. The drought was so severe that many brooks and streams that had never been known to fail dried up. The water in the Glencorse reservoir was wholly exhausted and the position of the Water Company became very grave when the millowners on the Esk demanded that the Crawley springs should be turned into the Glencorse burn, a situation that was only overcome by paying the millowners an indemnity between £4000 and £5000. That a further supply of water had become essential could no longer be doubted, and in 1843 the Company obtained an Act authorizing them to bring in three more riverlets at Listonshiels, Bavelaw and Black Springs which lie on the north side of the Pentlands with compensation water reservoirs at Threipmuir and Harlaw (Fig. 6.1). Notwithstanding difficulties in obtaining possession of the land, Jardine initiated the works vigorously but, having reached the age of 70, he retired in 1846.

Jardine's successor was James Leslie (1801–89), the son of an architect and the nephew of Sir John Leslie, Professor of Natural Philosophy at Edinburgh University. He started his engineering career with the Rennies and the earlier part of it was spent mainly on harbour works. It was not until Leslie had reached his middle thirties that he became concerned with waterworks when his first assignment was a report prepared jointly with Jardine for the Town Council of Dundee, further reference to which is made later.

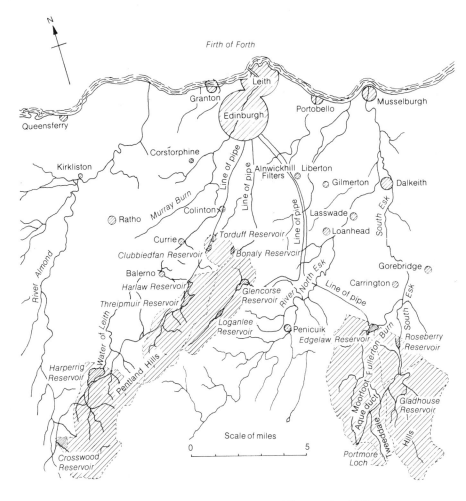

Figure 6.1 Edinburgh and District Waterworks, 1880

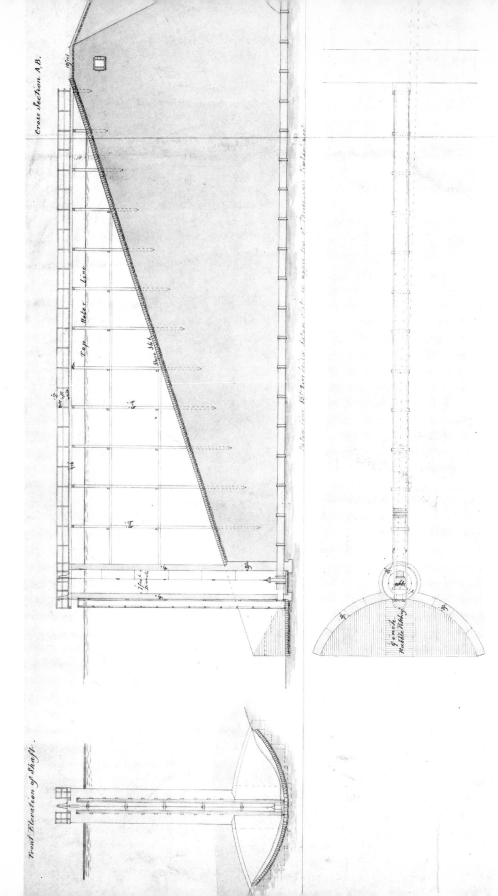

Figure 6.2 Bottom outlet works of Harlaw dam, 1848

The Threipmuir dam designed by Jardine was probably completed before Leslie took over, but his design for the Harlaw dam bottom outlet works dated 15 March, 1847, is shown (Fig 6.2). The discharge through a cast-iron pipeline laid on top of the dam foundations can be regulated by a sluice worked by a rod from the top of a masonry wet well with its foundations embedded near the upstream toe of the dam and supported against side-thrust by a circular wall. For valve inspection and main-tenance purposes, an outer sluice of oak working in guides can be let down and the water run off from the well. There was also a similar arrangement for an outlet works laid 40 ft above the bottom. Gangways supported on piers led out to the two masonry wet wells.

> Shortly before the completion of this reservoir, the inside slope of the embank-ment showed signs of slipping in consequence of its having been put together too hurriedly, without sufficient attention to the fact of its being composed en-tirely of hard boulder clay, which is difficult to consolidate without excessive wetting. This had the effect of slightly displacing the masonry of the tower.[7]

It was probably as a result of this experience that Leslie made a practice of specify-ing that the material in embankments should be placed in thin layers less than a foot thick, a practice which, probably unknown to Leslie, had already been adopted by Simpson. In 1883 the tower had stood for 35 years without further sign of move-ment and it is still standing today. The works authorized by the 1843 Act were com-pleted by Leslie in 1848.

While these works were yet in progress, however, it became more and more apparent that the yield from them would be insufficient and, probably at Leslie's in-stigation, the Company again applied to Parliament with the result that in 1847 it obtained powers to construct in the North Pentlands the reservoirs of Clubbie-dean, Torduff and Bonaly and in the South Pentlands to enlarge the Glencorse res-ervoir, also to construct an additional reservoir at Loganlea. The object in constructing the three former reservoirs was to store up the surplus spring water, and other pure water from the north side of the Pentlands, in order to maintain the supply to the citizens during periods of drought. The purpose of enlarging the res-ervoir at Glencorse, and of constructing an additional one in that valley at Logan-lea, was to store up such a supply as would at all times secure to the millers their statutory quantity, and enable the Company at the same time to keep the Crawley pipe always full. The Act of 1847 was the more interesting and important on account of its containing an obligation 'on the Company to furnish that supply on the system of constant service'.[8] Here one can detect the influence of Chadwick. This scheme was laid out by Rendel and Beardmore but the working drawings were made and the works carried out under the supervision of James Leslie.[9]

The Clubbiedean, Torduff and Loganlea reservoirs are much alike and a descrip-

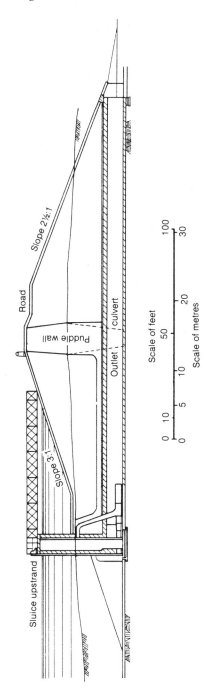

Figure 6.3. Harperrig dam, 1859 (redrawn from Fig. 6 of reference 7)

tion of one will suffice for all. The embankments were formed with slopes of 3 to 1 inside and 2½ to 1 outside with a width of 10 ft at the top which was 5 ft above top water level. A puddle wall in the interior of the bank, 8 ft wide at the top increased with a batter of 1 in 8 on each side down to the level of the ground, the depth of the puddle trench varying according to the nature of the material. Except that the bottom outlets discharged into tunnels driven into the solid rock and access to the tops of the wet wells was obtained by single-span steel girder bridges, the outlet arrangements at Torduff and Loganlea were similar to Harlaw. For the Clubbie-dean dam, reliance was placed on a single 21 in. diameter cast-iron pipeline buried beneath the embankment.

At Torduff reservoir some leakage has developed and remedial measures are in hand. At Clubbiedean reservoir it became necessary during the 1970s to grout the embankment and rock foundations because the limestone on which the embankment is founded was being dissolved in places, creating – on account of its age – leakage paths through the embankment.

The increased demands of the public again made it necessary to apply to Parliament for additional powers, and this time with James Leslie as the sole engineer an Act was obtained in 1856 authorizing the exploitation of the Colzium springs together with a compensation water reservoir at Harperrig (Fig. 6.3) which was completed in 1859. Leslie in this case introduced a great improvement in design by arranging that both the upper and the lower outlet should discharge into a bottom outlet culvert which had also been used for river diversion during construction. The wet well is square and is furnished with sluices outside and inside.

A still further supply being required, an Act to exploit the Crosswood springs was obtained in 1863. A reservoir, as usual, for compensation water for the mill-owners was constructed on the Crosswood burn. The design of the dam was similar to the Harperrig design and it was completed in 1868.

Leslie's methods of construction were admired by his contemporaries and in the discussion in 1859 on Matthew B. Jackson's paper on the Yan Yean Scheme, Henry Conybeare, the engineer for the Bombay Waterworks, is reported to have said that

> he had heard it often remarked by Engineers of waterworks, that the railways had introduced a loose way of making embankments which were thrown up with great rapidity but without sufficient attention being paid to their consolidation throughout. Hence failures had arisen from the dams not being water-tight. These were attributed chiefly to the earth being tipped from waggons. At Mr. Leslie's Edinburgh Waterworks all waggons were excluded, carts only being allowed, and the banks were formed in layers six inches thick, each layer being thoroughly indurated and punned by the constant passage of the carts used in spreading the successive layer. . . . Owing to recent accidents, distrust was felt if the dams were above a certain height, but if they were

formed as those at Edinburgh had been, there would be no difficulty in carrying the dams to any height. He considered Mr. Leslie's practice on these points a model for imitation.[10]

Specifications written by Leslie before the collapse of the Bilberry dam in 1852 allowed banks to be constructed in 9 in. layers[11] similar to Simpson (p. 88) but after 1852 he reduced the specified thickness to 6 in. and perhaps influenced by Captain Moody's advice at the Bilberry disaster inquest (p. 64), he also specified that

> the most clayey and earthy part of the stuff from the excavations is to be used for the heart of the embankment and more especially for the inner side, the more stony, gravelly or sandy portion, if any, is to be used for forming the slopes and more especially for the outer side of the embankment.[12]

The Harperrig and Crosswood embankments were among the best designed and constructed dams of their period.

The completion of the Crosswood scheme also completed the exploitation of the Pentlands which yielded a total of 6.3 mgd, of which 4.5 mgd, consisting almost entirely of spring water, came from the north side and the remainder from the south side. Following an Act passed in 1869, the works of the Edinburgh Water Company were taken over from the Company by a public Water Trust with representatives from the Corporations of Edinburgh, Leith and Portobello on 15 May, 1870.

In the view of many people the Edinburgh Water Company did not adopt a bold enough policy, and their schemes were always too little and too late. When complaints of a defective water supply arose in 1868, the three burghs of Edinburgh, Leith and Portobello resolved to undertake joint measures to obtain an adequate constant supply and appointed James W. Stewart, CE, as their engineer. Stewart drew attention to St Mary's Loch 33 miles south of Edinburgh and, supported by Bateman in a supplementary report, he recommended it as the most suitable source of supply. Bateman wrote:

> The district which has been selected by the Water Company as the most eligible for an extension of works is that which drains to the Fullerton Burn and the South Esk river. . . . The area of the drainage ground is about 14,500 acres of which 7,500 are on the South Esk and 7,000 on the Fullerton Burn . . . the Fullerton Burn was so foul on the occasion of my visit . . . that I cannot recommend it as a source of supply for the inhabitants although it might be used for compensation.

Assuming that with the necessary storage capacity the Fullerton Burn would be used only for compensation water, he estimated that the yield for town supply from the South Esk catchment area would be 8.4 million gallons which is very close to the average yield of 8.69 mgd subsequently established for the Moorfoot hills scheme.

Comparing the proposed long aqueduct that would be needed for the St Mary's Loch scheme with the 25¾ mile long aqueduct he had recently successfully completed from Loch Katrine for the Corporation of Glasgow, Bateman also wrote:

> The actual tunnelling on the Loch Katrine aqueduct was 13 miles – on the St Mary's Loch aqueduct it will be between 8 & 9 miles. The total length of cutting and tunnelling on Loch Katrine was about 22 miles – on the St Mary's Loch they will be about 12 miles. The St Mary's Loch tunnel will be of less magnitude instead of greater; for it is not the length of a tunnel which increases its magnitude but its size and its depth below the surface; and in these respects as well as in the quality of the material to be tunnelled through St. Mary's Loch has the advantage. . . . There is nothing that is not perfectly easy to cut through. To an observant eye the character and formation of the surface of the hills pretty clearly indicate the nature of the rocks which be beneath. Hard and abdurate rocks rise in rugged summits and bold escarpments and where there are alternating beds of hard and soft rocks, highly inclined . . . they form a furrowed surface, the hard rocks rising into ridges and the softer rocks, time and weather worn, into depressions or hollows. This description would suit the Loch Katrine district where the character of the rocks tunnelled through beneath was clearly shown on the surface and could be traced for miles across the country. Nothing of this kind is to be found in the line of the St Mary's Loch aqueduct. Smooth slopes and round-topped hills with a large quantity of detritus on the sides show the tender nature of the rocks which will be found to consist, not of the tough and stubborn mica slate and quartzose rock of the lower silurian which we met with near Loch Katrine but, for the most part, of the softer beds of the grey wacke and clay slate rocks which form the upper part of the same geological formation.[13]

Bateman did not deny that for a comparable yield the St Mary's Loch scheme would be more expensive but he argued that, as compared with a total yield of 8.4 mgd for the Moorfoot hills scheme, the St Mary's Loch scheme could be developed in stages to give a total yield of 24 mgd and that, in the long run, it would be cheaper. He therefore recommended the St Mary's Loch scheme and it was included in the 1869 Act for transferring the ownership of the Waterworks from the Water Company to the Trust but, after having passed the House of Commons, this part of the Act was thrown out by the House of Lords on account of some small inaccuracy in the deposited plans.

As was to have been expected when the Trustees had taken over from the Water Company as the authority responsible for water supply, they turned their thoughts again towards St Mary's Loch and, after having again consulted J. W. Stewart, took the first opportunity of re-introducing the measure.[14] After the Parliamentary notices had been published and the Bill deposited, a large amount of unrest regarding the measure began to be felt on the part of a considerable portion of the public. This uneasiness was very much caused by a series of letters in the *Scotsman* newspaper by a certain Dr Charles Wilson, a retired medical man and a shareholder in the Old Water Company, who signed himself 'A Physician': Making great play of the nature, habits and propensities of water fleas, he had a great aversion to the use of lake water notwithstanding the example of Glasgow – where the waters of Loch Katrine had been introduced to the great advantage of the citizens of the western metropolis.

When the parliamentary estimates came up for consideration by the Water Trust, James Leslie was convinced that the sum of £500 000 allowed for the cost of the project was too low, and declined to have his name on the plans. However, his views were adopted by only two of the Trustees and it was resolved to proceed with the Bill which was passed by a Select Committee of the House of Commons.

The decision of the House of Commons produced a very mixed state of feeling in Edinburgh, and the opponents of the measure were more than ever determined to get it thrown out by the House of Lords. During the interval between the passage of the Bill from the House of Commons to the House of Lords the walls were placarded with huge representations of a water flea, given the name *Daphnia pulex*, which produced the desired effect and stirred up the people against the measure. Never since the celebrated Disruption of the Church of Scotland in 1843 had party feeling in Edinburgh run so high nor so embittered as in the great water struggle.

When the Bill came before a Select Committee of the House of Lords, the Opposition contended:

(1) that the cost of the works would far exceed the sum of £500 000 specified in the Bill;
(2) the water of St Mary's Loch was insipid and unsuitable for drinking and cooking purposes; and
(3) an ample supply of water, of undoubtedly superior quality, could be obtained at less cost and in a much shorter time within the county of Edinburgh or its immediate vicinity.

In this last contention the opposition were ably assisted by Thomas Hawksley who, speaking off the cuff, staked his professional reputation that for a sum of £100 000 he could construct reservoirs in the South Pentlands (Glencorse Valley) and that there was sufficient water there to supply Edinburgh with 50 gallons per head per diem. As one wag under the title 'Hawksley's Edition of the Psalms of David' wrote:

> By Crawley streams we sat and wept;
> St Mary's we thought on:
> In midst thereof, we hung our harps
> The Pentland rocks upon.[15]

Leslie was examined on Hawksley's theory by the Committee, and it is much to his credit that even though he was a witness for the Opposition, it did not obtain his concurrence. Nevertheless, the opponents succeeded in having the St Mary's Loch Bill cast out by the House of Lords.

As James Colston wrote in 1890:

> It was done on a false issue. The Pentlands proposal has never been carried out; because the water was not obtainable except at a much larger cost than it could be had elsewhere. This the promoters of St Mary's Loch scheme knew at the time. It was a hard thing for them to suffer defeat, because of the Lords' Committee having lent their ears to bold engineering imaginative device, rather than to hard facts.[16]

More than a century later, but in a somewhat different way, the catchment area of St Mary's Loch is now being exploited in two equal instalments each estimated to yield 22.5 mgd by the Megget scheme. The Megget river discharges into St Mary's Loch and under the first stage, which is expected to be completed in 1983, the Megget reservoir is being created on this stream by an earth dam which exploits approximately half the catchment area of the loch. From the reservoir the water will be conveyed northwards by aqueduct and pipeline to Gladhouse reservoir built in 1879, Rosebery Treatment Works built in 1953 and Glencorse reservoir built in 1822, the last-named at 28.2 miles being the most distant of the three. In the second stage additional water will be obtained by pumping water from St Mary's Loch into the Megget reservoir. At the same time the water level in the loch will be brought under control by the construction of sluices at the outlet of the loch, the range of control being 4 ft.[17]

In 1870 James Leslie took his son, Alexander, into partnership and in 1872 James became Sole Engineer of the Trust. He and Thomas Hawksley were deputed to report on the best means of obtaining additional supplies and in 1873 they reported in favour of the Moorfoot hills scheme. With the South Esk catchment area used for town supply and the Fullerton burn catchment for compensation water, the scheme as constructed is similar to that described by Bateman.[18a] The design of the Edgelaw embankment on the Fullerton burn by the firm of J. and A. Leslie included a valve well just upstream of the clay corewall instead of a control shaft at the upstream toe of the dam, a retrograde step, possibly taken due to the influence of Hawksley who almost invariably used valve wells. On the other hand, an experience during exploration for this embankment illustrating the care taken by the firm in their site investigations is worth recording:

> Whilst trial-boring operations were being prosecuted to test the nature of the foundations for the puddle trench, what on a previous occasion had been taken for solid rock turned out to be merely a boulder although the bed of the stream and its left bank consisted of sound rock. A pit was accordingly sunk in the immediate vicinity of the original borehole but no firm bottom was reached at the level indicated. After proceeding further with this pit which was entirely through fine sand and required careful timbering, it was at length abandoned and the original borehole continued. The boulder was soon pierced and the boring rods went down an additional depth of nearly 30 feet without reaching solid rock. It was therefore considered advisable to look out for another site so that the embankment might be constructed in a more economical manner.[18b]

A better site was found about a mile further downstream. This careful site investigation is in striking contrast with that for the cut-off trench for the Silent Valley dam built during the 1920s in Northern Ireland where a boulder was also mistaken for solid rock but without the mistake being detected until after construction had already commenced. Because it was then too late to move the dam site elsewhere it became necessary to sink at great expense a cut-off trench 180 ft deep before a sound impermeable base was reached.[19]

Except for some slipping of the inner face of the Edgelaw embankment, no unforeseen difficulties were experienced during the construction period and these works in the Moorfoot hills were completed in 1880.

In order to comply with modern standards of safety the discharging capacities of the spillways have in all cases had to be increased, but this applies to almost all earth dams built during the nineteenth century. During this period in the development of her water resources, Edinburgh was most fortunate in having such an outstanding dam engineer as James Leslie in charge.

(b) THE DUNDEE WATERWORKS

As already stated, Leslie's first waterworks assignment was a scheme he prepared in conjunction with Jardine on behalf of the Town Council of Dundee for supplying the town with water from the Monikie district. The necessary Act was obtained in 1837, but was allowed to lapse.

In 1844 the Dundee Water Company[20] came into existence and consulted Leslie who revived the Monikie scheme (Fig. 6.4). His proposed headworks were a catchwater intercepting 3443 acres, a settling basin of 288 million gallons capacity and a clear-water tank of 36 million gallons capacity. He declared that normally the streams of the Monikie district were

> pure and to taste and appearance of good quality [but that] the water of all streams will, however, most probably be more or less muddy after heavy rains and, therefore, to obviate the necessity of taking it into the town before it has had time to settle in the large reservoir and to become pure, a clear water basin . . . capable of holding . . . nearly four weeks supply of the town, is provided immediately below the large reservoir. No filtration will be required . . . the supply of water will, by means of a floating sluice, be always taken from near the surface.[21]

Also proposed were an aqueduct 3 miles long and a 15 in. diameter cast-iron pipe 4 miles long from the clear-water tank to a service reservoir on the outskirts of the town at Stobbs Muir. Leslie's recommendations were accepted by the Water Company and the necessary Act was obtained in 1845. Without the catchwater but with an intake on the Monikie burn, these works were completed in 1848, the catch-water being completed 4 years later.

The storage capacity of the clear-water tank being relatively small, there must have been a great temptation to draw down the settling basin during times of drought but this would have been incompatible with its intended function. Instead, the Company obtained another Act in 1853 under which they constructed another reservoir on the north side of the settling tank and increased the storage capacity of the clear-water basin.

The first Monikie main, laid under the Act of 1845, proved very defective in capacity, delivering only about half the designed supply. In 1862, after the necessary Act had been obtained, a second 15 in. diameter main was laid. The demand for water continued to increase and another Bill was successfully promoted in 1866 for the construction of a dam to form an impounding reservoir on the Crombie burn, part of the storage capacity being reserved for compensation water. Except that it has a bottom outlet only, the design of the outlet structure with culvert of the Crombie dam is similar to the Harperrig design. After the completion of this dam, in 1868, the Monikie scheme gave a reliable yield amounting to 2 mgd excluding compensation water. James Leslie was the consulting engineer for these works at all stages of the construction, being responsible for the design and the preparation of contract documents, also for giving advice during construction.[22]

Under an Act dated 1869 the Magistrates and Council of the Royal Burgh of Dundee were constituted a body of Commissioners authorized to take over the lands and works of the private Water Company and the price to be paid by the Commission was fixed at £14 315.

Almost immediately after the Commissioners were appointed and the old Water Company's undertaking was vested in them, there was a water famine in Dundee and district.

> The supply at Monikie was almost exhausted and temporary help was obtained by supplementing the supply from the compensation water from Crombie etc. . . . The supply laid on to the water area was intermittent and restricted to a few hours per day. The Commissioners decided to construct new works to enable them to bring in a plentiful supply to the city and surrounding districts and appointed John Frederick La Trobe Bateman Esq. Waterworks engineer to submit a scheme.[23]

In the introduction to his report, Bateman made acknowledgements as follows:

> The reports of Messrs. Leslie, Fulton & Stewart and that of your Sub-Committee appointed to examine the localities referred to by the gentlemen named were placed in my hands. All these I carefully considered and after my arrival in Dundee, I received much valuable information from Mr. Robertson, Convenor of the Committee, and from Mr. Duncan, the late Manager of the Water Works.[24]

Accompanied by Robertson and Duncan, Bateman visited the existing waterworks and the proposed sites for new works.

Both John Fullerton and J. W. Stewart, in their reports written during 1865 and 1868 respectively, proposed that the Isa river should be exploited. Leslie, on the other hand, in a report written in 1865, considered that the Loch of Lintrathen with the Melgam river diverted into it would be a better source of supply and Bateman quoted Leslie as stating 'that it would afford a supply of unquestionably good and pure water, and much more than amply sufficient for the supply of Dundee for many years to come.'[25]

In 50 years the population of Dundee had almost trebled from 31 000 in 1811 to 90 417 in 1861 and it had further increased to about 115 000 in 1870. Bateman wrote:

> The rapid increase in the last nine years is owing mainly to the large extension of manufacturers connected with the development of the Jute Trade. For the wants of the various manufactories there is no proper or sufficient supply of Water. They have to depend on very trifling local sources and on the water caught in ponds from heavy rain; and a large demand for water for manufacturing purposes exists which it is very important to supply.[26]

On the basis of a future population of 180 000 in Dundee including its immediate neighbourhood and a future population of 60 000 in the neighbouring towns of Arbroath, Carnoustie, Forfar and Kirriemuir (also 50 gallons per head per day including commercial consumption for the former and 30 gallons per head per day for the latter), Bateman arrived at a total of 10.8 mgd, but the scheme he proposed was for 12 mgd. This was subsequently referred to by him as being a first instalment only.

Bateman then turned the reader's attention to the source from which the water was to be obtained and wrote:

> There are some nearer sources which, I understand, have attracted the attention of some of your townspeople; but, owing to their limited extent, the small amount of rainfall, the character of the manure used in the cultivation of the soil and the nature of the crops produced, they are, in my opinion, unsuitable and not worth your attention.
>
> If I may be permitted to quote myself 'The supply to large towns ought to be sought for in those mountain districts where the largest amount of rain falls, where there is little or no population, where manured lands scarcely exist, and where copious springs are constantly supplying the purest and softest water.'
>
> These considerations naturally point to the Grampian mountains as the proper source of supply to Dundee and its neighbouring towns. They lie at no great distance and are easily accessible – their geological structure ensures the purest and softest water – their great elevation a most copious rainfall; and their steep and almost uncultivated slopes secure a rapid delivery of the rain which falls upon them in an uncontaminated condition.
>
> The nearest stream in these mountains, at a sufficient elevation to supply the higher parts of Dundee is the River Melgam at Lintrathen; and it is also in all other respects the best and most desirable source to which you can resort.[27]

The Melgam river and the Loch of Lintrathen combined have a catchment area of 18 975 acres, and to provide storage capacity for both water supply and compensation water amounting to about 8 mgd, Bateman proposed that an embankment should be constructed to raise the water level in the Lintrathen Loch about 20 ft.

Bateman considered that, for the small yield of 2 mgd obtained, the existing Monikie works with a total storage capacity of about 650 million gallons were over-reservoired and he wrote: 'If the present Works, with their large storage reservoirs, had not been constructed, the best route [for the aqueduct] would have been direct to Dundee, but under existing circumstances, there can be no question of the propriety of conducting the water to the existing Works.'[28] As shown on the map (Fig. 6.4) as the 'Parliamentary Route 1871', he therefore recommended an aqueduct 21 miles long from the Loch of Lintrathen to the Crombie reservoir, 13 miles of which consisted of a covered conduit not under pressure and the remaining 8 miles of 27

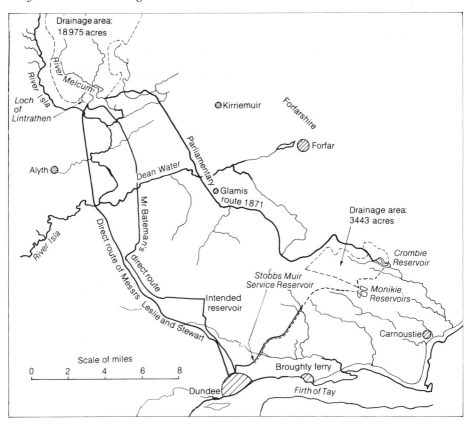

Figure 6.4 Dundee Waterworks including alternative routes proposed in 1872 for main from Lintrathen Loch (redrawn from contemporary drawing)

in. diameter pipeline across the valley of Strathmore, the route selected being the one giving the shortest length of piping and the least pressure. The length over which the pressure exceeded 400 ft head of water was limited to 2½ miles, and it nowhere exceeded 500 ft (Fig. 6.5). He also recommended a third main, 20 in. diameter, between Gagiewell and Stobbs Muir reservoir.

Bateman's scheme was adopted, the necessary Parliamentary plans were submitted and the Commissioners were authorized to carry out the necessary works under an Act which received the Royal Assent in 1871. However, a dispute then arose as to whether to proceed with the Parliamentary route – which was strongly supported by the convenor, William Robertson – or a direct route to Dundee, this plan being supported by some of the other Commissioners including Hugh Ballinghall. Easton Gibb, who as a contractor had recently built under the direction

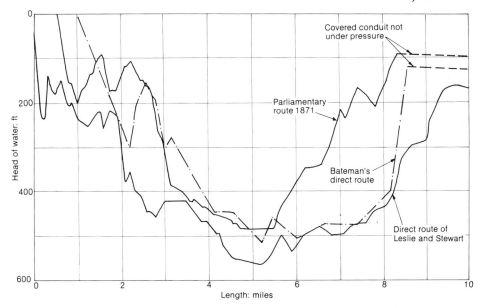

Figure 6.5 'The lengths of and pressures upon the pipes crossing Strathmore Valley', plotted from diagram by J. F. Bateman, 1872

of James Simpson the 24 mile long Aberdeen water supply aqueduct, was a friend of Ballinghall and helped him with technical advice in his opposition to the Parliamentary route.[29]

Perhaps because of his advocacy of the unsuccessful St Mary's Loch scheme, J. W. Stewart was regarded as being an expert on aqueducts and pipelines and he was asked to give his opinion. He strongly recommended that cast-iron pipes should be used exclusively on a direct route between Lintrathen and the service reservoirs in Dundee instead of a combination of pipes, aqueducts and reservoirs as proposed by Bateman.[30] At the meeting of the Water Commission held on 20 October, 1871, the Commissioners by a majority, with the Convenor dissenting, accepted Stewart's recommendation and resolved to abandon the Parliamentary route recommended by Bateman.

On 31 October, 1871, James Leslie and J. W. Stewart were then instructed to survey the district between Lintrathen and Dundee and to prepare Parliamentary plans for a direct route. In their joint report dated 6 December, 1871, they reported that this had been done. They stated that 'after due deliberation' they found 'that the most eligible mode of conveying the water from Lintrathen to Dundee was by iron pipes'.[31] Instead of making a recommendation on the quantity of water to be brought in as a first instalment, they also gave estimates for alternative schemes with quantities delivered to Dundee varying between 4 and

12 mgd. The Commissioners decided that the first instalment should be 8 mgd, requiring a 27 in. diameter pipeline. Bateman was not content to have the cup dashed from his lip and he sent an unsolicited report dated 9 January, 1872, to the Water Commissioners which began as follows:

> After your decision to adopt what has been called 'the direct Route' and to apply to Parliament for powers to abandon the works laid out by me . . . which were authorized by the Act of last Session; and your appointment of other engineers to carry out your wishes, I thought it better to reserve the remarks I felt bound to make, in answer to the objections urged to my recommendations, until the surveys of the engineers had been completed, their plans deposited and their reports and estimates furnished.
>
> I pass over, as unworthy of notice, the charges of unfairness and inaccuracy which have been brought against me – of mapping out gigantic new schemes – of squandering money and destroying present property for the purpose, it is insinuated, of pocketing a commission on the outlay; nor do I intend to enter into a minute examination of the audaciously inaccurate estimates (by Stewart) which were put forward in October last for the purpose of deprecating my views and of prejudicing the public mind against the scheme I had laid out for the supply of the town.[32]

Bateman also complained that considering how much his professional reputation was affected by the course which had been pursued, it would have been but common courtesy to have sent him at the earliest opportunity a copy of the Leslie and Stewart report and the plans to which it referred, instead of first learning of them through the press. He wrote:

> The system of conveyance adopted by Messrs. Leslie & Stewart differs very greatly from that which I should have recommended in the adoption of a direct route. . . . They adopt cast-iron pipes for the whole distance, going as nearly straight from point to point as the configuration of the country will allow. The result is that the pipe is under pressure throughout its whole length – the maximum pressure being about 560 feet and for 6 miles together varying from 400 feet to 560 feet [Fig. 6.5]. There is not, so far as I am aware, any line of main pipe of similar size and length under such heavy pressure. No engineer accustomed to the working of pipes under pressure would willingly incur the attendant risks. It is not only the strength of the iron itself that has to be considered but the difficulty of maintaining the joints under the excessive pressure.[33]

Bateman then put forward his own proposals for a direct route in which over a length of 4¼ miles the pressure would have varied between 400 and 510 ft.

For the three alternative routes Bateman gave his own cost estimates, in which he claimed that both his routes were cheaper than Leslie and Stewart's direct route and he concluded his report by expressing the hope that he had said enough 'to convince you that the decision you had arrived at was an erroneous one. In the interests of the town you represent I trust my endeavours to do so may not be in vain.'

Leslie and Stewart evidently disagreed with Bateman's estimates, in particular his estimated cost for covered conduits, and his last communication to the Dundee Water Commissioners is one dated February 5, 1872, in which, full of resentment, he wrote:

> I should not trouble you again upon the questions which have given rise to so much discussion nor make any observations upon Messrs. Leslie & Stewart's reply to me if it had not been that in this reply my estimates are for the first time impugned. I am prepared to defend the course I have taken and to substantiate every statement I have made either before a referee or a Parliamentary Committee, but I cannot, in the meantime, allow the public to be misled by such false estimates as have been put upon the works I proposed.

Bateman must, with some justification, have felt particularly angry with Leslie for having refused to endorse Stewart's estimates for the aqueduct for the St Mary's Loch scheme, but being now prepared to accept them for the proposed pipeline for the Lintrathen scheme. He continued by describing the numerous places such as for the Manchester Waterworks and the Halifax Waterworks where he had constructed concrete conduits, and their costs which were well below the figure he had used for estimating purposes and which Leslie and Stewart had increased by over 50 per cent. Despite Bateman's protests, the application to Parliament for the direct route went ahead and it was sanctioned by an Act in 1872. According to the writer of Leslie's obituary 'in the promotion of this scheme his hands were materially strengthened by the co-operation of Mr. Hawksley.'[34]

A report dated 27 May, 1873, headed 'Dundee Water', by J. and A. Leslie starts:

> By Minute of 6th March, communication on 12th of that month, 'the Engineers' were requested as soon as possible to make out the plans and specifications of the whole works necessary for bringing the water from Lintrathen to Dundee, and including the high water level reservoir, – that is to say the works more especially under the department of Mr. Stewart.

For the very same reasons that Bateman had advocated such a reservoir, J. and A. Leslie wrote:

> In the event of an accident to the main pipe between Lintrathen & Dundee, the

town will, so long as there is no intermediate reservoir, be dependent for its supply on the maximum discharge of the Monikie pipes, together with the storage of the existing town reservoirs, which are not of sufficient capacity to maintain for 6 days a supply of more than 5 million gallons per day. It is therefore obvious that when the daily requirements of the town exceed this quantity, additional storage must be provided near Dundee in order that a full supply may be kept up during any temporary suspension of a supply from Lintrathen for repairs on the pipe or otherwise.

However, they added:

This reservoir is not absolutely necessary for several years to come and it may be sufficient, in the meantime, in order to prevent any undue pressure on the pipes to have a small overflow cistern at the end of the 27 inch main at Clatto [the proposed site of the reservoir].

Stewart in no way accepted the need for a high-level reservoir[35] and a decision was taken to commence the construction of the works without it. The contract drawings for the embankment at Lintrathen were completed by December 1872 and a contract for the headworks was awarded to Easton Gibb.

Subsequent events are described in a report[36] to the Water Commissioners dated 1913 which states:

while the works authorised by the [1872] Act were in progress, the Commissioners discovered that the work was to cost more than had been estimated for and that an additional reservoir on the line of piping from the Loch would be necessary to maintain a continuous supply to the city. The Dundee Water (Additional Powers) Act 1874 was obtained for this and other reasons.

Clatto reservoir was constructed. A later entry in the same report states:

The main pipe laid between Lintrathen Loch and Catto proved very unsatisfactory and untrustworthy, leaking and bursting continually. The requirements of the water area were ever increasing and it was found expedient to lay down a duplicate pipe so as to ensure a constant supply. For this and other purposes the Act of 1882 was obtained.

Having been for 25 years responsible for Dundee's water supply under the old company, Leslie no doubt resented Bateman – a younger man – being called in, and probably felt justified in supplanting him. However, as after-events showed, Bateman was a much better and more experienced engineer on aqueducts than

114

either Leslie or Stewart, and if he had been allowed to proceed with his own scheme he would have saved the Dundee Water Commissioners a lot of trouble and expense on burst pipes and the consequential interruptions to the water supply.

Leslie also took his son-in-law, R. C. Reid, into partnership and under the name of Leslie and Reid his firm has become the oldest British waterworks consulting engineering firm still in existence. During his lifetime, the firm was responsible for works for the water supply of Dunfermline, Berwick-on-Tweed, Dunbar, Peterhead, Dalry, Thurso, Irvine, Bathgate, Kirkwall, Galashiels, Bothwell, Hawick, Peebles and St Andrews.

7 John Wignall Leather (1810–87) and the Bradford Waterworks

The Bradford Waterworks Company was authorized by an Act dated 1838, and in the same year they engaged George Leather and Son to advise them on the best method of increasing the water supply. The firm reported in favour of bringing certain springs at Manywells in the Hewenden Beck Valley, about 7 miles from Bradford, to that town and were then instructed by the Water Company to complete Parliamentary plans for the project. The scheme (Fig. 7.1) consisted of a compensation reservoir on the Hewenden Beck opposite the Manywells Springs, a storage reservoir at Chellow Dean and a service reservoir in Bradford with a line of pipes conveying the water from a well at Manywells to the service reservoir. These works were executed between 1842 and 1844.[1]

There was then a pause in construction until in January 1850 George Oxley, the Manager of the Company, wrote to Wignall Leather intimating 'the wish and determination of the Directors to take such measures during the coming summer as will bring all the water that flowed from Manywells' into supply.[2]

It would appear that at some time previously the Chellow Dean reservoir had been full with water running to waste, and that the Directors had decided for themselves that more storage capacity was needed. Four months later Oxley wrote again to Wignall Leather referring to his earlier letter. He complained bitterly that the summer was passing away without anything having been done and he added

> unless you can give them [the Directors] your services in good earnest so as to enable them to set about the enlargement of their works with that promptitude which they consider the case fully justifies them in requiring, they have fully resolved to call in the assistance of some other professional gentleman without further delay.[3]

Wignall Leather's reply is lost but it was obviously conciliatory and one can speculate that because the water consumption was increasing rapidly and would make bigger drafts on the available storage capacity at Chellow Dean in the future, he also expressed his doubts whether additional storage capacity would improve the

116

situation. He seems to have been unwilling to commit himself until some gauging of the yield from Manywells, which he had in progress, gave him better records. In his next letter, dated 27 June, 1850, Oxley wrote:

> I am glad to find you do not think I have scolded you without cause. Perhaps I ought not to differ from you in the view you take of our position and resources without great deference; but this I know, that facts are stubborn and figures sometimes false. . . . [We are] relying upon a supply as uncertain as the clouds, and unless it should please Providence to send us some wet weather shortly, our reservoir will be as dry as a desert in the course of a month or so. . . . The calculations in reference to the gauge are no doubt necessary but whatever these figures may bring out, they will not prove to the Directors what common sense and experience has made plain to everybody, that more reservoir work is of paramount importance. . . .
> Another store reservoir . . . should be made forthwith.[4]

The upshot of this was that a second storage reservoir was constructed by Wignall Leather at Chellow Dean.

In 1851 Wignall Leather was instructed to devise a scheme which would add considerably to the existing source of supply; he reported in favour of utilizing the Hewenden Beck catchment area and, by means of a tunnel, also part of the Worth river catchment area.

There then followed a Parliamentary contest in the 1852–53 session with the Bradford Corporation who, advised by J. F. Bateman, had a rival scheme based on exploiting the river Worth. The outcome of this contest was that both schemes were thrown out.[5]

Wignall Leather then devised new proposals based on exploiting catchment areas in the Wharfe and Aire valleys and also further development of the Hewenden Valley. These works (Fig. 7.1) comprised the following:

(1) A branch aqueduct which, after tapping springs over a length of 4 miles in the Wharfe Valley, joined a main aqueduct from a storage reservoir at Barden (today known as the Lower Barden reservoir) which passed in tunnel beneath a storage reservoir at Chelker (water being able to be admitted to or withdrawn from this reservoir through a branch pipeline) and then entered another tunnel across the watershed to more springs over a length of 5 miles in the Aire Valley before arriving at another service reservoir near Bradford, the total length of the main aqueduct being 17½ miles of which nearly 4 miles was in tunnel;
(2) a compensation water reservoir in the Wharfe Valley at Grimwith;
(3) a compensation water reservoir in the Aire Valley at Silsden; a storage reservoir at Stubden in the Hewenden Valley and a conduit from Stubden to the Upper Chellow Dean reservoir.

117

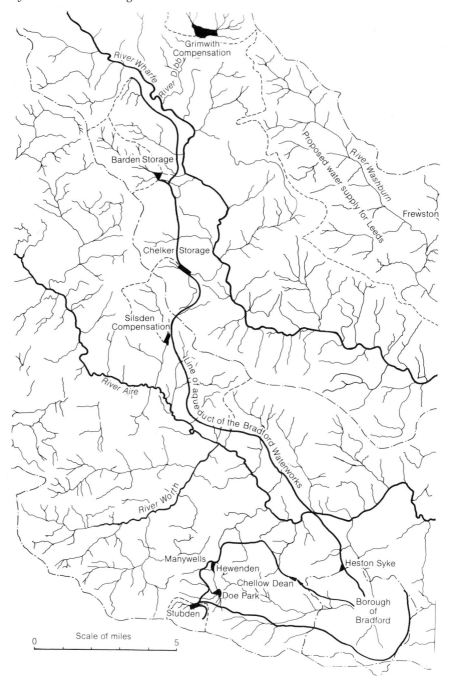

Figure 7.1 Bradford Waterworks (as conceived by J. Wignall Leather), 1864

These bold and far-sighted proposals were adopted by the Water Company and later the Corporation agreed to purchase the undertaking of the Company, and also to support Wignall Leather's scheme in Parliament. With the exception of the Stubden and Doe Park reservoirs, and notwithstanding opposition from mill-owners and landowners in both Houses of Parliament, an Act authorizing the Works was obtained in 1854. Together with a new conduit for supplying the high-lying parts of Bradford the Stubden and Doe Park reservoirs were authorized by a subsequent Act dated 1858 at which time a catchwater to the Chelker reservoir (Fig. 7.2) was also authorized. J. Wignall Leather's designs for the five main dams are shown (Fig. 7.3). The designs were such that 'having gone to great expense and trouble to make an embankment to retain the water, an easy access is afforded to its entry into the very heart of the work, where it will be sure to find any weak place that may exist either in the puddle or the masonry.'[6]

The transfer of the waterworks from the Company to the Corporation took place in October 1855, and from the annual reports which Wignall Leather submitted to the Corporation from October 1857 to 1863, also the annual reports of the Water-works Committee from October 1857 to October 1877, it is possible to follow the progress of these works. The works took far longer to construct than estimated and the greatest difficulty was experienced in making and keeping the reservoirs watertight. Several of them gave trouble after Wignall Leather ceased to be respon-sible for them. It was not until Thomas Hawksley started using a cementation process for sealing fissures in rock for the Cowm and Tunstall dams, about 1877, that a strong tool for controlling leakage from reservoirs started coming into use[7] and in the early Victorian period reliance was of necessity placed on ensuring that leakage was clean, also on keeping both the leakage and the embankment under close observation. On this problem J. F. Bateman wrote:

> Almost all leakages tell their own story, and give evidence which may generally be implicitly trusted. If the water issues without force and perfectly free from discoloration or matter in suspension, there is no danger although the amount may be considerable. It is an evidence either that the water passes through fissures of rock, strata, or through sand or gravel, without waste of material. It is possible, nevertheless, that water may have passed through or in contact with the earthwork or puddle of an embankment, which it may have wasted or carried away, and may thus have lost the discoloration which it would have inevitably obtained by passing subsequently through a bed of sand or gravel before it made its appearance at the surface. This is an improb-able supposition when the water issues close to the foot of a bank, but should it occur still there is no immediate danger, and the leakage and its attendant cir-cumstances, if continually and carefully observed, will disclose the true state of the case in ample time to allow of measures being taken to prevent mischief.

BRADFORD CORPORATION WATERWORKS.

Plan and Section
OF A
PROPOSED AQUEDUCT OR CONDUIT

for intercepting Water now flowing in or to the

MARCHUP BECK AND HEATHNESS GILL BECK,
OR THEIR TRIBUTARIES,

and diverting or conveying the same to and into a Reservoir authorized by
"The Bradford Waterworks, Act 1854," and now in course of construction near Chelker House,
in the Township of Draughton & Parish of Skipton,

and which **PROPOSED AQUEDUCT OR CONDUIT** *will pass*

FROM, THROUGH, TO, OR INTO THE SEVERAL

TOWNSHIPS OF SILSDEN, ADDINGHAM & DRAUGHTON,

in the several Parishes of

KILDWICK, ADDINGHAM AND SKIPTON,
all in the

WEST RIDING OF THE COUNTY OF YORK.

JNO W LEATHER, C. E., LEEDS.

NOVEMBER, 1857.

Figure 7.2 Example of lettering for 1857 parliamentary plans

If the leakage is stationary in quantity, or decreases, the circumstance in either case is a satisfactory sign; if it increases but still remains clear, then there is a probability of the existence of the condition of things supposed, and a settlement of the bank, following a waste of material and immediately over the spot at which it has occurred, may be looked for. Immediate danger, however, from such a cause, if that be the only one, is not to be apprehended; but of course a reservoir in such a state must be drawn down, and means taken for remedying the evil.[8]

The contracts for the aqueduct from Barden, to and including the service reservoir, and for the four reservoirs at Grimwith, Barden, Chelker, and Silsden were awarded during 1856. The contracts for the Hewenden Valley works were awarded soon after. The Aire Valley section of the conduit, including the crossing below the river Aire, was completed by October 1859 but water could not be taken into supply until after the Silsden compensation water reservoir was completed during 1861. By October 1861 the whole conduit, including the tunnels, was completed but no water could be abstracted from the Wharfe catchment because the Grimwith compensation water reservoir was not ready to be used.

However, by October 1863 Wignall Leather could write:

All your Conduits are completed. The same may be said of all the seven Reservoirs connected with these new works, except Barden Reservoir and Doe Park Reservoir – and the work in progress at these places will be completed within a few weeks time.

All the reservoirs, except the Barden and Chelker reservoirs are, or have been recently, full and overflowing. The Chelker reservoir has been within five feet of top water line, and would have been filled had you been in possession of its principal feeders, which were and are necessarily shut off (by the requirements of your Act) until the Grimwith compensation reservoir is certified to be completed. This reservoir has been full and overflowing for a month past; the notice that application will be made for the necessary certificates from the Magistrates of the fact of its satisfactory completion has been given, and I see no reasonable ground to doubt that such certificate will be granted accordingly. You will very shortly be in the position to take the same step with respect to the Doe Park reservoir, and, these certificates obtained, you will be in undivided possession of a district capable of yielding a supply of water more copious in proportion to your population than any other in the Kingdom, of a quality rarely to be obtained, and far removed from the possibility of contamination.

We have had many difficulties and disappointments to contend with; I think we now see the end, and I trust, indeed I do not doubt, that you will ere long be

121

Figure 7.3a J. Wignall Leather's designs for three dams

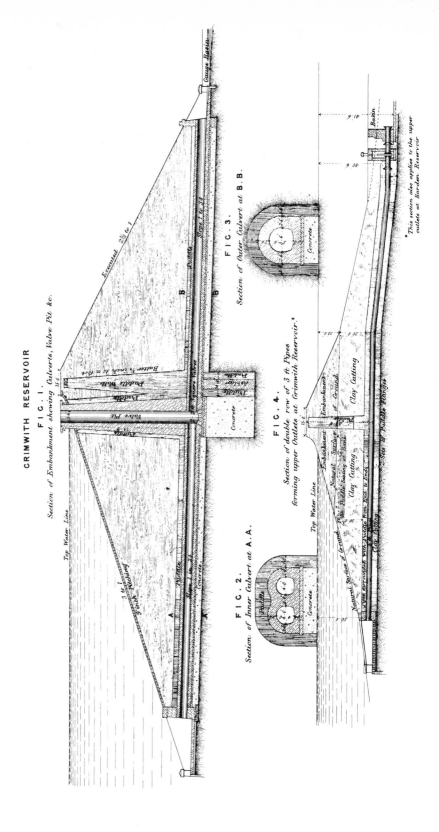

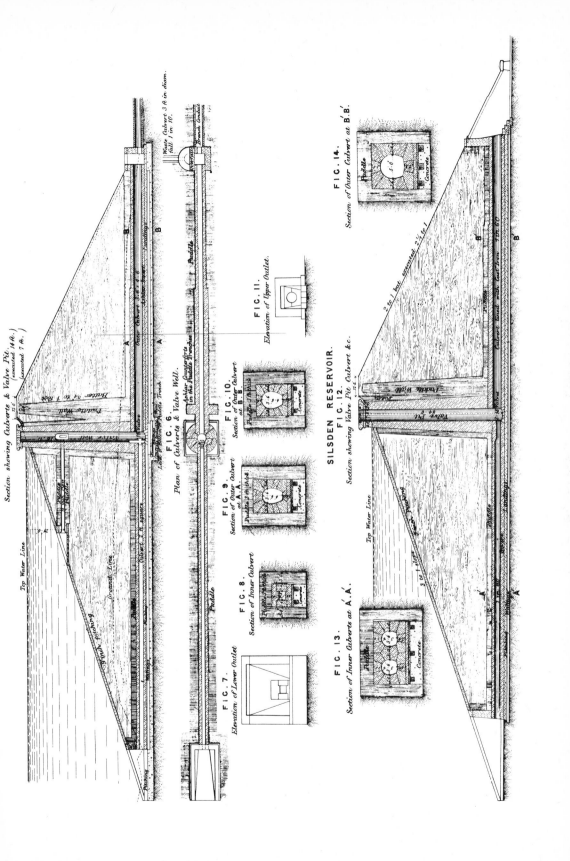

SILSDEN RESERVOIR.

FIG. 6.
Plan of Culverts & Valve Well.

FIG. 7.
Elevation of Lower Outlet.

FIG. 8.
Section of Inner Culvert.

FIG. 9.
Section of Outer Culvert at A.A.

FIG. 10.
Section of Outer Culvert at B.B.

FIG. 11.
Elevation of Upper Outlet.

FIG. 12.
Section shewing Valve Pit Culvert &c.

FIG. 13.
Section of Inner Culverts at A.A.

FIG. 14.
Section of Outer Culvert at B.B.

Section shewing Culverts & Valve Pit.

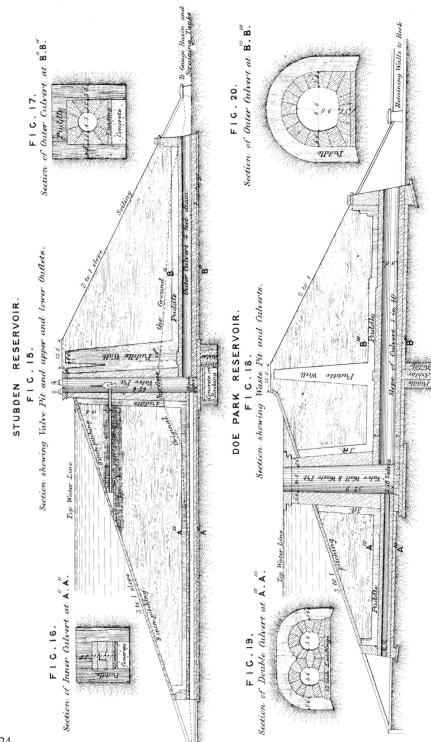

STUBDEN RESERVOIR.

FIG. 15.

Section showing Valve Pit and upper and lower Outlets.

FIG. 16.

Section of Inner Culvert at A.A.

FIG. 17.

Section of Outer Culvert at B.B.

DOE PARK RESERVOIR.

FIG. 18.

Section showing Waste Pit and Culverts.

FIG. 19.

Section of Double Culvert at A.A.

FIG. 20.

Section of Outer Culvert at B.B.

Figure 7.3b J. Wignall Leather's designs for two dams

124

amply compensated for the spirit you have shown in carrying out so large a
measure of improvement, by finding it not only self supporting, but a source of
considerable and constantly increasing profit in itself, and of no small aid in
promoting the prosperity of the Town and District.

Unfortunately Wignall Leather's hopes for the Barden and Doe Park reservoirs
were not fulfilled. The crisis in his relations with the Corporation may have been
precipitated by the collapse of the Dale Dyke dam designed by his cousin, John
Towlerton Leather, on 11 March, 1864, but at all events by October 1864 he was no
longer employed by the Corporation and responsibility for the waterworks was
handed over to the Corporation's Waterworks Manager, Charles (later Sir Charles)
Gott.

As can be seen from Fig. 7.3, for four of the main dams the method of regulating
discharges from the reservoirs adopted by J. Wignall Leather was by means of a
valve well close to the clay puddle wall which intercepted a masonry culvert built in
a trench beneath the dam. Except that Leather designed the valve well to also act as
a waste pit, the fifth dam (Doe Park) is similar to the other four.

While this arrangement was better than naked pipes below embankments, some
of its disadvantages were:

(1) a considerable length of culvert on the upstream side is inaccessible when there
    is water in the reservoir;
(2) on account of differential earth pressure, the well is liable to be thrown out of
    the vertical;
(3) as the well is connected at its base with the culvert, its inability to resist differen-
    tial earth pressure and settlement is liable to cause fractures accompanied by
    crushing on both sides of its junction with the culvert and in this way water may
    penetrate into the heart of the embankment, thus seriously endangering the
    work;
(4) the masonry or concrete pier brought up from the bottom of the trench for the
    purpose of supporting the culvert where it crosses the puddle clay trench was
    often counter-productive and broke the back of the culvert owing to the settle-
    ment of the ground on either side of the pillar under the weight of the embank-
    ment.

What occurred at each dam was as follows: The Grimwith embankment, which
has recently been raised substantially, was originally 83 ft high. Construction commenced in 1856 and the work was sufficiently advanced that impounding was able
to commence in 1861 but in October Wignall Leather reported 'as it was then found
that a leakage occasioned by unequal settlement of the inner culverts and valve pit
had not been perfectly stopped, we deemed it prudent ro run down the water with

a view to insertion of iron shielding'. No further trouble with leakage was reported and these measures were apparently successful. In October 1864 the Waterworks Committee reported that a magistrate's certificate had been obtained for the reservoir and that it had been handed over to the millowners on the River Wharfe.

The Lower Barden embankment is 72 ft high. When Wignall Leather left, work on the dam stopped and the Water Committee wrote:

> The Barden Reservoir is not in a satisfactory condition. The work which was in question at the beginning of the year, for the purpose of reaching and making good some deficient parts of the embankment have failed. Your Committee have now asked Mr. Bateman, Civil Engineer, to examine the Reservoir, and to give his opinion and advice on the course which should be adopted, and the whole matter is now under consideration.

Presumably on the advice of Bateman, the first cut-off trench was abandoned and work on a new cut-off trench approximately 90 ft upstream of the original trench commenced in 1866. Referring to the excavation and close timbering of the trench, the Water Committee in 1869 reported:

> The operations have proved to be peculiarly and exceptionally difficult. The stratum of clay upon which the puddle work is based has continued at an unusual depth throughout the entire length of the embankment – the depth at the south end being upwards of 60 ft, and all the measures above it being mere drift stone, gravel, and irregular deposit. The clay stratum has, however, been followed, and the trench is being turned up the two sides of the valley, from the ends of the embankment, for a sufficient distance to cut-off the loose and pervious measures up to the water level.

This turning up and following the sides of the valley instead of excavating into the hillside is characteristic of J. F. Bateman's work in the Longdendale Valley described in Chapter 9. The Barden reservoir, although not quite complete, was finally brought into use in 1873, that is 17 years after commencement, and was at last found to be watertight.

The Silsden embankment is 100 ft high. Because of the slippery nature of the material of which it was constructed, this embankment gave Wignall Leather anxiety during construction and he flattened the outer slope from 2 to 1 to 2.6 to 1 and also introduced ribs of rubble. As at Grimwith he also had some trouble with differential settlement of his culvert where it crossed the puddle trench and he inserted iron shielding. These measures appear to have been successful as no further trouble with this reservoir is reported.

The Stubden embankment was about 66 ft high. Construction commenced in

Figure 7.4 Thomas Hawksley FRS, John F. Bateman FRS, Sir Robert Rawlinson and J. Towlerton Leather

1859 and the work was so far completed that impounding was able to start in 1862 and the reservoir then remained in use for 5 years, but in October 1867 the Water Committee reported:

> In the early part of the year, a leakage of water was found to be taking place from the reservoir. The water found its way into the outer culvert, and increased in quantity so rapidly that precautions of an exceptional and special character had to be taken. The water . . . was lowered 18 ft . . . but the leak still continued to increase and presented such an appearance as to cause great anxiety about the supply of water for the high level district during the summer.

Temporary repairs were successfully executed without emptying the reservoir and further repairs were carried out in the dry in 1868. The reservoir continued to be a source of anxiety as leakage was noticed from time to time and a part of the culvert on the outside of the puddle trench had to be lined with cast-iron plates.

In 1875 A. R. (later Sir Alexander) Binnie succeeded Gott as Waterworks Manager and immediately put in hand the construction of a new tunnel outlet terminating upstream in a cast-iron valve tower connected with the hillside by a light Warren-girder bridge. The original culvert outlet was abandoned and removed; during its demolition it was found that not only had the masonry of the valve shaft been pushed considerably out of the perpendicular but also that the line of pipes to the upper forebay was broken near the valve shaft which must have been the source of a considerable amount of leakage. The puddle clay in the corewall and in the cut-off trench was found to be of excellent quality.

As originally designed and constructed, the Doe Park embankment was 60 ft high. During 1864 Gott executed repairs to the embankment after carrying out some investigations of a practical but hazardous nature. The Corporation started filling the reservoir again on 1 January, 1865. At the request of the Water Committee, J. F. Bateman inspected the embankment on 27 January and reported as follows:

> The reservoir has on one or more previous occasions failed to retain water with safety after the works have been supposed to be finished and the reservoir has been filled. These failures appear to have arisen mainly from two causes:
>
> 1. From the fact of the puddle trench not having been carried down nor tied at the ends to sufficiently retentive strata; and
> 2. From imperfections in the puddle wall itself, which allowed water to pass through and create what must have been dangerous leaks.
>
> It was the wish to discover the places at which these imperfections existed and to remedy the evil that induced Mr. Gott to adopt the bold and hazardous experiment which was condemned in the early part of last summer [by Robert

Rawlinson during a visit to the site] and which was abandoned in consequence of the correspondence with the Home Secretary. This was to sink a trench on the outside of the puddle-wall, retaining such a quantity of water in the reservoir as would keep its surface several feet above the bottom of the trench, so that the pressure would force the water through the imperfect parts and indicate the places where repairs were necessary. In this way Mr Gott appears to have discovered where the imperfections were, and he has consequently been able to repair them without reconstructing the embankment. He has also deepened and continued the puddle-wall so as to tie it to more retentive ground than was done at first.

The quantity of water issuing at various points on both sides of the valley near the foot of the bank and through the joints of the masonry of the culvert was considerable amounting to about 200,000 gallons per day (900 cu.m. per day). It was, however, in all cases except one, perfectly clear and colourless, indicating that no waste of material is taking place. In the case of the single exception, the discoloration did not arise from waste of material, but from the ochrous character of the water which gave it a reddish turbid appearance. . . . I am of the opinion that there is no dangerous leakage from the reservoir. The quantity is large, considering the comparatively small height of the bank much more than could be desired – but so long as it remains stationary in quantity with the reservoir full, colourless and free from matter in suspension, and no unusual or uneven settlement takes place, no mischief is accruing.[9]

The reservoir continued in service but a few months later it was found that though much leakage was stopped 'there was a fault in the puddle at a considerable depth and nearer to the middle of the embankment than the last work had extended' beneath where the crest 'sank between two and three feet in depth and breadth'.

Rawlinson was instructed to make a second visit to Doe Park and on this occasion he approved of the repairs that Gott was carrying out. After the defective puddle clay was replaced there was apparently no further major trouble but in October 1866 the Water Committee reported that 'in the early part of the year there was a small leak in consequence of shrinkage and consolidation of part of the new puddle work; this was, however, speedily repaired and did not interfere with the use of the Reservoir.' After this date, this reservoir is no longer referred to in the Committee's reports.

With hindsight one can attribute Wignall Leather's troubles mainly to two causes: one was the difficulties with unequal settlement commonly experienced with masonry culverts crossing puddle trenches as described by Wood[10] and A. R. Binnie,[11] the other that he did not base his cut-off trenches on sound impervious strata, nor did he extend them far enough into the hillside.

8 Thomas Hawksley, FRS (1807–93)

In Chapter 1 Hawksley's part as a witness before the Health of Towns Commission and in promoting the Nottingham Inclosure Act is discussed; in Chapter 2 his quarrel with Chadwick is exposed. This chapter describes Hawksley's professional career.

(a) NOTTINGHAM AND OTHER PUMPED WATER-SUPPLY SCHEMES

Thomas Hawksley was the son of a manufacturer in Nottingham and was educated at the local grammar school. He is reputed to have displayed at an early age an interest in studies of a scientific nature, particularly mathematics, geology and chemistry. At the age of 15 he left school and was apprenticed to a local architect and surveyor. When the source of water supply of the first water company in Nottingham became insufficient, a second company came into existence and Hawksley, though only in his early twenties, was appointed about 1830 by the new company to undertake the construction of the Trent Waterworks with a pumping station adjoining the river at Trent bridge where clean water was obtained by filtration through natural beds of sand and gravel.

Hawksley designed his water distribution on the constant supply system and his great achievement in this respect is to have succeeded with this system where others before him had failed.

> The most natural and obvious way of supplying water is to keep the pipes constantly charged under pressure so that any consumer has only to open his tap to draw fresh water from the main. And no doubt this was the first thing attempted, but the taps and fittings would soon leak and get out of order causing, if neglected, such waste as would speedily exhaust the capability of the works.[1]

Herein lay the reason for the strong opposition of the engineers of the London Water Companies, in particular Wicksteed and Simpson, to the constant water

130

supply system but Thomas Hawksley, being of an independent turn of mind, determined to develop just such a system for his waterworks.

> He saw the desirability of returning to the original plan of keeping the supply pipes always charged under pressure, the only problem being to prevent the waste by leakage. It may be asked by what means he contrived to effect this, when no one had effected it before? The answer may be expressed in very simple words, though it took long study and perseverence to carry it effectually into practice. It was merely by contriving fittings which would not readily get out of order, and by so arranging them that if they did get out of order, they could and should be easily repaired. There were great difficulties with the plumbers but Mr Hawksley's plan was to begin by getting them under reasonable control when all else became easy.[2]

In 1845 the two waterworks companies at Nottingham were amalgamated by an Act of Parliament and Hawksley then took charge of the joint enterprise which bore the name of the Nottingham Waterworks Company. He afterwards constructed more works for obtaining water from wells in the New Red Sandstone and he remained the Engineer until the water supply was taken over by the Corporation in 1880.

The sinking of mines in north-east Durham had demonstrated conclusively the availability of very large quantities of underground water from the magnesium limestone and the Sunderland Water Company came into existence by Act of Parliament in 1846. The Company engaged the services of Thomas Hawksley and built a large pumping station at Humbledon, the engine house for which still remains, although disused (1972). By a further Act in 1852 the Company became the Sunderland and South Shields Water Company with an extended statutory area of supply and within 25 years four large pumping stations designed by Hawksley were constructed.

> Each of these required shafts to be sunk; engines, boilers, their houses and chimneys to be erected; reservoirs to be constructed; pipelines to be laid; dwellings to be built for the operators and stations to be landscaped. Fulwell was commenced in 1852; Cleadon was under way in 1863; Ryhope (1868) and Dalton (1879) continued the expansion.[3] (Fig. 8.1a)

The empirical rule was that no new station should be within 2 miles of any other. Of these pumping stations, Ryhope – where there are two double-acting, compound, rotative beam engines each 33 ft long between pump rod centres and weighing 22 tons – is the only one which still exists with the steam plant in its original condition (Fig. 8.1b). After a century of supplying water, pumping at Ryhope

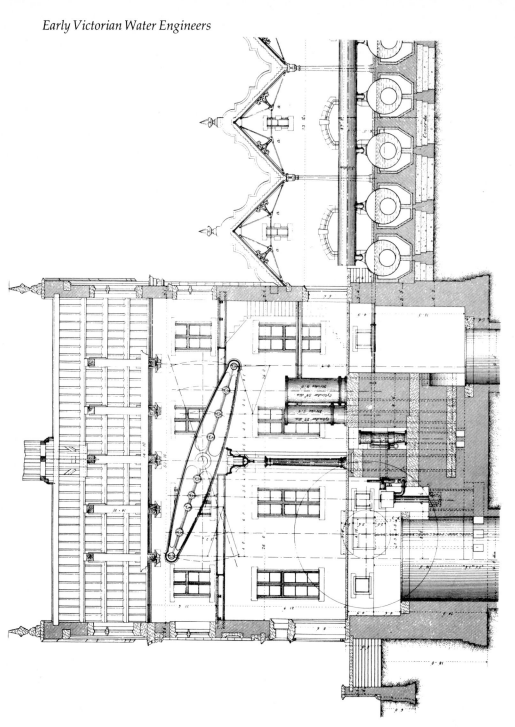

Figure 8.1a   Ryhope pumping station, North East Durham, 1858

Figure 8.1b   Beam engines at Ryhope pumping station, 1980

ceased in 1967 but fortunately a trust has been able to preserve the station 'for the benefit of all who would come and savour the unique experience of watching a large beam engine in motion'.[4]

Besides Nottingham, and Sunderland and South Shields, there were many other towns for which Hawksley designed pumped water supply schemes including Derby, Darlington, Stockton, Middlesbrough, Norwich, Great Yarmouth, Lowestoft, Barnstaple, Bridgwater, Hinckley, Lichfield, Newark, Northampton, Southend, Weymouth and Workington. Abroad he designed pumped water-supply schemes for Stockholm and Altona.[5] Although it is sometimes alleged that the pavilion with loggia at the north end of the Serpentine in Kensington Gardens was designed by the Prince Consort with the Petit Trianon of Versailles in mind, [6] in fact it was once a pumping station designed by Thomas Hawksley (Fig. 8.2).

The cost of constructing waterworks varies very much according to the features of the locality, its geological structure and the kind of schemes, whether pumping or gravitation, for the place to be supplied. In his evidence before the Royal Commission on Water Supply in 1869, Hawksley stated that, as a general rule, the cost of pumping schemes was only about one-third that of gravitation schemes, and even when the cost of coal, labour and machinery was capitalized they were very much cheaper.

Figure 8.2 Serpentine pumping station circa 1858 in Kensington Gardens

(b) THE EXPERT WITNESS

On expert witnesses Jeremy Bentham wrote:

> Persons of this description though in English law confounded with witnesses and not without advantage treated as such, are in fact a sort of assistant to the judge and as such treated by the Roman law.

Having thus quoted Bentham, Lord Macmillan commented:

> The expert witness, therefore, is in quite a special position. He is an assistant in the ascertainment of truth; he is the purveyor of information on which decisions are to be arrived at, and to the truth and validity of that information his professional credit and reputation are pledged.[7]

It is doubtful whether this was understood or accepted in early Victorian times.

In an age when it was often only rich men who could afford to pay fees for expert witnesses whereas the inhabitants at large and especially the labouring classes, were usually unable to afford them or to obtain hearings at Parliamentary Committees, the scales were inevitably weighed down on the side of wealth. Chadwick complained that:

> Men of science receive retainers: and, the past experience will show, give evidence according to the retainers on one side or the other as may serve with the interests of the party retaining them. . . . All the world knows upon what conditions the lawyer speaks; that what he gives as facts are the facts of his client; the advocates's cited cases and not his assertions are relied upon. But the science of the scientific man is taken to be his own science and not the science of his client made up for his cause.[8]

Although not given in evidence before a Parliamentary Committee, as an example of a case where it is hard to avoid the conclusion that some of the engineers were, to a greater or lesser extent, partisan, one can refer to the engineering reports written after the collapse of the Dale Dyke dam.[9] None of the five, including Hawksley, acting for the Sheffield Water Company admitted that there was any fault in the construction of the dam, whereas the reports written independently by each of the nine engineers engaged by the Sheffield Corporation expressed views which added up to a powerful indictment of the dam's construction.

Hawksley's achievements at Nottingham attracted the notice of Chadwick and, as has already been described in Chapter 1, he was chosen by the latter to be one of his principal witnesses at the Health of Towns enquiry. Hawksley's subsequent brilliant career was partly due to him being, as Chadwick discovered, an outstandingly good witness and he became one of the most famous professional witnesses of his time. According to one source:

Mr Hawksley might be described as an invincible witness. His appearance in a case was heralded by the introduction of piles of statistics and other data which he had sent before him. Let a question arise about the fall of rain in any part of the district that was affected by the Bill, or the capacity of the smallest of the streams, out came a mass of figures relating to the subject which appalled the opposing counsel and made the younger members of committee groan in secret. Hawksley had spent so many years supporting and opposing Parliamentary schemes, it seemed as if he had at length reduced all the tactics of counsel to formulas and had tabulated all their combinations. He displayed a manner that was almost contemptuous when efforts were made to entrap him, and it was difficult to resist the impression that he was more annoyed at the efforts to waste the time of the committee. His memory was marvellous for details and precedents. No style of cross examination was effective against him. The courtly Hope-Scott, who was so terribly efficient through the simplicity of his attacks, used to be foiled by Mr Hawksley as easily as he withstood the mighty strokes of the present Lord Grimthorpe who seemed born to wield a battle axe or a two-handed sword, or the straightforward thrusts of Mr Rodwell. A Parliamentary engineer who is in request can hardly fail to be without some of the spirit of the old Condottiere; like the counsel and agents, his business is to make the best fight he can for whatever side that pays his fees, whether promotors or opponents, Mr Hawksley somehow did not convey that impression.[10]

Examples of Hawksley's parliamentary work are the evidence he gave in connection with water supplies for Edinburgh already described in the previous chapter, and for Dundee.

For the latter city, Hawksley was the chief and leading supporter of the direct route in the great water controversy of 1871–72 and when, as had been foreseen by Bateman, many bursts occurred in the trunk main, he and T. E. Harrison, an associate of Robert Stephenson, were called upon by the Water Commissioners to give advice on how to keep the pipeline in repair.[11] Whilst in Scotland Hawksley's parliamentary work did not bring him any engineering work, in England after having successfully steered a Bill through Parliament he was frequently called upon to then be the consulting engineer for the construction of the project.

(c) THE LIVERPOOL WATERWORKS

The position regarding Liverpool's water supply prior to 1845 has been described in Chapter 1; and as already stated, two private companies provided the bulk of the supply. In 1845, the Liverpool Guardian Society for the Protection of Trade requested an enquiry into the business of water supply.[12] The society quoted the companies' shares, which stood at three times and six times their face value, and stated that the water supply was 'not only miserably inadequate but the most expensive in the country'.[13] An enquiry in which a lively interest was taken by the press was held by the Special Committee of the Highways Board at which evidence was produced on many abuses and defects such as one row of ten houses being without water for 7 months because of the failure of the previous tenants to pay water rates, many cases of water remaining on for no longer than 1 hour at intervals of 2 days, and in some cases even then coming on only in the middle of the night. The main conclusion of the Special Committee was that 'The inhabitants ought not to be dependent on mere trading companies for that most necessary article of life but that supply should be in the hands of a public body.'[14]

Having been encouraged by the 1845 enquiry to seek extended powers from Parliament, the Liverpool Council sought to gain control of the private water companies. Another large-scale enquiry relating to their purchase commenced in February 1847 and, as before, the overwhelming weight of evidence was against the private companies. The Corporation decided to act quickly and with compensation for the companies agreed at £537 000, the Liverpool Corporation Water Act received the Royal Assent in July 1847. From that month, the supply of water to Liverpool became the sole responsibility of the Corporation which now had to concern itself with the considerable problem of expansion.

Two widely varying water supply schemes were proposed, one being an extension of the well system as recommended by Simpson and the Borough engineer, Newlands, and the other being a gravity scheme from the Rivington district as recommended by Thomas Hawksley.

> A fiery debate, in press, private lobby and on public platform ensued. It was obvious that the argument ranging round the Rivington Pike Scheme was on cost. The initial estimate in 1847 had been £200 000 and by 1850 it had risen to £450 000. From the outset those in favour of the Rivington Scheme, labelled Pikists, enjoyed a majority in council. . . . Parliamentary assent was obtained to undertake the scheme but in 1850 there was a reversal of the political situation and the anti-Pikists found themselves to hold the majority in the council chamber. Their joy was however short lived, for they found that the contracts for construction of Rivington Pike Waterworks had been signed and sealed making it virtually legally impossible to renege. Nevertheless, an attempt was made and a court of inquiry was called.[15]

The referee was Robert Stephenson and the Council undertook to abide by his arbitration. He estimated that for a supply not exceeding 8 mgd the Simpson and Newlands scheme was the cheapest, but for a supply exceeding this amount, the Rivington Pike scheme, which he estimated could supply 12–13 mgd 'with absolute certainty' was the cheaper scheme and in March 1850 he reported in favour of the latter.[16] With compensation water, subsequently fixed by Parliament to be 8.3 mgd, a yield of more than 20 mgd was required to meet Stephenson's guarantee which was not fulfilled. Nevertheless it was good policy to start looking for water elsewhere instead of continuing to exploit the local wells, with the risk of pollution and salinity due to over-exploitation.

The catchment area of the Rivington scheme embraces 10 000 acres of moorland in the catchment areas of the rivers Ribble and Douglas. When designing the Bradford Waterworks, J. Wignall Leather relied on spring water without filtration for the domestic supply, and the same practice was followed at Longdendale by Bateman as described in Chapter 9. However, Hawksley used filters to obtain a clean and wholesome water supply.

The scheme as designed by Thomas Hawksley (Fig. 8.3) consisted of five reservoirs with a total storage capacity of 3040 million gallons tapping the springs in this catchment area, 4 acres of slow sand filters and a pipeline with a nominal internal diameter of 44 in. and a length of 17.3 miles (the longest major water supply main in

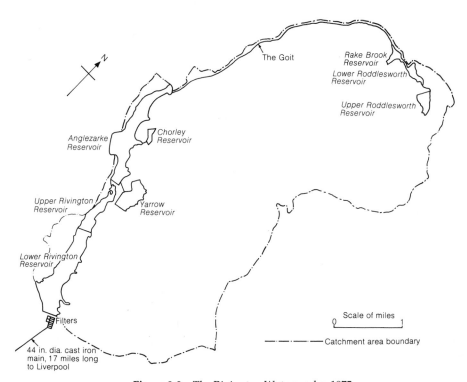

Figure 8.3 The Rivington Waterworks, 1875

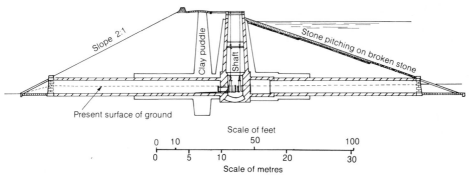

Figure 8.4   Lower Rivington reservoir, 1857 (redrawn from contemporary drawing)

existence at the time it was built). The slow sand filters are still in use.[17] All the dams are of similar design – a trench below ground level which was filled with puddle, and an earthen embankment within which is a clay puddle corewall above ground level. The maximum height above original ground level of the embankment varies between 36 and 84 ft and, in general, the upstream slope is 3 to 1 and the downstream slope 2 to 1. The cross-sections showed that the shoulders on each side of the clay corewall were to be constructed in concave layers 4 ft thick sloping towards the corewall, a practice that Hawksley appears to have soon discontinued. In the three main reservoirs, Lower Rivington, Upper Rivington and Angelzark, there are three vertical supply shafts 30–41 ft deep and one compensation water supply shaft 41 ft deep sited a short distance upstream of the clay corewall built of blue brick which intercept horizontal culverts beneath the embankments, the culverts being lined with blue brick (Fig. 8.4).

> In constructing the tunnels and shafts provision was made, and toothings were left out, to give support to the stoppings in building in the valves. In this part of the work great care was taken to have all the bricks cut to fit their particular places, and to soundly bed them in cement. In each of the shafts there were four valves, and two lines of pipes – two valves being on each pipe for facility in case of repair (Fig. 8.4). In all cases the size of the outlet tunnel was determined by the area draining into the stream and the maximum rainfall; and the tunnel was of such size as to take the water in floods, during the construction of the works.[18]

Hereafter such shafts are referred to as valve wells.

The other two reservoirs, Rake Brook and Lower Roddlesworth, were constructed mainly to supply compensation water, and had different outlet arrangements. They were integrated into the remainder of the scheme by an open channel 20 ft wide at the bottom and 3¾ miles long (known as the Goit) which served not only to convey surplus water from the upper reservoirs to Rivington but also to intercept water from the intermediate gathering ground.

While these works were under construction the Chorley Waterworks were acquired by the Liverpool Corporation by Act of Parliament in April 1856; this included the High Bullough reservoir within the catchment area and increased the united storage capacity to 3100 million gallons. The High Bullough dam had been designed by J. F. Bateman.

As discussed below, Hawksley overestimated the maintainable yield from the Rivington reservoirs as being 22 mgd, whereas experience showed later that it was scarcely more than 16 mgd.

In the main embankment of the lower Rivington reservoir a slight depression appeared near the compensation shaft in 1932. A trial hole was sunk and it was found that a portion of the clay puddle had perished in an irregular manner extending to a depth of 44 ft. In no case was it found that the core had perished for the full width but it had approached to 2 ft of the width. This was repaired with new clay.[19] With both supply and compensation water tunnels laid in the bases of the embankments one might have expected more trouble, but apart from this one incident no significant damage up to the present day (1981) appears to have occurred.

In 1860 the Corporation obtained powers to construct the Upper Roddlesworth reservoir, completed in 1865, which served only to increase the total storage capacity for water coming off the catchment by 6 per cent and did not effectively increase the supply. Although this reservoir was not constructed under Hawksley's supervision, and it does not appear to have been designed by him, some of the experiences with it are interesting and worth recording.

The reservoir is formed by an embankment 1190 ft long with a maximum height of 69 ft above original ground level. A clay puddle wall was carried to within 3 ft 3 in. of the top of the bank. From time to time this embankment has caused considerable trouble due to swallow-holes appearing on the upstream side of the clay corewall. In February 1904 a hole 5 ft across by 8 ft deep appeared, and was refilled with puddle. Twenty-one months later another hole measuring 4 ft across and 1 ft deep appeared at the same spot. Excavation revealed a circular shaft 3 ft in diameter. The excavation was carried down 33 ft and a small spring was disclosed at the bottom.

> In the meantime, close search was made in Liverpool but the only information found was a report from the Water Engineer to the Committee in which he referred to difficulties he was experiencing with a spring at the bottom of the trench; later he reported having successfully overcome the difficulty.[20]

In order to deal with this spring at the bottom of the vertical shaft pitching stone on edge was laid in the bottom . . . a 12 inch cast iron pipe was carried vertically up the trench from this foundation with a 4 inch cast iron outlet carried into the reservoir, and fitted with a reflux valve at 13 feet below sill level, the level to which water used to rise in the trial hole. Seven feet of broken stone and gravel was placed around the bottom of the standpipe, the remainder of the excavation being refilled carefully with puddle. The work was completed on the 2nd June 1906, since when there has been no further movement at this point.[21]

In January 1908 another subsidence at a different location occurred. In this case the swallow-hole formed entirely within the upstream slope just clear of the puddle clay wall. The diameter of the hole was approximately 4 ft near the surface, gradually increasing to 7 ft at 20 ft below the surface and then gradually reducing to 3 ft at 26 ft 6 in., where the ground became solid and excavation ceased. In this case also running water was found which was dealt with in a similar manner to the first swallow-hole.[22] Although not so fatal in their consequences, it is interesting to compare these swallow-holes with those encountered on the Bilberry dam, and discussed in Chapter 4.

A mistake made in the construction of the Upper Roddlesworth dam was that the toe was built of sand which turned into 'running sand' when attacked by water, with the consequence that when a considerable amount of run-off from the high ground on each side of the valley flowed onto a berm on the downstream slope during the very heavy rain on the night of 20/21 January, 1954, some of the sand was washed away and a slip took place. (The incident is somewhat similar to that which occurred to the Bilberry embankment on 29 May, 1944.) A good drainage system was installed both on the downstream slope of the embankment and to convey water draining from the higher lands at each end of the bank, so that it is carried away clear of the embankment.[23]

One of the many arguments in favour of the Rivington scheme had been that it would not only provide a constant water supply but that it would also provide the motive force for an arterial drainage system. The proud boast of the Pikists had been that the water would flow not in gallons but in torrents. However, such was the growth of population and the increased demand for water that by 1872 there had been a complete turn of events. The water rate had steadily climbed and the promised constant supply was no longer available.

A satirical weekly, *Porcupine*, in a series of articles entitled 'Our Water Supply in Peril', compared the widespread euphoria which greeted the initial supply of Rivington water with the disappointment 16 years later and wrote 'Now in Liverpool we have not a constant supply and we have constant anxiety.'[24] At that time in 1872 the Yarrow reservoir, for which parliamentary powers had been obtained in 1860, was under construction; but as it was also within the Rivington catchment area, it had only a small effect in increasing the water supply when it was completed in 1875.

In the early spring of 1874 the first decisive steps were taken to develop a new area of supply. Joseph Jackson, an engineer from Bolton who had administered completion of the Yarrow reservoir after the death of Thomas Duncan – the Borough Engineer in 1868 – was requested by the Water Committee to review all reports of schemes which had been published since 1826.

Six potential sources were considered by Jackson. One source some 85 miles north of Liverpool was Ullswater. Three sources some 65 miles north of Liverpool were Haweswater, Lake Windermere and the headwaters of the rivers Lune and Hodder, the last being 20 miles east of Lake Windermere. One source some 45 miles south-west of Liverpool was Bala lake proposed by Robert Rawlinson in 1846 and 1866. The remaining source, which was also the one recommended by Jackson, was the catchment area of the upper Brock, a tributary of the river Wyre, and the adjacent catchment areas exploited by means of catchwaters.

On the upper Brock at Admarsh, some 40 miles north of Liverpool, Jackson proposed to make a reservoir with an embankment 110 ft high. The area draining directly into the proposed reservoir was only 4250 acres but a further 6000 acres in Wyredale were to be tapped by catchwater conduits discharging into the reservoir. There was to be no compensation water supply and it was assumed that the mill-owners would accept instead reasonable payments in cash. Jackson estimated that, with no compensation water, the yield would be a daily supply of 20 million gallons.

An alternative scheme which allowed for 10 mgd as compensation water in addition to the supply of 20 mgd per day included two additional smaller impounding reservoirs each requiring embankments about 100 ft high, one on the river Wyre and the other on the river Calder, and also longer catchwaters tapping larger catchment areas.[25]

In May 1874 the Water Committee decided to get two independent second opinions on what would be the best scheme, from Thomas Hawksley and J. F. Bateman. Thus after a lapse of about 18 years, the Corporation was again employing Hawksley, and in his report dated 15 August, 1874, he endorsed Jackson's proposals.[26]

Bateman, who was aided by his chief assistant G. H. Hill, in his report dated 14 August, 1874, contended, on the other hand, that Jackson's proposals for constructing a reservoir on the Upper Brock and exploiting the Wyresdale catchment area with catchwaters would be more difficult and costly than he estimated. Referring to the proposed 110 ft high dam, he wrote:

> The material of which it would have to be formed – being, from the nature of the country, nearly all clay – very flat slopes would have to be provided to

prevent slips, and ample time would have to be allowed for consolidation. An embankment of this height, even supposing it successfully completed, and no unusual difficulty experienced in obtaining a secure foundation, could not be safely raised to its full height in less than 7 or 8 years.

He also demonstrated that to be effective in intercepting floodwater necessary to achieve the desired yield, the catchwaters would have to be larger and more costly than Jackson had estimated. Instead, Bateman put forward a proposal that the Boroughs of Liverpool and Manchester should undertake a joint venture for developing Ullswater as a source of supply. He stated that Manchester, though much better off than Liverpool for a supply of water, was not more than 5 or 6 years in advance of its necessities. His report included a breakdown of costs which showed up most favourably the proposed joint venture.[27]

Matters took a new turn in November 1877 when the attention of the Water Committee was drawn towards the valley of the River Vyrnwy as a possible site for the development of a gravitation scheme. As described elsewhere Bateman had considered this valley in 1865 as a possible source of supply for London[28] but it was left to Hugh Williams, a civil engineer from Wigan, to realize that it was a suitable source for Liverpool. Williams drafted a scheme which he entrusted to the Chairman of the Water Committee and he alleged that there was an understanding between the Chairman and himself that, if the Council decided to investigate his proposals further, he would be employed as the consulting engineer. In this he was disappointed. The Borough Engineer, G. F. Deacon, who subsequently received an honorary doctorate from Liverpool University and became an eminent consulting engineer, was requested by the Chairman to investigate the area and to submit a report to Council at the earliest possible date. Deacon placed his report, in which he endorsed the scheme, before Council on 18 December, 1877. Still no action was taken on a new gravitation scheme and in April 1879 *The Irish Times*, making a general report on Britain's water resources, wrote: 'Probably there is no place with anything like the population of Liverpool that goes on obstinately boring at the strata beneath their feet and as a consequence is obliged to drink its own sewage, more or less diluted.'[29]

From the original choice of six likely schemes only Ullswater remained to oppose the proposed new site at Vyrnwy. Of the two, the cost-conscious members of the Liverpool Council were generally in favour of the joint project with Manchester but by midsummer 1879 it was becoming clear that, despite overtures from their counterparts in Liverpool, the Manchester Water Committee were not enthusiastic towards the joint Ullswater venture and after a meeting between representatives of the two Councils on 11 June, 1879, it was abandoned.

After the abandonment of the Ullswater Joint Venture, Deacon made a preliminary survey of the Vyrnwy valley in which he deduced from surface

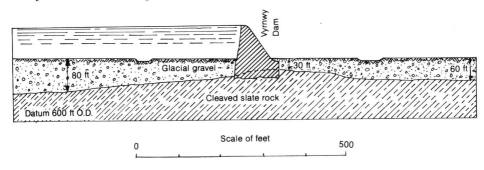

Figure 8.5 Longitudinal section of valley at Vyrnwy dam site (G. F. Deacon), 1880 (redrawn from Fig. 6 of reference 30)

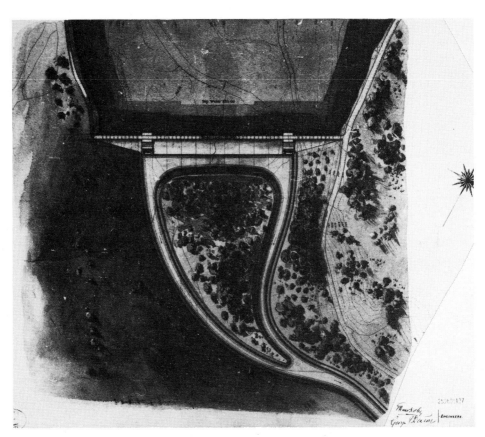

Figure 8.6 Plan of Vyrnwy dam dated 26 May, 1881, signed T. Hawksley, George F. Deacon as Engineers

144

indications that it was the site of an old glacial lake whose waters were at one time held up by a rock barrier or rock bar (Fig. 8.5). He estimated that the cost of the project would be £1 250 000 and for the Parliamentary plans he located the centre line of the dam where he inferred that the rock bar lay. An application was made to Parliament for the necessary powers, Hawksley and Deacon were associated as Engineers for promoting the Bill, and it received the Royal Assent on 6 August 1880.

Before deciding on the final line Deacon then investigated the area thoroughly with numerous borings and shafts in order to determine the contours of the underground rock on the basis of which the final centre-line, which was nearly identical with the original one, was fixed. Deacon estimated from the information obtained

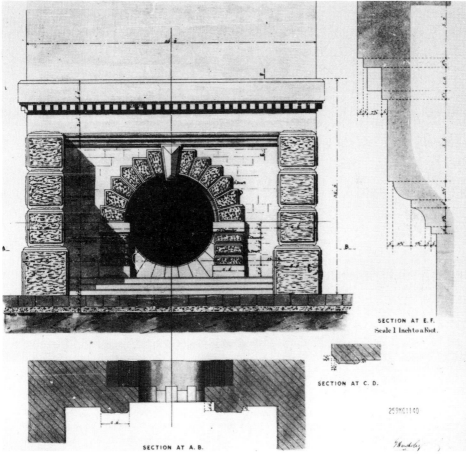

Figure 8.7 Elevation Vyrnwy dam tunnel dated 13 August, 1884, signed T. Hawksley

Figure 8.8   Artist's impression prior to construction of Vyrnwy dam

from this survey that a deviation in the centre line up or down the valley of only a quarter of a mile would have added from £300 000 to £400 000 to the cost of the project, a good example of the value of thorough exploration of a dam site before commencing work.[30]

At a meeting of the Water Committee on 2 March, 1881, Hawksley was engaged as Engineer-in-Chief for the project including the 68-mile-long aqueduct from Vyrnwy to Liverpool. It was also decided that he should have the assistance of G. F. Deacon, or another engineer who would be appointed by Council after his suitability was assured.

At this time Hawksley was in his early seventies and had had considerable experience on large projects whereas Deacon, in his late thirties, had had none. It was normal practice for the authority's own engineer to be associated with the authority's consultant for promoting a Bill, and Hawksley was also willing that Deacon should be associated with him on the general design of the dam. For the detailed design of the work, and for the supervision of construction, however, he was not willing to allow the association as Joint Engineer with Deacon to continue. Accordingly eight drawings which had been prepared in Hawksley's office showing the general design of the dam in plan (Fig. 8.6), elevation and cross-section at various locations were signed by both Hawksley and Deacon as Engineers on 26 May, 1881, but no later detailed drawings of the dam such as the detail of the tunnel outlet

146

Figure 8.9 Vyrnwy dam under construction

shown (Fig. 8.7), nor any drawings of the aqueduct prepared in Hawksley's office were signed by Deacon. An artist's conception of the dam as originally conceived, which differs only in some of the details from the work as executed, and a photograph of the work under construction, are shown (Figs 8.8 and 8.9).

The project proceeded normally until February 1885 when, as a result of requests having been made separately to them, Hawksley and Deacon submitted estimates for the total cost of the project as shown in Table 8.1.

Table 8.1 Comparative cost estimates on Vyrnwy project (£)

	Thomas Hawksley	G. F. Deacon	Parliamentary
Money already spent	1 104 588	1 044 489	
For completion in 1889	1 079 162	729 019	
TOTAL	2 183 750	1 773 508	1 250 000

The Council was disturbed that the two engineers should entertain such widely differing assessments of the total cost, and was dismayed by the estimated increases above the parliamentary estimate. Hawksley took offence when one or two of the more excitable members declared that the engineers had betrayed them, and handed in his resignation. With the resignation of the Engineer in Chief the Water Committee was thrown into disarray and the Chairman was urged to placate Hawksley, which apparently he succeeded in doing until a second argument broke out.

As far as he was concerned, Hawksley had been placed in overall charge of the Vyrnwy project and, on this understanding, he was willing to accept overall responsibility for it. However, it had been brought to Hawksley's notice that although the Water Committee had undertaken that he should be engaged as Engineer in Chief at the meeting on 2 March, 1881, the Council a fortnight later had entered into a separate agreement with G. F. Deacon. 'That, that gentleman was to act in conjunction with me!'[31] Hawksley, who had not been aware of this agreement, was not told of it until 4 years later and then unofficially. 'Mr. Deacon claims to be not merely my assistant for the purposes expressed in my agreement but to be professionally united to me as the joint engineer of the undertaking for all other purposes.'[32]

On 19 May, 1885, G. F. Deacon addressed a formal letter to the Town Clerk in which he made the unmistakable assertion: 'My present position under my own agreement is that of joint engineer with Mr. Hawksley.'[33] Hearing of Deacon's assertion of his position according to his own agreement with the Council, Hawksley demanded clarification of the situation from the Town Clerk: 'If the answer is, that Mr. Deacon is considered to be joint engineer with me, I must still persist in vacating my agreement.'[34]

After Hawksley's resignation, a further dispute with him arose, on which the *Liverpool Daily Post* wrote:

> In the settlement of accounts between Hawksley and the Corporation, a dispute arose chiefly owing to the contention of the latter that Mr. Hawksley should not have withdrawn from his important position until the entire work was brought to a state of completion. The matter was brought to arbitration proceedings commencing before Mr. F. A. Bosanquet, Q.C. . . . on March 29 1888. Mr. Hawksley based his claim on an agreement signed in March 1881. Numbers of expert witnesses and others were called, and it was not until August 11, 1888, that Mr. Bosanquet made his award which was all in favour of Mr. Hawksley, to whom the Corporation was ordered to pay £14,123 over and above the sums which they had already paid him, to pay his costs, their own costs and the costs of the arbitration.[35]

With someone else appointed in his place as City Engineer, the completion of the project was left solely in the hands of G. F. Deacon as the Water Engineer, and he completed the first instalment of the scheme enabling water to be delivered to Liverpool in 1892. The last instalment was completed in 1910.

(d) OTHER IMPOUNDING SCHEMES

After the collapse of the Dale Dyke dam in 1864 described in Chapter 13, Thomas Hawksley succeeded J. Towlerton Leather as consulting engineer to the Sheffield Water Company and he reconstructed the Dale Dyke dam at a new site a little further upstream from the original site. The reconstructed embankment (Fig. 8.10) is a typical example of Hawksley's earthwork. On behalf of the Water Company, he also completed an earth dam at Agden, constructed a new reservoir at Strines and a reservoir at Damflask to which further reference will be made.

Other places supplied by Hawksley from high gathering grounds were Leicester, referred to in Chapter 1; Leeds, where he succeeded J. Wignall Leather as the Corporation's consulting engineer; Barnsley; Boston; Haslingden; Merthyr; Rochdale; Watford; Wexford; Bridgetown (Barbados); and the Weardale District in Newcastle and Gateshead, County Durham.

Space does not permit a description of all Hawksley's works but the Waskerley, Smiddy Shaw and Tunstall dams in the Weardale District will be briefly referred to as being representative of his talents. For the 1870s Waskerley and Tunstall were both very large dams and, with the possible exception of the lower Rivington dam also designed by Thomas Hawksley, the former probably exceeded in volume any other dam that had previously been built.

The first to be built was the 90 ft high Waskerley dam constructed between 1868 and 1872. There is a culvert in a trench below the dam foundations and releases from the reservoir are controlled by a single valve in a valve well (Fig. 8.11). The outlet arrangements may appear to be similar to those at Rivington, also those discussed in the previous chapter, but there is one important difference in that Hawksley introduced slip joints – thus making the rigid culvert to some extent articulated. As stated by Yordi:

> The weakness of the 'slip joint' method lies in the fact that the settlement must be uniform and the range of vertical movement small otherwise jamming will take place with crushing of the abutting faces, which will probably be accompanied by fracture.[36]

There are clear indications that Hawksley recognized the need for uniform settlement, because where the culvert crosses the clay it is allowed to float in it with slip joints where it enters and leaves the puddle clay and also slip joints adjacent to the valve well. The valve well is also entirely surrounded by puddle clay, but Hawksley ignored the effect of differential pressure due to the 3 to 1 upstream slope which will now be described.

An eyewitness wrote:

> When the embankment was constructed they could not succeed in getting the

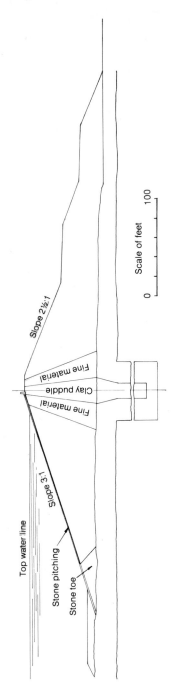

Figure 8.10 Reconstructed Dale Dyke dam, 1875

earthwork to set absolutely evenly, and a greater weight went on one side than the other, and threw the shaft out of the perpendicular to the extent of 1ft 10ins. in a height of about 70 feet. Open cracks, in which he could put his little finger, resulted.[37]

This movement caused great anxiety but after 7 months it ceased and after 9 months the valve and capstan were fixed in position. The cracks were caulked and the shaft was backfilled with concrete to 30 ft above the bottom, the valve being embedded in the concrete. Impounding then proceeded normally with no further trouble. The valve can never be replaced except with great difficulty, but after more than a century it is still operating satisfactorily. The shaft as it is today with its capstan off centre is shown (Fig. 8.12).

This incident did not deter Hawksley from using valve wells but it is interesting to note that in the case of the valve well of the Damflask dam for Sheffield's water supply (Fig. 8.13), he originally built it with the shaft protruding above the upstream slope in the same way but, no doubt as a result of his experience at Waskerley, he subsequently moved the upstream slope further forward and constructed a retaining wall so as to obtain, so far as practical, uniform pressure on both sides of the shaft. This must also have been beneficial in giving better distributed pressure on the two articulated sections of culvert and more uniform settlement.

The Waskerley and the Damflask valve wells were both built of brick, cement mortar being used for the lowest courses and lime mortar for the remainder. In the case of Waskerley, masonry was substituted for brick where the well appeared above the surface. The culverts were also built in brick and an interesting detail is that Hawksley used moss in the slip joints. So far as the author is aware, valve wells designed by Hawksley have not given trouble after they were built and, with one exception at Rivington, they seem to have been reasonably watertight.

The Smiddy Shaw reservoir, sited on the edge of a moor with embankments on all four sides, commands the Consett ironworks in the valley below and was completed in 1875. Having no natural drainage area of its own it is fed by catchwaters. In hard winters ice very readily forms on the water surface to such an extent that it creates an airtight barrier between the atmosphere and the unfrozen water below. The outlet arrangements are similar to those for the Waskerley reservoir but when water was withdrawn from the reservoir during these freezing conditions, a vacuum beneath the ice was created which interfered with the abstraction of the water. To overcome this, pipes (as shown in Fig. 8.14) were built into the bank to admit air below the ice.

At the Tunstall reservoir the dam is 82 ft high and there is a tunnel at one end. Releases through the tunnel are controlled by two valves in series in a valve well. The advantage of this arrangement is that by leaving the upstream valve, referred to as the guard valve, normally open and by using the downstream valve, referred to as the operating valve, for controlling releases, the guard valve can be closed temporarily when it is necessary to repair or replace the operating valve, thus avoiding the risk of a difficult and expensive operation such as occurred at the Vartry waterworks, described elsewhere.

The cut-off trench in the hillside at one end was originally backfilled with puddle clay, but when the reservoir was only partially filled, it was found that water was passing through rock beyond the end of the puddle trench in large quantities. In extending the cut-off trench by tunnelling methods, the puddle clay was partially replaced with brickwork. When this was completed

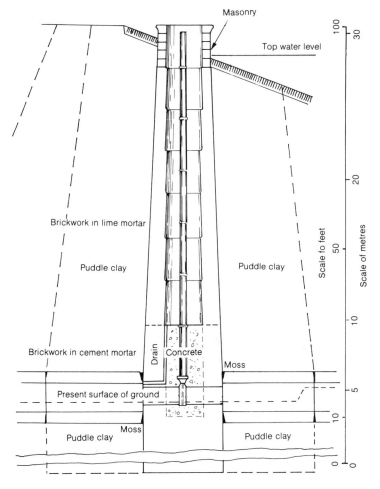

Figure 8.11   Waskerley valve well, 1872 (redrawn from contemporary contract drawing)

it was found that the water was passing near the base of the brickwork which supported the puddle; and holes were bored from the surface on the inside of the puddle wall at a distance of 10 feet from it, and cement grout was poured into them. The percolation of water was in this way completely stopped in 1879 when the reservoir was brought into use.[38]

This process, now known as grouting, was first used by Hawksley at Rochdale's Cowm embankment completed in 1877[39] but Cowm and Tunstall share the distinction of being the two embankments where grouting was first used on earth dams anywhere in the world.[40]

The Damflask reservoir was constructed during the 1860s for supplying compensation water to millowners. When impounding began Hawksley found, to his disappointment that after reaching a height of 30 ft the water escaped through a band of jointed and fissured rock at one end of the dam puddle trench and reappeared as a spring at the foot of the byewash. The reservoir was not required for use, consequently no funds were allotted by the Company to enable Hawksley to carry out remedial measures, but after the works were acquired by the Sheffield Corporation in 1888, a wing trench 2200 ft long and 80–100 ft deep was constructed, which

Figure 8.12   Top of Waskerley valve well

entirely cut off all percolation. It took 5 years to complete, and cost £53 000.[41] Nearly 30 years passed before the reservoir came into constant use in 1896.[42]

So few impounding reservoirs for water supply had been built during the first half of the nineteenth century that estimates of yield from them were guesswork. Quoting from the evidence Hawksley gave in 1847 at the Parliamentary Preliminary Inquiry on his Rivington scheme, Lloyd has written: 'He stated the produce from the watershed would be equal to a supply of 23½ million gallons per diem' and 'the extent of the storage exceeds 2,500 million gallons'. Following this, in answer to the question 'what is the average fall of rain you have estimated this supply from on that district per annum?' he said 'we propose to gather three feet' which from the area is equivalent to 22 mgd. Two days later, Hawksley further stated, 'if the evaporation be deducted from the mean fall on the district, the remainder is the quantity which may be safely calculated upon being received in the reservoir'. It may be concluded that Hawksley based the quantity he could supply on the average run-off of the catchment area. At that time, such appears to have been the general opinion.[43]

After the Rivington scheme was put into operation, it soon became apparent that the effective yield was less than 22 mgd. In 1864, 1865 and 1866 the average was less than 16½ mgd, the yield in 1865 being only 14½ mgd.[44]

As a result of this experience, and also experience with impounding reservoirs gained elsewhere, Hawksley was able in the evidence he gave to the Richmond Commission in 1868 to formulate his rules. Pointing out that in wet years, when a reservoir is full, the excess goes over the waste weir and is lost:

> The first thing to be done is to ascertain the average of the rainfall over a very large number of years. From that deduct one sixth, that being the quantity which will inevitably be lost over the waste weir . . . The next thing to do, from the residual quantity is to take off the amount of evaporation.

Hawksley then went on to say:

> We find by the reservoirs of the great magnitude which I am going to mention we can store and regulate (that is the thing wanted) the rainfall of three consecutive dry years, and we find (and it is a very curious fact again, but it comes in justification of what I have already said) that the average rainfall of the three consecutive dry years . . . is exactly one-sixth less than the average of the whole.[45]

Following a droughty period in the 1880s, including a severe drought in 1887, Hawksley's rule was modified by A. R. Binnie who recommended that the average rainfall of the three consecutive driest years should be taken as being one-

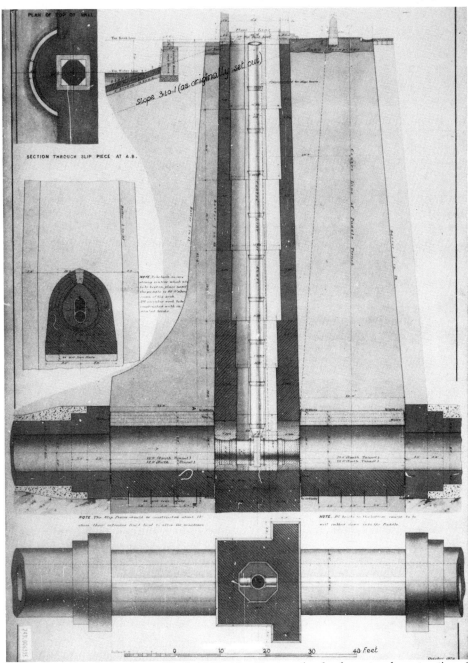

Figure 8.13   Damflask valve well built 1867 with widening of embankment and construction of retaining wall undertaken subsequently

Figure 8.14   Smiddy Shaw dam, 1875 – air pipe on left

fifth less than the long-term average.[46] With storage of sufficient capacity to equa-
lize the erratic run-off from a catchment area in the 3 consecutive driest years, the
stage was reached of numerically estimating the yield from 80 per cent of the
average rainfall which became known as the 'reliable yield'. Counsel found that
this rule was one which laymen could readily understand and until 20 years ago it
remained generally accepted for Parliamentary purposes. The value is equivalent
to the run-off in a hypothetical 80 per cent rainfall year.

In 1852 Thomas Hawksley had moved to London and established himself in
Great George Street where he continued to follow his profession until his death 40
years later. Whilst the number of impounding schemes which Hawksley designed
was much exceeded by his great rival Bateman, he designed more pumped water-
supply schemes than any of his contemporaries. He claimed that he was responsible for more than 150 waterworks.[47] Though he never directly presented any
Paper to the Institution of Civil Engineers – his office being near – he participated,
as the minutes show, in many discussions and took a great interest in its affairs,
serving on various committees from time to time. Whilst with the general public it
was only the railway engineers who held the centre of the stage, with the engineering profession it was otherwise. Of the five persons who were elected presidents of
the Institution of Civil Engineers during the 1870s, two of them were waterworks
engineers, one being Thomas Hawksley (1872–74) and the other J. F. Bateman
(1878–80), the subject of the next chapter.

9 J. F. La Trobe Bateman, FRS (1810–89)

(a) EARLY WORKS AND THE REPAIR OF THE BILBERRY DAM

Among the many interesting and important subjects to which the present desire for sanitary improvement has recently directed public attention, none have a higher claim upon that attention, nor are more intimately mixed up with the health, the comfort and the well-being of our town populations, than the questions of an abundant supply of good and wholesome water, the complete and proper drainage of our houses and our cities, and the purification of the streams and rivers into which the sewage of our towns is allowed to flow. Scientific research, and the experience of daily life, are constantly bringing to view the close connection which these questions have with the mortality, the comfort and the moral habits of our rapidly increasing population.

The tendency to herd together in large cities for purposes of convenience and employment, the rapidity with which many manufacturing towns have sprung into existence or increased in size, – outstripping all preparation or arrangement for the physical comfort and well-being of their inhabitants, – the deterioration of the dwellings of many of the older towns and the closer packing of the labouring classes for want of proper house accommodation, have all contributed to enhance the evils attendant upon a deficient supply of water and imperfect drainage. The spread of manufactures and the valuable commercial purposes to which the waters of the country have been applied, have led to the deterioration of most of the streams to which the inhabitants formerly resorted for the supply of their domestic wants, and suitable natural supplies of water have now become either wholly deficient or lamentably inadequate to meet the demands of health and comfort. Systems of artificial supply have to be adopted, and in many cases these are attended with so much difficulty and expense, that every effort to inculcate right principles of supply, and to afford accurate information for the government of those engaged in carrying out works of so much value to the community, is entitled to attention and respect.

157

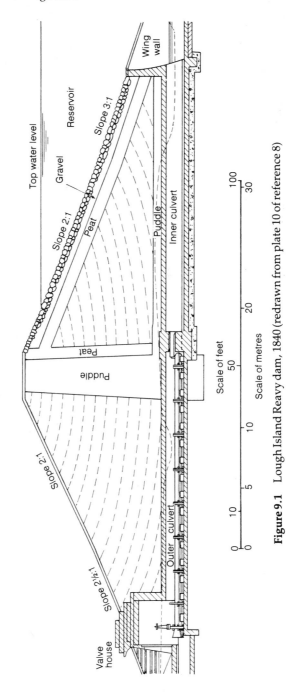

Figure 9.1 Lough Island Reavy dam, 1840 (redrawn from plate 10 of reference 8)

With these words John Frederic Bateman (who late in life added his mother's maiden name of La Trobe) began his address to the British Association in 1855.[1] He had a brilliant career, particularly as a dam-builder, and the number of dams in the United Kingdom constructed under his supervision far exceeded those of any of his contemporaries or even of his successors. He is the only British water engineer so far to have been the subject of a full-length study, and the author is much indebted to P. E. Russell for the use he has been able to make of his thesis.[2] In this chapter it will be possible only to concentrate on the more outstanding of Bateman's many projects.

Bateman was born in 1810 near Halifax; his father was an unsuccessful businessman but his mother's family were prominent members of the Moravian sect and of Huguenot origin. Young Bateman was sent to Moravian schools where the precepts of Comenius (1592–1670) were still followed that older pupils 'should learn the important principles of the mechanical arts both that they may not be too ignorant of what goes on in the world around them and that any special inclination towards things of this kind may assert itself with greater ease later on.'[3]

After leaving school Bateman was apprenticed to a surveyor and mining engineer; at the age of 23 set up on his own as 'a civil engineer, land surveyor and agent',[4] and in the following year he investigated the causes of floods, and their consequences, in the River Medlock which led to his studying hydraulic questions more closely.[5]

In the spring of 1834, a by then well-known Manchester engineer, William Fairbairn (engine-maker of Canal Street, Ancoats) was asked by a group of millowners in Northern Ireland to make a report concerning the all-year-round availability of sufficient water power. Fairbairn was asked because he was known to the millowners from previous installation of waterwheels in Northern Ireland.[6] Although able to deduce the water requirements, Fairbairn himself was more interested in mechanical engineering and did not wish to undertake the surveys. Here occurred a great turning point in Bateman's life, in that Fairbairn invited him to make the surveys on his behalf. This association, once established, proved to be fundamental to Bateman's career as a water engineer and, in due course, he also became Fairbairn's son-in-law.

In Fairbairn's book[7] on the Bann reservoirs, published in 1836, the drawings at the end of the book are signed by Fairbairn as Engineer and 'J. Fred.[c] Bateman' as Surveyor. However, when the Act was passed that year, Bateman was appointed Engineer to the Bann Reservoirs Company. Bateman also wrote two papers for the Institution of Civil Engineers, the first one in 1841 on the completion of the Lough Island Reavy reservoir,[8] work having begun in 1837, and on the whole scheme in 1848 on the completion of the Corbet Lough reservoir,[9] which required an embankment only 10 ft high.

Referring to the first reservoir, there were no rainfall or river flow records at the

159

site. 'There seemed, however, to be a prospect of obtaining sufficient water to justify the reservoir being laid out as large as the circumstances of the locality would allow. This was accordingly done.'[10] Subsequent experience fully justified this expectation.

One principal, and three smaller, embankments were required to impound the water to a height of 35 ft above lake level, the main embankment (Fig. 9.1) being 40 ft deep at the discharge culvert where it attains its greatest height. The main embankment had a clay corewall and cut-off trench, the clay being worked in regular 8 in. thick layers. In addition it had a lining of peat 3 ft thick brought up on the inside of the puddle and also on the face of the water slope, well worked and trodden together in an almost dry state. A course of gravel about 18 in. thick was laid over the peat on the water face, and above that stone pitching 2 ft thick.

Peat being of a light and fibrous character, Bateman's theory was that, in the event of a leak occurring it would attract the fibres which, by degrees, would stop the holes sufficiently for the silt to settle over and effectively close the aperture. J. Smythe carried out laboratory experiments on dried turf, as used by Bateman, as adjuncts to the clay corewall of the Rhodes Wood dam which he found expanded 20 per cent under water, absorbed 55 per cent and increased 241 per cent in weight; he also advocated the use of peat as a protection to puddle.[11] Peat continued to be incorporated occasionally, one example being as relatively thin blocks on both sides of the clay corewall of the Lliw dam built in 1862–67, but after about 1870 it was no longer used.

An interesting feature was that the embankments 'were formed in concave layers 3 feet thick, each layer being completed before another was commenced, steps being cut in the ground where necessary to receive the layers'.[12] Bateman's object, no doubt, was to avoid slip planes which he fancied might otherwise occur between layers. Particularly on the sloping surfaces the layers were much too thick for good compaction with horse and cart or wheelbarrow.

A culvert was constructed in the solid ground under the embankment to discharge the water; it is divided in the centre by a solid piece of masonry through which three 18 in. pipes passed, one of which was closed and not used. The inner half of the culvert is open to the reservoir and the outer half contains two pipelines controlled by valves at the downstream toe of the embankment. The inner culvert is laid upon a bed of concrete 18 in. thick and was intended to have been surrounded by puddle 12 in. thick, the excavation being made just sufficient for this purpose (see Fig. 9.1). All would probably have been well if the puddle surround had been in place, but unfortunately the superintendent, without Bateman's concurrence, substituted rubble backing for the puddle which, to complete the mischief, he carried on past the solid masonry and through the centre puddle to the outside of the bank from the inside of the reservoir. The consequence was that under a pressure of only 12 ft of water the water leaked through the joints of the inner culvert and passed through the rubble to the outside culvert. Not wishing to incur the expense of Roman cement (which had been invented by Edgar Dobbs in 1810) Bateman tried to make hydraulic mortar according to some instructions just then published by Vicat; but in the end had to resort to picking out the joints and caulking them well with oakum to within 2 or 3 in. of the face, finally filling the remainder with Roman cement. These repairs were made in 1839 and 1841 and served reasonably well until 1867 when there was subsidence in the pavement close to the breast wall of the forebay and greatly increased leakage. After a visit made to the site by Bateman in October 1867 extensive repairs were carried out which appear to have been completely successful.[13]

As had been the case with the Bann Reservoir Company, the person employed as Engineer for the purpose of promoting a Bill through Parliament was not necessarily the same person who would be the Engineer responsible for the subsequent design and execution of the project. Thus the so-called Engineer for promoting the scheme was, in some cases, a prominent citizen engaged as much for the influence he could wield as for any technical ability he might have. In such cases the task of getting the works built might well be deemed the responsibility of the Surveyor who also gave evidence and who, after a Bill received the Royal Assent, then became the Engineer for construction of the project. In this way an able young man could change his status from that of a Surveyor to that of an Engineer.

This happened with the Glossop Dale Reservoirs scheme for which Bateman was first Surveyor and subsequently, after the passing of the Act in 1838, Engineer. Three dams were sanctioned but only the 65 ft high Hurst dam (Fig. 9.2) was built. Instead of a central clay corewall and cut-off trench, Bateman in this case designed his dam with a clay blanket 5–6 ft thick on the upstream face as the watertight membrane, the blanket being joined to a clay-filled cut-off trench which ran along the foot of the upstream slope. As designed the blanket was protected from wave action by pitching stone 18 in. thick laid on 2 ft of gravel or soil. For some unknown reason this particular embankment appears not to have been constructed in accordance with the design because when some works of improvement and alteration were carried out in 1955/61 no defined clay layer was found; nevertheless the cross-section is of interest in showing a type of design adopted by Bateman with success on several occasions to be described later. The discharge culvert, or tunnel, which extended from the upstream forebay to a short distance beyond the dam centre line, is built of brick on a concrete foundation and is enveloped in puddle clay 2 ft thick. Beneath the downstream slope of the dam the outlet is continued as a 15 in. diameter pipeline with a control valve at the downstream end, both features being considered bad practice after 1864. Whilst it is not recorded that the outlet tunnel and pipeline gave trouble, during 1959–61 both were sealed and a siphon drawn-off arrangement was substituted.[14]

As was the case also at the Bann reservoirs, the cross-section shows that the

161

162

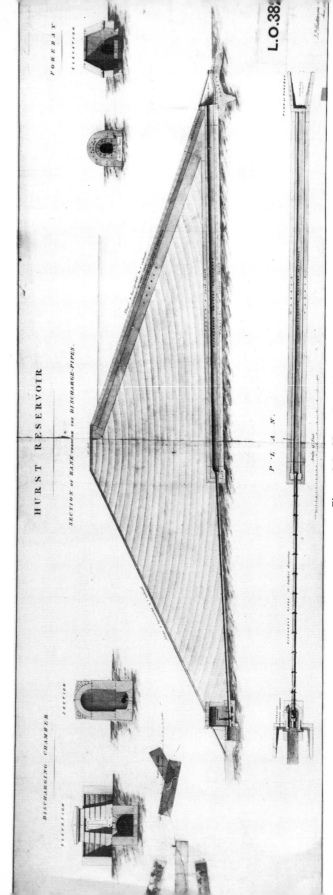

Figure 9.2 Hurst dam, 1840

embankment was to be formed in concave layers some 3 ft thick. After the completion of this dam in 1840[15] Bateman, at the age of 30, won for himself recognition as an Engineer for both the promotion and execution of projects.

Bateman was also consulted by several other water companies and local authorities in Lancashire. At Bolton[16] in 1849 he raised for compensation water the embankment of the Belmont reservoir from 70 to 86 ft high, an interesting account of which is given by Swales,[17] and in 1850 the Dingle dam was built for water supply. He was also Engineer for St Helen's,[18] Stalybridge and Mossley[19] and Blackburn.[20]

It may be remembered that in September 1845 Hawksley declined to undertake any further works for the Towns Improvement Company.[21] Chadwick thereupon invited Bateman[22] to become one of the Company's Engineers and his name appeared on their prospectus, which must have made it better known. The Company was near the end of its existence but Bateman was asked to estimate the cost of works at Chorley[23] and subsequently was the Engineer on his own behalf.[24] The High Bullough dam designed for Chorley (Fig. 9.3) and completed in 1850 has a pipeline embedded in concrete in a trench beneath a 50 ft high embankment as the reservoir outlet. Where it crosses the puddle trench the pipeline is supported on two masonry piers and the discharge valve is at the downstream end of the pipeline. At the upstream end there are two openings.

The stone blocks shown on the section and in plan were presumably intended as supports for a long rod, or possibly a chain, but the purpose of the rod or chain is not known. It may have been intended to be used for opening and closing a flap valve on the upper opening. In all probability the lower opening was used for diverting water during the construction period and was closed permanently by a cast-iron cover-plate before impounding began.

By modern standards the pipeline buried beneath the embankment with a control valve at the downstream end is a bad arrangement, and the fact that the dam has survived without giving serious trouble indicates that the foundations were good, and that the caulking of the joints in the pipeline was well done.

The *Westmorland Gazette* of 17 August, 1844, gave notice of a proposal 'to form a vast reservoir at Kentmere so that the waters accumulated in winter may furnish a better supply in droughty seasons than has otherwise been enjoyed . . .'. After a public meeting during the following week, a Provisional Committee of local mill-owners was formed and they called in the services of Bateman.[25]

The Kendal Reservoirs Act, signed by Queen Victoria on 21 July, 1845, followed. The preamble to this Act reads:

> Whereas it is expedient that Reservoirs should be constructed . . . for the Purpose of affording a better and more regular Supply of Water to the Mills and Manufactories upon the said Streams respectively, and by means thereof of

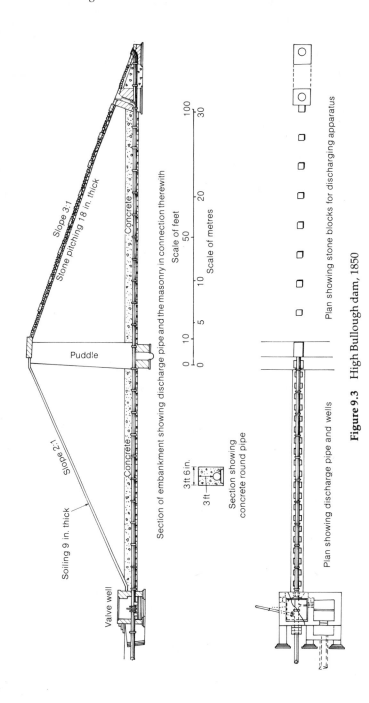

Slope 3:1

Stone pitching 18 in. thick

Concrete

Concrete

Puddle

Soiling 9 in. thick

Slope 2:1

Valve well

Section of embankment showing discharge pipe and the masonry in connection therewith

Scale of feet

Scale of metres

0   10   50   100

0   5   10   20   30

3 ft 6 in.

3 ft

Section showing concrete round pipe

Plan showing discharge pipe and wells

Plan showing stone blocks for discharging apparatus

Figure 9.3 High Bullough dam, 1850

cleansing the said Streams, and thereby promoting the Health of the Persons residing upon the Banks of such Streams. . . .[26]

The Act authorized the construction of five dams of which only the Kentmere Head dam[27] (Fig. 9.4), completed in 1848, was built.

Most fortunately Bateman's specification for the construction of this dam has been carefully preserved.[28] The clay corewall was specified to be worked in courses 8 in. thick, each layer to be completed to its full extent before the next layer was laid; 'the puddling to be done by soaking each course 12 hours in water and then cutting it lengthways and crossways and treading it, each course to be cut and worked into the one below'. The bank was to be constructed in concave layers 2 ft thick on the water side and 4 ft thick on the outer side of the corewall; 'the inner part of the bank to be composed of the most adhesive material and so laid, carted over and watered in dry weather that it shall become either quite or nearly watertight, the outer part of the bank to be composed of dry or stony material'.

Instead of supporting the pipeline where it crossed the puddle trench on pillars, Bateman in this case specified an arch (Fig. 9.4) as follows: 'the pipes to be supported in passing through the puddle upon a stone platform formed by throwing an Arch across the puddle trench so that the pipes may have equal bearing throughout and can be at the same time surrounded by Puddle at the Centre of the bank'. The detailed drawings of the arch no longer exist but it was probably narrow, not more than one stone wide. The method of construction may have been that, after bringing up the clay in the puddle trench to the level of the underside of the pipeline, timbered trenches were excavated in the puddle clay to the shape of the arch and the stones were then placed in position with the clay acting as centring. Finally, with or without removing the timbering, the slot above the arch was backfilled with puddle clay. The laying of the pipeline would then have been able to proceed.

For the culverts, the specification reads:

> The culverts to be excavated out of the solid ground a trench being cut for them no wider than sufficient to contain the masonry of the sides without backing. To be built of good flat bedded Stone or Slate set in hydraulic mortar and covered 3 feet with Puddle or pounded clay united with the centre puddle of the bank.

The inner culvert having open communication with the reservoir was specified to have an opening of rectangular shape 4 ft high by 3 ft 6 in. wide.

It was also specified that 'the inner or mouth of the inner culvert be covered with an iron grating part of which must be moveable by means of a rod or chain worked by a Crab or other Apparatus on the top of the bank.' This would appear to have been some mechanical arrangement for raking the iron grating under water to free it when necessary of debris. With the bars running from the top to the bottom of the grating, perhaps the device consisted of hinged rods moving in vertical planes between the bars which could be lifted or lowered by a lever on the crest of the embankment.

Since the Reservoir Safety Act (1930) the dam has been inspected periodically. When the first inspection was made in 1933 it was found that at least one of the pipes through the dam was broken and all the pipes were renewed. The inspecting engineer would not sanction the use of either the valve 'F' or the valve 'C' for controlling the outflow and a new valve was fitted (not shown on Fig. 9.4) which closed off the end of the inner culvert. The operating rods for this valve were carried up the stone-pitched slope to a large handwheel on the crest of the dam.[29] The consequence of this was that the inner culvert of rectangular shape was now subject to water pressure, a condition for which it had not been designed by Bateman, and the entrance to this culvert collapsed in 1964. With a steel tube, made of old oil drums welded together through the middle to allow water from the reservoir to gain access to the gate well, the culvert was grouted up. It was expected that when in due course the thin shell of the pipe corroded, the concrete surround would provide an adequate watertight pipeline but the culvert had to be grouted again in 1977 before all the voids in the stonework surrounding the pipe were filled.

Another work also undertaken in 1965 was a permanent lowering by 3½ ft of the top water level of the reservoir by cutting a new 45 ft long spillway 3½ ft deep into the existing spillway. The reason for this was that there had been a further progressive consolidation of clay core during the past 120 years. This had brought the top of the core down to such a level that when the reservoir was in flood the top water could penetrate the fill above the core, spill over to the downstream fill and thus in time wet the downstream fill sufficiently to weaken it so that an earth slip could have taken place. The normal remedy for such a decline would have been to have raised the core to its former level but the cost factor outweighed the benefit of the storage capacity involved. The dam was thus fully restored to a safe and sound condition.[30]

The collapse of the Bilberry embankment in 1852, and the evidence given by Captain Moody, have been described in Chapter 4. Moody also inspected the Holme Styes embankment and reported unfavourably on its condition. He found leaks in the valve pit and the culvert which were running 'considerably muddy' and depressions in the bank. He was very scathing about the top water level of the reservoir having been raised by a wall across the entrance to the spillway, which he condemned as being a most dangerous practice. He recommended the Commissioners to send for a hydraulic engineer and to carry out his instructions.[31]

The Commissioners called in Bateman and shortly afterwards the Holme Reservoirs Act 1853 received the Royal Assent. With Bateman named as the Engineer, this Act authorized the raising of funds for the purpose of rebuilding the Bilberry

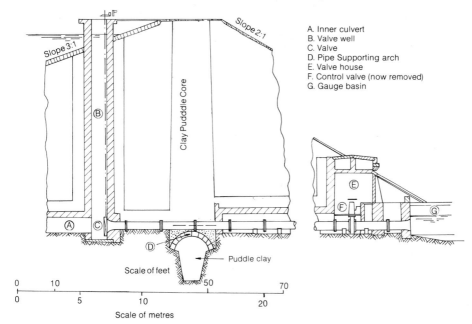

A. Inner culvert
B. Valve well
C. Valve
D. Pipe Supporting arch
E. Valve house
F. Control valve (now removed)
G. Gauge basin

Figure 9.4 Kentmere Head dam, 1848. This drawing does not show the valve which was fitted in 1936 to enable the inner culvert to be shut off. The operating rods for this valve are carried up the stone-pitched upstream face of the dam and the valve is operated by a handwheel near the top of the valve well (redrawn from Fig. 6 of reference 25)

embankment and for carrying out repairs to the Holme Styes and Boshaw Whams reservoirs. The Commissioners were also replaced by newly appointed Directors.

Adopting the same methods in principle as he had designed for the Hurst dam (Fig. 9.2), the evidence points to Bateman having blanketed the upstream slope of the Holme Styes dam and the adjacent sides with a layer of puddle clay protected by sandy fill and pitching as shown on an 1857 drawing (Fig. 9.5). A rare opportunity to examine the work done, at a location normally under water, occurred when during the summer of 1975 the reservoir level was drawn down lower than it had been for several decades and a crater was discovered. During an air raid on Sheffield in the winter of 1941–42, sticks of bombs were unloaded and, from other bomb craters on the same alignment, all the evidence points to one bomb having landed under water on the embankment where it exploded on impact. An examination of the crater before it was refilled revealed conditions which were consistent with the design of blanket and toe trench shown on the 1857 drawing.[32]

Under the 1843 Holme Styes Act the reservoirs were required to be inspected by an engineer once a year, and in 1872 Thomas Barham Foster, who was Bateman's nephew, offered his services for making an annual inspection and report for £21

167

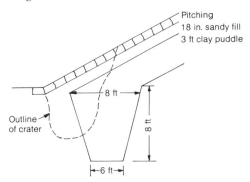

Figure 9.5   Holme Styes dam – detail from drawing dated 1857

plus expenses. He wrote: 'Under Mr. Bateman, I reconstructed the Bilberry Reservoir and Holme Styes some 16 years ago so I am fully acquainted with the details of their construction both external and internal.'[33] Neither Moody nor Foster referred to the Boshaw Whams embankment and any repairs that were necessary to it would appear to have been minor.

In July 1854 a contract for the reconstruction of the Bilberry embankment was awarded to some contractors for £5500. The new embankment was on the site of the old one but with the centre line 30 ft upstream of the old one. The crest level of the new embankment was 14 ft lower than the old one but the top of the waste shaft was lowered by only 10 ft, thus allowing a freeboard above top water level of only 4 ft whereas previously it had been 8 ft. The width of the crest was 18 ft. The upstream slope was approximately 3 to 1 and the downstream slope 2 to 1.

Bateman specified that before other work began a temporary aperture for stream division was to be made through the westerly wall of the waste shaft. In addition, he specified that a masonry barrel culvert with an internal diameter of 2 ft should be constructed along the base of the embankment at its deepest point. For the last 30 ft at the reservoir end this culvert consisted of a 9 in. diameter cast-iron pipe terminating in a small masonry chamber at the upstream toe of the embankment and able to be closed by a blank flange.

For making the reservoir watertight, a layer of puddle clay was placed on the water face of the embankment and on the floor and sides of the reservoir for a considerable distance from the embankment. This puddle was protected by a layer of earth and gravel over which was stone pitching, on similar lines to his Hurst design (Fig. 9.2). The thickness of the clay puddle was 4 ft on the face of the embankment and 2 ft elsewhere.[34] The means which Bateman adopted for making the reservoir watertight would appear to have been similar to what George Leather was proposing should be done when he visited the works in July 1843.

Bateman was evidently conscious that the spillway capacity was inadequate and subsequently, in 1867, a supplementary spillway was constructed on the north side of the reservoir, the Engineer named in the contract documents being G. H. Hill who was Bateman's chief assistant. The spillway was 50 ft long, the crest level being 5 ft below the top level of the dam and it discharged into a 10 ft wide bywash channel.[35]

It is interesting to follow the subsequent history of the dam.

On 12 August, 1933, the first inspection of the Bilberry reservoir under the Reservoirs (Safety Provisions) Act 1930 was made by E. J. Silock, MICE of Silcock and Simpson of Westminster and Leeds. Referring to the masonry culvert underneath the embankment he wrote:

> The [reservoir] end of the pipe is covered with a blank flange so that no water can reach the tunnel through the pipe. There is, however, a continuous flow of water of varying volume down the culvert. This water is quite clear but contains iron and leaves a ferruginous deposit on the sides and bottom of the culvert and the stream. The water issuing from this channel would appear to come from a spring situated under the embankment, but the discharge from the spring is affected by the water level in the reservoir and also by rainfall . . . at times there have been indications of discolouration of the water, which might be construed as a danger signal.

The leakage varied between 60 000 and 600 000 gallons per day (3 litres per second to 30 litres per second). Silcock also found that a settlement of 12–15 in. had occurred over part of the upstream slope of the embankment.[36]

No remedial measures were undertaken, and when J. P. Beveridge inspected the reservoir under the Act 10 years later he found that the leakage from the culvert had increased to a continuous flow varying between 100 000 and 1 million gallons per day (5–50 litres per second) depending on reservoir level, and rainfall and that the settlement in the depression in the upstream slope had increased to 20 in. He also presumed that there was a spring under the embankment.[37]

There is no doubt that the spring referred to by Silcock and Beveridge was the same spring as was encountered during the excavation for the cut-off trench for the first embankment in 1839 and which subsequently caused its collapse. Clearly they were both unfamiliar with the history of the first embankment. In his specification Bateman wrote: 'Any springs arising in the base of the bank to be turned into the 2 feet barrel culvert.' Whilst Bateman does not state precisely that the primary purpose of the masonry culvert was to intercept this spring, without it doing so there could not have been any successful reconstruction of the embankment and this would appear to have been its main purpose.

In 1936 the Huddersfield Corporation decided to take steps to construct a reservoir on the Digley Brook immediately downstream of the Bilberry reservoir, also to purchase the Bilberry, Holme Styes and Boshaw Whams reservoirs, and obtained the necessary Act in 1937. A contract for constructing the Digley embankment and other works was actually awarded at the beginning of 1939 but before starting work the contractor was allowed to withdraw and construction was postponed indefinitely until after the war.[38]

It thus came about that when the greatest storm in living memory in the Digley valley occurred, on 29 May, 1944, the embankment was still as reconstructed by Bateman. Fortunately the additional spillway had also been constructed as without it the embankment would certainly have failed a second time. As it was, the run-off from the adjacent valley sides on to the top of the embankment, coupled with waves breaking over it from the reservoir whilst the wind was high, washed away parts of the embankment (Fig. 9.6) and created, for a short time, a highly critical situation; fortunately the wind soon moderated. Three lives were lost and the storm also caused a considerable amount of damage in Holmfirth. No doubt because it occurred during wartime, this catastrophe received very little publicity.[39]

Shortly after the war the Huddersfield Corporation again put in hand the construction of the Digley embankment and it was completed in 1954, G. H. Hill and

Figure 9.6   Bilberry dam after storm of 29 May, 1944

Sons being the consulting engineers. At the same time, without lowering the crest of the Bilberry embankment, the top of the waste shaft was lowered again, this time by 11 ft, and the reservoir now serves only as a silt trap (Fig. 9.7). The top water level of the Digley reservoir is 15 ft below the crest of the Bilberry dam and the greater part of the downstream slope is now submerged.

(b) THE MANCHESTER WATERWORKS

Dr John Dalton (1766–1844), the famous chemist and natural philosopher, for many years contributed to the Manchester Literary and Philosophical Society rain-gauge readings; the gauges were situated along the line of the Rochdale Canal and over the Pennine chain of hills by Blackstone Edge. The readings had been regularly furnished by the Canal Company to Dr Dalton but, unknown to him, the rain-gauges were all fixed on the ridging of the roofs of the houses of the persons in whose custody they were placed, thus 'overlooking the circumstance . . . that every wind which blew would be deflected upwards by the sloping roof of the home, – would rush with increased velocity over the ridging and carry away the rain which ought to have fallen into the gauge'.[40] These records appeared to show

Figure 9.7 Bilberry dam in 1980

that less rain was received by a gauge the higher it was placed, and it was erroneously assumed by many that less rain fell on elevated land than on low land.

When Bateman was engaged with George Leather by some objecting landowners in opposing a scheme for obtaining additional supplies of water for the town of Oldham in the Parliamentary Session of 1838, he opposed the scheme on the basis of the current theory that less rainfall fell on elevated than on low ground, and Oldham's Bill was lost.[41] However, a few years after this, the readings which Bateman had obtained from rain-gauges situated at both hilly and low sites in various parts of the country began to cast doubts in his mind on the validity of this theory, and it was then that he discovered that the records sent to Dr Dalton were from rain-gauges on the roofs of houses. Bateman continued his observations and in 1844 contributed a paper on the subject to the Manchester Literary and Philosophical Society.[42] In the discussion on this paper he commented on the positioning of rain-gauges and he contended that more rain fell on elevated land; not less, as had previously been believed. Bateman also expounded these opinions to a meeting of the Statistical Section of the British Association in York in September 1844.[43]

One of those who attended the September 1844 meeting of the British Association in York was Edwin Chadwick and, in reply to a letter dated 8 October, 1844 from a certain town councillor of Manchester, he wrote:

> For all purposes it would be of the greatest importance that you should get the advice of trustworthy engineers, of whom I am sorry to say there are marvellous few – a more ignorant or more jobbing set of men, less to be trusted as the difference of their estimates and their expenditure will show, than the common run of men who dub themselves with the title of engineer and pretend to science I have rarely met with. . . . You would do yourselves great credit by a report from Mr Hawksley. Young Mr Bateman's paper read before the British Association was thought so well of by Mr John Taylor the engineer and others that he was recommended to the Council for an application for another paper and he, I think, would be worth your consideration at Manchester.[44]

This unsolicited testimonial on behalf of Bateman may have helped him in subsequently being selected by the Manchester City Corporation to be their Engineer for new waterworks.

Thomas Hawksley prepared the Lancashire Waterworks scheme to which reference has already been made in Chapter 1, and a Bill was laid before Parliament in 1846. Opposition to this came from the Manchester and Salford Waterworks Company in the form of a Bill based on a hastily prepared scheme proposing the construction of reservoirs in Lyme Park, engineered by Simpson.[45] The Lancashire

Waterworks Bill was also opposed by the Corporation on the grounds that the supply of water to a city or town should be controlled by the inhabitants of that city or town, and to allow another company in would necessitate the purchase of two companies instead of only one at some later date. Neither Bill was successful and the Corporation was left to fulfil the obligation it had imposed on itself. This it did by calling upon Bateman, who had already been employed by the Corporation during the committee stage, to supply a scheme for supplying Manchester and Salford with water.[46] Thus began an association with the Manchester Corporation that was to continue for many years.

It is not proposed to discuss the various negotiations with millowners or the rival schemes, including another by Hawksley, that were then put forward, which have been fully described elsewhere,[47] but to go straight to the Act which received the Royal Assent on 22 July, 1848. This Act authorized, *inter alia*, the exploitation of the Etherow river in the Longdendale Valley lying some 12–16 miles to the East of Manchester, the construction of two small reservoirs on the Arnfield and Hollingworth brooks respectively, and the acquisition of the water company.[48]

The Longdendale project, and the Rivington project concurrently under construction for Liverpool, were the first major works of the kind in the country. There was thus very little experience to act upon and there was a lack of reliable rainfall records in the district.

Across the main valley between the village of Tintwistle and Woodhead a series of embankments were constructed which form a chain of separate reservoirs for impounding the waters of the river Etherow; three such embankments named Woodhead, Torside and Rhodeswood were constructed in the first stage (Fig. 9.8).

The works in Longdendale were commenced in August 1848, the Woodhead embankment and a tunnel at Mottram being the first two works to be taken in hand, and continued for nearly 30 years until the spring of 1877. Bateman wrote a history of these works which was published in 1884. However, this was written late in life, with the consciousness of a long and difficult task successfully achieved. A better idea of the difficulties Bateman as a younger and less experienced dam-builder faced can be gained from the earlier reports he wrote from time to time to the Water Committee of the Manchester Corporation, from whom he held back nothing. Bateman was most fortunate in having the support of a wealthy corporation and it says a great deal for the city fathers of Manchester that they responded to Bateman's frankness by continuing to give him their support through all his difficulties.

At the time when site investigations were undertaken by Bateman, sinking shafts below groundwater with the crude and cumbersome pumping machinery then available presented a much more difficult problem than today, and boring in rocks was also slow and difficult. Bateman records with disappointment how one boring 7 ft deep into what appeared to be solid rock was subsequently found to

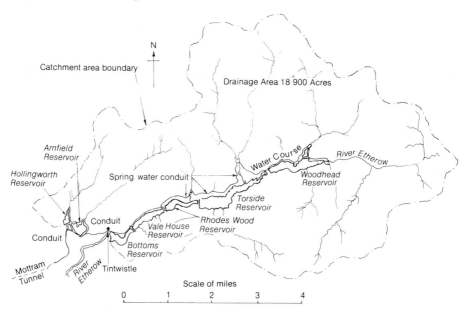

Figure 9.8 Longdendale reservoirs, 1876 (redrawn from map in reference 40 dated 1884. To avoid confusion with the spring water conduit, the flood water course on the north side of the Torside, Rhodeswood, Vale House and Bottoms reservoirs has not been shown)

have been in a boulder 9 ft thick. Probably also the client was loth to spend much time and money on site investigation, a problem that not infrequently still occurs today. As a pioneer Bateman in 1847 did not have the experience in interpreting the results of site exploration that he subsequently acquired.

Longdendale is in the Yoredale shales and sandstones which, in the valley, are very disturbed. These disturbed geological conditions are not due to any major horizontal regional movements or faulting; they are due to localized movements. The present valley system of the Pennine Chain was formed long before the Glacial period and the first valleys were narrow and deep. As a result of the removal of the overlying load by the rivers, uplift in the valley floors and rebound of the strata on both sides of the valleys occurred. The uplift affected the strata near the surface considerably but had less and less influence with depth until regions of stability with no damage to the sandstone or shale beds were reached. The release of stresses in the pre-Glacial period also resulted in the beds of shale and sandstone on both sides of the valleys becoming jointed in directions parallel to them for considerable horizontal distances, even beyond the reach of the ice when the valleys were subsequently moulded to gentler slopes by the glaciers. One consequence of this was that when the glaciers retreated many landslides occurred.

After having completed the Rhodeswood and Torside embankments, Bateman wrote a report in which he described his experiences in excavating cut-off trenches in this strata, and it is interesting to compare the geology of the Longdendale Valley with the geological conditions in the Derwent and Ashop valleys where the Howden and Derwent masonry dams were also built in the Yoredale rocks 50 years later. Bateman wrote:

> When the original scheme for supplying Manchester with water was laid out, the valleys of Longdendale seemed especially suited to the purpose of collecting water and of constructing reservoirs to store. There was no other equally extensive track of unoccupied ground, and no valley which apparently presented equal facilities for the construction of large and efficient reservoirs. The geological character of the district appeared eminently favourable, consisting for the most part of retentive beds of shale, with abundance of clay and other suitable materials for the construction of the embankments – and it was not until the ground was fairly cut into in the search for suitable foundations for the clay puddle of the banks, that the hidden difficulties with which we had to contend were fully exhibited. The valley down which the water flows is but the main fissure of the district. It has been produced by an upward force and was originally but a crack in the crust of the earth, accompanied by an infinite number of minor parallel cracks, which, though not visible at the surface, extend longitudinally down both sides of the valley. In cutting the puddle trenches such longitudinal cracks were constantly discovered and crossed, and it was impossible in all cases, to penetrate far enough into the hill to cut off all which could communicate in any way with the main valley which had subsequently to be filled with water. – Another feature of the district was the multitude of landslips which had occurred from the gradual melting or perishing of the soft beds of shale and the falling of harder material which rested upon them and were thus undermined. Many of them were visible and were easily avoided but to a certain extent there was nothing to indicate their existence, or to enable you to determine by any examination which could be made short of cutting for a puddle trench, what was terra firma and what was slipped material.[49]

The engineer for the Howden and Derwent dams wrote:

> The Derwent valley and the adjoining Ashop valley contain many old landslips, and one at the junction of the two valleys is very extensive, being apparently ¾ mile in length. The Ashop valley in particular for a considerable distance shows signs of continuous landslips. The Yoredale beds are wrinkled or folded in the valley bottoms and also sometimes to a less extent a little higher

175

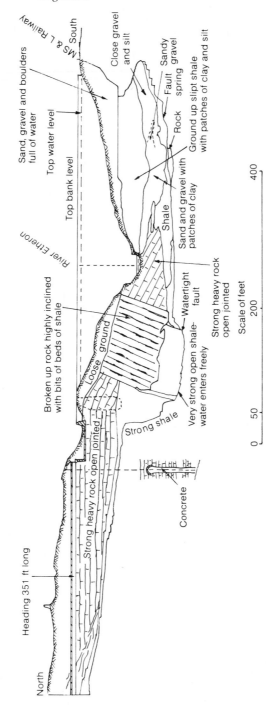

Figure 9.9 Geological section of Woodhead dam site (source: H. Lapworth, 'Geology of dam trenches', *Proc. Instn Wat Engrs*, 1911)

up. Sometimes the strata are curved into a long roll without being faulted, but in the bottom of the valley they are tilted up sharply, the central part being reduced to a powdered mass. In excavating through these wrinkles, the disturbed area gradually became less as greater depths were reached, until it was represented by only 2 or 3 feet of crushed sandstone. Below this level there were still indications of some disturbance, but they were very slight when the bottom of the narrow trench was reached, and appeared to be dying out. There is little doubt that the Yoredale shales and sandstones if undisturbed would prove fairly watertight for reservoir construction, but in this area they have been so broken up, shattered, and generally disturbed, that it is impossible to make reservoirs without excavating to great depths and incurring consequent additional expense.[50]

The last sentence refers to the great depths – 190 ft below the surface – to which the cut-off trench had to be sunk at one part of the Howden dam. In the Derwent dam the greatest depth necessary to secure watertightness was 108 ft.

The Derwent Valley Water Board originally intended to also build three dams in the adjacent Ashop valley but as a result of the costly experience gained at the Howden and Derwent dam sites, also the evidence of continuous landslips for a considerable distance in this valley, these projects were abandoned.[51] Pioneering in similar geological strata, it is not surprising that Bateman encountered so many difficulties. It is greatly to his credit that he persevered and in the end overcame them.

Bateman designed the first Woodhead embankment as a conventional earth dam with a clay puddle corewall and cut-off trench in the centre. The site was a narrow part of the valley, one side of which consisted of an ancient and extensive landslip which had pushed over the river and formed a steep escarpment on the other side (Fig. 9.9). The water was to be released from the reservoir through two 48 in. pipelines laid side by side with about 1 ft between them and with valves at the outer ends. The diameter of the pipelines was fixed having regard to river diversion during floods and was much larger than was subsequently required for water release. The pipes were supported by a stone pillar under each pipe; they were satisfactorily tested in their places by water pressure and were then surrounded by and embedded in concrete.

In his report of October 1849 to the Water Committee on the Woodhead reservoir Bateman wrote:

I fear that the sinking of the puddle trench on the Derbyshire side of the embankment to a secure foundation is going to be a difficult and troublesome work. The borings which have been made to ascertain the character of the strata previous to the commencement of the work have proved deceptive –

They indicated the presence of rock at about 20 feet below the surface of the ground, the superintendant mass being evidently slipped material from the hills above – what was supposed to be solid rock turns out so far to be large loose blocks some of them many feet thickness and in some cases rest one upon another in such a way as to deceive the most experienced borer. It has been found necessary to go to a considerably greater depth than was anticipated and we have not yet reached a satisfactory foundation. This will materially retard the progress of the work as well as increase the cost. [52]

The Woodhead and Torside reservoirs were both intended to store turbid water, and the original intention had been to complete the Woodhead embankment first. In view of the difficulties being experienced at this site, however, Bateman recommended that a contract for the completion of the Torside embankment should now be let. A limited amount of work had already been done at this dam site under an earlier contract. Any hesitation which the Water Committee may have had in accepting Bateman's recommendation was removed when, following the collapse of a weir intended to divert the river into a flood water course, the Woodhead embankment (which had reached a height of 24 ft above the discharge pipes) was overtopped and breached by a flood 5 days later. The water thus let loose rushed down the valley destroying fences, crops, bridges and buildings in its course for 5 miles down the river. Before the end of 1849 a contract for the completion of the Torside embankment was let.

In dry weather, when the streams and springs were unswollen by rain, the water was beautifully clear but as soon as the volume was increased by sudden rain the water was stained by peat and in that condition unfit to drink. By means of narrow slots in front of weirs (Fig. 9.10), water when small in quantity was conveyed away by watercourses beneath the tops of the weirs to be delivered direct to Manchester or, if more than sufficient for the wants of the town, into store in Rhodeswood res-

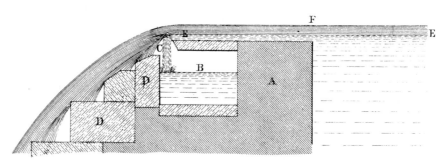

Figure 9.10   Slotted weir, 1852

ervoir. When the springs and streams fell below the quantity required, the deficiency was made up by drawing from Rhodeswood reservoir. At other times when the streams became swollen by rain and turbid, the weirs were so designed that at higher discharges the water jumped over the slots and was delivered to the Woodhead and Torside reservoirs. From the former reservoir the water was released into the river as compensation water. From the latter reservoir it could be used either as compensation water or, after being left undisturbed for several months to allow sediment to settle out, it could go into the potable water supply system. The Rhodeswood reservoir was the furthest downstream and this layout resulted in a flood-water course being required which would convey flood and compensation waters past the Torside and Rhodeswood reservoirs, especially past the latter.

For diverting the river during construction of the Torside embankment, a flood-water course was excavated in the solid rock on the north side of the valley.[53] Below that, and alongside the Rhodeswood reservoir, a large channel 35 ft wide and 10 ft deep was projected and partially executed when further progress was halted by the movement of a landslip. In his report of December 1850 Bateman wrote:

> I have for some time been watching the progress and considering the best means of preventing the movement of an old landslip on the northerly side of the Rhodes Wood reservoir across which the diversion of the river has to be carried. . . . The ground has been well known to have been constantly though slowly moving forward for years – the public road having to be altered from time to time in consequence. Before the commencement of our work the Turnpike road had moved about 3 feet in thirteen years and the slip was nearly in a state of rest. Since however we cut across the foot of it in the construction of the river diversion the movement has been much more rapid. A good deal has been done to prevent this by draining off swampy places and by the diversion of streams which were soaking into and saturating the mass but so far without any material benefit.[54]

During April 1851 Bateman reported that the ground was still moving at a rate of ¾ in. a day.[55] Bateman first constructed a single-span bridge across the flood channel, the foundations of which extended well into the undisturbed rock below the slip plane. He then placed a heavy mass of earth on the bridge and the adjacent relatively flat area which thrust against the hillside, and thereby prevented any further movement.[56]

In February 1851 Bateman reported:

> As the Woodhead embankment rose in height, symptoms of weakness were found in the discharge pipes, which near the centre of the bank appeared to be

179

yielding slightly under the pressure of the super-imposed mass. To remedy this, internal cylinders have been inserted for a length of about thirty yards in one line of pipes and are now being placed in the second. The evil appears entirely obviated and the reduction in the size of the pipe is now in no degree material, the only object for which it was originally made of such large diameter being to aid in discharging the floods during the early execution of the work before the embankment had obtained any material height. [57]

During the first few days of February 1852 the rainfall was extremely heavy and, as described in Chapter 4, the resulting flood on the river Holme on the eastern side of the Pennines precipitated the collapse of the Bilberry dam and had disastrous consequences for people and property in the vicinity of Holmfirth. The same rain-storms had also passed over Longdendale only 10 miles away on the western side of the Pennines and on 10 February, 1852, *The Times* reported:

> The great reservoirs which are constructing near Woodhead, 15 miles above Manchester, by the corporation of that town, were filled so full of water on Sunday that the engineer was under considerable apprehension that the Tor-side Reservoir, the embankment of which is not yet completed, would burst, and he very prudently despatched messengers down to the inhabitants below, warning them of the danger; but by keeping the water back as much as possible in the upper reservoir at Woodhead, and by employing a great number of excavators to cut an extra channel for the overflow from the Tor-side, so as to keep it off the embankment, the disaster was happily averted. The inhabitants, for miles down the valley of the Etherow, on which the reservoirs are situated, were in a state of panic during the whole of the day, and were removing their furniture and valuables with the greatest precipitation. Mr. J. Lees, of the firm of Messrs. Lees and Co., manufacturers, had several carts and waggons at work for many hours in moving his furniture. The quantity of water stored in these reservoirs is so vast that had they burst the loss of life and property must have been immense. The quantity of water stored in the Bilberry reservoir, which has committed such devastation at Holmfirth, is as a bucketfull compared with the water in the Woodhead and Tor Side. So great was the accumulation of water that Mr. Bateman had to discharge during many parts of the day at a rate of 3,200 cubic feet of water per second, to prevent the disaster.

As to what happened at the Rhodeswood reservoir, Bateman wrote:

> The excessive rain of February 1852 set in motion an ancient landslip of about 40 acres in extent lower down the valley than the one already described. On this ground, which exhibited no indication of moving, a contractor's village

... had been erected. This village was moved downwards about 8 inches during the night of the 6th February; and the masonry of the waste weir and waste water course of the Rhodeswood reservoir was crushed and disturbed. The completion of the embankment which formed, when finished, a buttress to the sides of the valley and the addition of weight to the toe of the moving mass arrested the movement.[58]

On this occasion, Robert Stephenson and I. K. Brunel were consulted and approved the measures that were adopted.

The Torside reservoir, having been completed, was gradually being filled in October and November 1854 and was within 9 ft of being full, the depth of water being then about 80 ft, when on 17 November fractures occurred in both discharge pipelines and a considerable quantity of water escaped near the outside slope. The reservoir was emptied as quickly as possible through one of the pipelines, the other being too badly damaged to be able to be used and in December 1854 Bateman wrote to the Water Committee:

> Since my last Report I have had the cause of this accident more closely investigated. It appears certain that the Embankment has been stretching itself upon its base and carrying the pipes with it apparently both upwards and downwards so as to leave them asunder near the centre. In which direction the greatest movement has occurred I am not yet able to determine but the total amount of elongation in the south range of pipes is from 3½ feet to 5 feet. This range is the most seriously damaged but the mischief is principally confined to a short length of about 22 feet immediately on the outside of the puddle in the centre of the bank – for about 15 feet the pipes are crushed into an elliptical form having about 6 inches greater diameter horizontally than vertically. Elsewhere they are almost uninjured. Some of the joints are drawn asunder in the north range but the elongation appears to have been less there and the injury is comparatively trifling. Both ranges of pipes may be temporarily repaired and I have given instructions to that effect. . . . In lieu of the present pipes which it is unfortunate it would be dangerous any longer to rely upon, I have to recommend the driving of a tunnel.[59]

In his report to the Council dated in January 1855 on this accident Bateman wrote:

> I believe every precaution which human foresight could conceive was taken to prevent such an occurrence. The pipes were sunk a considerable depth into the solid ground below the base of the bank and embedded in a great mass of concrete (except at the centre where they were supported on stone pillars and surrounded by puddle) and each end abutted against substantial ashlar stone buttresses which were carried deep into the solid ground. [Bateman added

that] the probable cause of the movement is the existence of a bed of hard [*sic*] clay of from 5 to 8 feet thick which forms the bed of the valley. The clay rests on a few feet of gravel beneath which there is a close water-tight rock into which the puddle of the bank has been securely tied. It is not unlikely that this bed of clay . . . has yielded a little or allowed the superincumbent mass to slide upon its surface.[60]

Early in 1855, whilst temporary repairs to the pipelines were proceeding, Bateman had holes drilled through the pipes to discover if the puddle clay was still in contact and reported:

It is evident from these experiments that after the pipes had been drawn asunder . . . the pressure of the water has forced away a portion of the puddle in the immediate neighbourhood of the fractures and filled up the vacancy with sand and gravel. . . . Under these circumstances it would not be advisable to store any water in the Reservoir until the puddle around the pipes has been effectively repaired. This will be a work of considerable difficulty.[61]

Instead of attempting to repair the puddle clay round the pipelines, it was decided to adopt a quite different solution. Quoting Bateman again:

A new puddle trench was sunk into the clay near the foot of the inner slope and the upper part lined with puddle clay 5 or 6 feet in thickness. The water was discharged by means of a tunnel in which two pipes are introduced – one of 48 inches in diameter which draws off the water to about 20 feet of the bottom and another of 24 inches in diameter which, as a syphon, will draw off the water to the bottom, the outer end being introduced into the Rhodeswood reservoir immediately below at a level low enough for the purpose.[62]

Bateman's report of April 1855 to the Water Committee on the Rhodeswood reservoir reads:

The south range of pipes has been overhauled, any slight imperfections repaired and a piece in the centre well strapped together. In the north range one or two pipes appear to be defective and it will be necessary to introduce a few cylinders before strapping the centre piece together.[63]

Presumably the object of strapping pipes together in the centre was to prevent drawing of joints in contact with the clay core where leakage would be particularly dangerous.

Bateman seems afterwards to have decided that the pipelines were not at fault because in his History he wrote:

At the Rhodeswood reservoir the pipes were laid in the same manner as at Torside, the most southerly one, however, being laid in a chase cut out of the solid rock and surrounded with concrete. The outer ends of the two discharge pipelines were closed by 3 feet valves, and no trouble of any kind has been experienced here. Owing, however, to imperfect workmanship in the puddle wall of this embankment, some time after the reservoir was filled, water was observed to escape. The bank was cut open to the defective spot and a layer of sandy material was discovered to have passed through from one side of the puddle wall to the other and through this the water had escaped. This was cut out, the puddle restored and the embankment raised to its full height.[64]

In 1856 Bateman ceased to be personally responsible for the direct supervision of the operations but he remained the Corporation's Consulting Engineer.[65] During May 1860 he reported that the restoration of the Rhodeswood bank was not complete but was capable of holding water to within about 14 ft of the top, that at Torside where trouble had been experienced with slipping of the puddle clay lining, the defects were greater than had been expected before the water was drawn down and that at Woodhead the leakage remained the same in quantity as it had done during the last 18 months. He expressed his concern that without these dams being watertight, and therefore not capable of being kept full, the demand for water would soon exceed the available supply. All three reservoirs were, in due course, made watertight but Bateman pointed out that space for two more reservoirs was available in the Longdendale Valley, and partly because of his concern at the water supply situation at that time and partly with a view to making a major increase in the supply, he proposed that they should be built. They would be able to store water for compensation, thus releasing the Torside reservoir to become a second reservoir for the storage of spring water.[66] Bateman's proposals were accepted and the necessary Act for constructing these two reservoirs was obtained in 1865.

The designs of the Vale House and Bottoms embankments are similar and a cross-section of the former is shown (Fig. 9.11). Whilst Bateman still used concave layers, instead of specifying in general terms the distribution of the finer fill material to the centre and the coarser to the outer parts of the embankment, he now showed on the cross-sections definite zones for two classes of fill material, clayey or moist adhesive material placed in layers 2 ft thick in the inner zones on both sides of the puddle clay corewall and rock, gravel or stoney material in layers 4 ft thick in the outer zones. This more positive action by Bateman may well have been prompted by Moody's testimony in 1852 at the inquest after the collapse of the Bilberry dam.[67]

To protect the puddle at the bottom of the trenches from being eroded by water seeping through joints in the rock, a layer of concrete about 5 ft thick was placed at the bottom of the trench before placing the puddle clay at both dam sites. The cross-section of the Vale House dam also shows a drainage pipe embedded in masonry used to divert a spring encountered in the cut-off trench.

Bateman recorded that

> there was no material difficulty in the construction of the Vale House reservoir . . . but very heavy masonry was required at the northerly end of the embankment of the Bottoms reservoir for the foundation of the waste weir and the various works there which had to be constructed upon a thick bed of clay which overlay the flagstone rock and which it was apprehended might slip. The works were, however, successfully carried out although when partially completed a heavy flood carried away a portion of the embankment in consequence of the insufficiency of a temporary trough which had been constructed for the passage of flood-waters.[68]

The reader is now referred to the problems Bateman faced in the construction of the first Woodhead dam. A considerable amount of water had to be pumped out of the excavation and the river itself was diverted over it in a large wooden trough. The south end of the bank was the main problem and in a report dated 9 January, 1858, to the Water Committee, Bateman wrote:

> In the execution of the work the shale was followed as a foundation for the puddle as far as it was possible to do so and without danger to the stability of the Sheffield Railway [Fig. 9.9]. A gravel bed, no doubt the old course of the river lay immediately above the shale . . . it was found desirable to fill in the trench as fast as it was bottomed to the shale with puddle to prevent the sides from slipping in. When this puddle had been carried completely across the river and raised to the level of the old course it was supported by a brick buttress built in Lias Lime while the driving into the hillside towards the railway was continued with a view of still adhering to the shale or getting past the old shingle of the former river course. This mode of proceeding had eventually to be abandoned or, notwithstanding the immense amount of timbering which was employed to support the sides while the trench was being sunk, the whole hillside with the railway upon it would have slipped into the bottom.[69]

When the work was far advanced and the reservoir was filled to some depth, the leakage was greater than anticipated. It was hoped that the ground would silt up and the leakage decrease from natural causes but, this not proving to be the case, Bateman then adopted

> a simple mode of reducing it by boring holes of 5 or 6 inches diameter down to the gravel through which it was expected the water passed and then filling in

ashes and other materials for the purpose of choking which were forced down by a column of water brought in pipes from a little distance at a higher level than the surface of the water in the reservoir.[70]

The other materials used were sand, lime and woollen waste. Bateman found that ashes with a small occasional amount of woollen scribblings formed the best choking ingredients.

With the water level 30 ft below top water level, the depth of water in the reservoir being between 35 and 45 ft, the total discharge was reduced considerably from 4 cu. ft/s before 'choking' commenced to 0.6 cu. ft/s after 12 months, the leakage remaining perfectly clean.

The 'choking' mixture used by Bateman in the mid-nineteenth century has its descendant today in the muds made of bentonite oil mixtures with fillers used by engineers in the oil industry. At the Dokan dam, built during the 1950s, a problem arose on how to carry out grouting against flowing water in some limestone fissures and a mud in the ratio 50 kg bentonite, 30 litres diesel oil and 0.5 kg cotton flock was used with spectacular success in temporarily clogging the fissures, thus arresting the flowing water for a sufficient length of time to enable flash setting grouts, injected immediately after the mud, to harden.[71]

After 12 months the reservoir water was allowed to rise to about 20 ft below top water level, but even at this level half the storage capacity was lost and there were also incipient signs of erosion such as the water becoming cloudy occasionally, so it was eventually decided to abandon the first dam and to build a new one.

As regards the new work, Bateman in his History wrote:

> By careful boring which occupied 8 years a place was at length discovered at which continuous shale [sic] existed right across the valley from top-water on one side to top-water on the other and at this spot a new embankment has been formed. . . . The old bank was left in and the hollow between the two filled up.[72]

A longitudinal section clearly labelled that of the second embankment, from which Fig. 9.9 was drawn, is also included in the History but it does not show shale continuous to above top water level on both sides. The cut-off trench of the first embankment had been filled with puddle clay, whereas the second one was filled with hydraulic concrete where it was in fissured rock or pervious strata. Whilst puddle clay cannot resist erosion, concrete can do so; and this feature alone is probably sufficient to account for the success of the second Woodhead dam which was deemed to be watertight. For the new outlet from the reservoir a tunnel was driven in solid ground under the hill on the northerly side of the valley.

In view of the difficulties he had experienced in extending the cut-off trench into

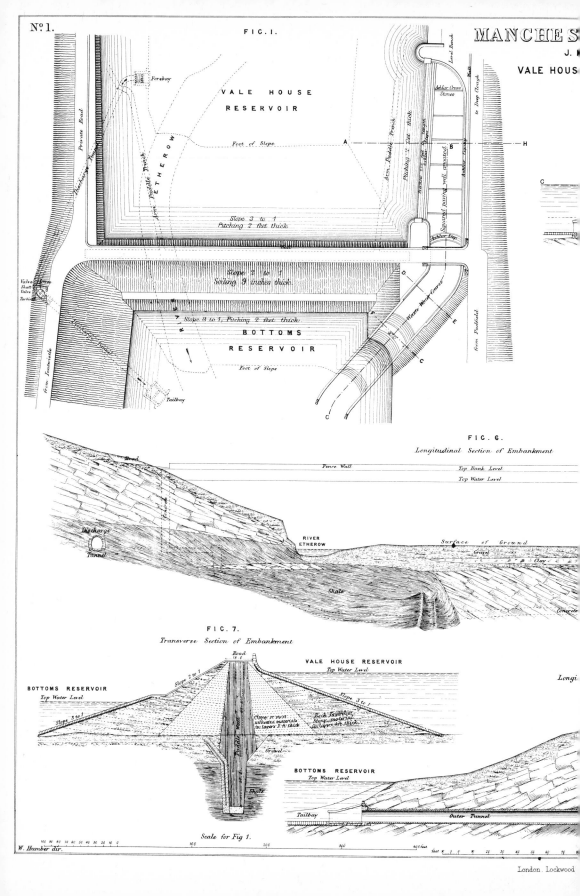

No. 1.

FIG. 1.

MANCHES

J.

VALE HOUS

VALE HOUSE
RESERVOIR

Forebay

Foot of Slope

Private Road

Arm Puddle Trench

Discharge Tunnel

Arm Puddle Trench

Pitching 2 feet thick

Ashlar Cross Stones

Level Bench

to Deep Clough

Ashlar Byewash

Squared paving well cemented

Slope 3 to 1
Pitching 2 feet thick

Ashlar Steps

Waste Water Course

Valve House
Shaft Valve
Turbine

Slope 2 to 1
Soiling 9 inches thick

from Padfield

Discharge Tunnel

Slope 3 to 1, Pitching 2 feet thick

from Footbridge

BOTTOMS

RESERVOIR

Foot of Slope

Tailbay

FIG. 6.

Longitudinal Section of Embankment

Road

Fence Wall

Top Bank Level

Top Water Level

Discharge
Tunnel

RIVER
ETHEROW

Surface of Ground

Gravel

Clay

Shale

Concrete

FIG. 7.

Transverse Section of Embankment

Road
18 0

VALE HOUSE RESERVOIR

Top Water Level

Slope 2 to 1

Slope 3 to 1

BOTTOMS RESERVOIR

Top Water Level

Slope 3 to 1

Clays or most
cohesive materials
in layers 2 ft. thick

Rock Travelled
Stone material
in layers 5ft thick

Longi

Gravel

Puddle Wall 40 ft

Shale

BOTTOMS RESERVOIR

Top Water Level

Tailbay

Outer Tunnel

Scale for Fig 1.

W. Humber dir.

London, Lockwood.

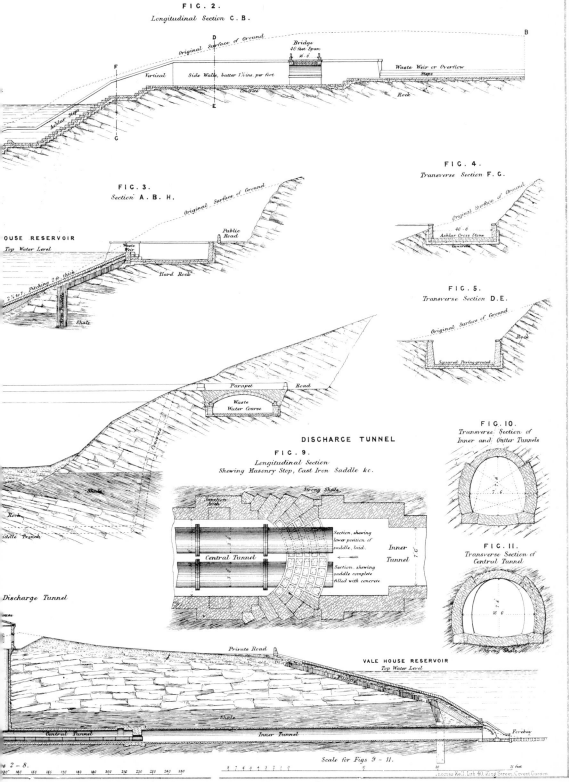

FIC. 2.
Longitudinal Section C.B.

Original Surface of Ground

Bridge 40 feet Span

Waste Weir or Overflow Steps

Vertical

Side Walls, batter 1½ ins. per foot

Concrete

Rock

Ashlar sur.

FIC. 4.
Transverse Section F.G.

FIC. 3.
Section A.B.H.

Original Surface of Ground

OUSE RESERVOIR
Top Water Level

Public Road

Waste Weir

Original Surface of Ground

40.0 Ashlar Cross Stone

Concrete

2½ to 1 Pitching 2 ft thick

Hard Rock

Shale

FIC. 5.
Transverse Section D.E.

Original Surface of Ground

Rock

Squared Paving grouted

Parapet   *Road*

Waste Water Course

DISCHARGE TUNNEL

FIG. 10.
Transverse Section of Inner and Outter Tunnels

7.6

FIC. 9.
Longitudinal Section Shewing Masonry Step, Cast Iron Saddle &c.

Strong Shale

Junction Arch

Central Tunnel

Section, shewing lower position of saddle, laid.

Section, shewing saddle complete filled with concrete

Inner Tunnel

7.6

FIC. II.
Transverse Section of Central Tunnel

Shale

Rock

addle Trench

10.0

Strong Shale

Discharge Tunnel

ouse

Private Road

VALE HOUSE RESERVOIR
Top Water Level

Shale

Central Tunnel   *Inner Tunnel*   *Forebay*

s 2 - 8.

Scale for Figs 9 - 11.

Court, Ludgate Hill.   Thomas Kell Lith 40, King Street, Covent Garden.

the hillsides at Woodhead, Bateman developed the use of arm trenches at the other dam sites as shown for the Vale House dam (Fig. 9.11). An arm trench can be used when, owing to excessive depth, there is difficulty in cutting off a water-bearing bed which outcrops in the reservoir. The bottom of the trench is in watertight strata and the water-bearing bed is partly cut off by the concrete and puddle clay in the trench, the remainder of the outcrop being concreted or puddled over as in the example. Bateman describes an arm trench at the Torside dam where the puddle clay lining covering the water-bearing beds, being on too steep a slope, from time to time gave way and was being replaced with concrete.[73]

The catchment area of the Longdendale Works, including also the Hollingworth and Arnfield reservoirs, was assessed as being 18 900 acres and the average rainfall over it is about 54 in. In 1847 Bateman assumed that 36 in. of run-off could be collected and estimated that the gross yield would be 36.9 mgd. Storage requirements to obtain this yield were thought to be equivalent to 80–90 days supply.[74]

In 1860 the gross storage capacity of the Longdendale Works was 4360 million gallons. As a result of experience gained during a drought in 1852, Bateman reduced his estimated run-off to 33 in. but increased his estimated gross yield slightly to 38 million gallons, the storage capacity available being equivalent to 120 days supply.[75] Droughts again occurred during 1864 and 1865 and the need for still more storage capacity became apparent. As a result of a recommendation by Bateman in 1874 that 30–50 days additional storage capacity should be provided, reservoirs were constructed elsewhere on the system and the gross storage capacity was increased to 6040 million gallons, equivalent at 38 mgd to 159 days supply.[76] From the gross yield, 13.6 mgd has to be released as compensation water, leaving an estimated balance of 24.4 mgd for water supply. As mentioned later, an even more severe drought occurred in 1884 and, according to one authority, the reliable yield after giving compensation water is not more than 20 mgd.[77]

The inhabitants of Hyde were alarmed when one day the 40 in. diameter pipeline from the Mottram tunnel to Manchester burst, but a self-acting valve on the main closed automatically and avoided any serious damage. Bateman had foreseen that just such an eventuality could arise, and at his instigation Sir William Armstrong designed and manufactured self-closing valves for him, which were used on various mains of the supply and distribution system.[78]

Bateman found that, as compared with pipes cast with the socket upwards, those cast vertically with the socket downwards were greatly superior and could take the strain of 'caulking up' better. He therefore followed a precedent which had already been set by James Jardine in 1821 in insisting on all cast-iron pipes for the Manchester Corporation being made in this manner.[79]

A third very important innovation was the system of coating the pipes, inside and out, according to a process patented by Dr Angus Smith. Bateman wrote that an examination of some 36 in. pipes, which were coated by this process and which had been laid for upwards of 30 years, showed that no corrosion had taken place inside in that time and that the pipes were still as clean as when first laid.[80] Dr Angus Smith's process quickly became established and was universally adopted.

At the end of his *History and Description of the Manchester Waterworks*, published in 1884, Bateman devoted 20 pages to the Thirlmere scheme and although he did not live to see this major scheme constructed, no account of his career would be complete without a brief reference to his part in it.

The increase in demand for water in the early 1870s was such that another major source of supply had to be considered, and Bateman put forward in 1874 the proposal that the Boroughs of Liverpool and Manchester should undertake a joint venture for exploiting Ullswater as a source of supply, to which reference has already been made in Chapter 8. In addition Lake Thirlmere had been suggested, and when the proposed joint venture collapsed, Bateman in 1876 then put forward this source for Manchester alone. This recommendation was accepted by the Council and the necessary Act was obtained in 1879.

For the yield from the catchment area, Bateman gave limits of 40–50 mgd;[81] the actual reliable yield has been found to be within this bracket but close to 40 mgd.[82] On account of a trade depression and reduced demands for water, no action except the setting-out of the line of the aqueduct between Thirlmere in the Lake District and Manchester (a distance of nearly 100 miles) followed during the period 1879–84.

However, after a severe drought lasting from April to November in 1884 which had drawn down the reservoirs considerably, Bateman reported that it was most unlikely that the storage would be re-filled by the rains in the coming winter months of 1884–85 and that provision for the next summer's supply would not, in such circumstances, be satisfactory.[83] The Corporation therefore decided to proceed with the execution of the Thirlmere scheme, but with what must have been a great blow to Bateman's ego, they appointed G. H. Hill to be the Sole Engineer for the design and execution of the works.

George Henry Hill (1827–1919) became a pupil of Bateman in 1843, and 6 years later became one of his assistants on the Longdendale Works.

> The ability which he displayed during this time in dealing with great natural difficulties arising from land-slips, floods, foundations, etc. when reliable records and experience in such matters were comparatively limited led to his being transferred to Scotland for the execution of the scheme which Mr. Bateman had designed for the water supply of Glasgow from Loch Katrine. After supervising the construction of the Works at Lochs Katrine, Vennacher and Drunkie, as well as those on the first 15 miles of the aqueduct thence towards the city, he was, in 1861, placed in charge by Mr. Bateman of his practice in the North, with offices in Manchester.[84]

In 1859 Bateman had set up his office at 16 Great George Street, Westminster, and had bought Moor Park Estate near Farnham in Surrey. Even though there was a well-established train service between London and Manchester, Bateman must have delegated a great deal to Hill. Hill's, for example, is the only name and signature as Engineer which appears on the contract drawings dated 11 March, 1871, for the 55 ft high Bollinhurst dam, completed in 1872 for the Stockport District Waterworks. With such authority, his status today would certainly have been that of a partner, even if only a salaried one, instead of being a chief assistant.

In 1872 Hill became a member of the Institution of Civil Engineers, and that might have seemed an appropriate time for Bateman to take him into partnership; or in 1875 when he was seriously ill and Hill had to carry the whole load. It was not until 1880 that he did so, however, and the partnership was dissolved some 5–7 years later.[85]

The first stone of the Thirlmere embankment was laid in 1890, a year after Bateman's death. 'During the opening ceremony many speeches were made but Bateman's name appears to have been mentioned only once by G. H. Hill and not at all by the civic dignitaries.'[86] The works were completed in 1894.

Hill had two sons whom he took into partnership, and the firm of G. H. Hill and Sons still exists.

(c) THE GLASGOW WATERWORKS AND OTHER SCHEMES

A water company known as the Glasgow Company was established by Act of Parliament in 1806. Under the advice of James Watt, and Thomas Telford who furnished plans for the works, the Company constructed on the north bank of the river Clyde filtering beds and ponds and erected two steam engines made by Boulton and Watt. However, these filtering beds were soon found insufficient and unsuitable, and a new system was constructed on the south bank. The filters formed there, which were inspected by Simpson when he visited Glasgow in 1827, consisted of a brick tunnel or culvert built along the south bank below river bed level. The river bank at this place consisted entirely of sand and the joints of the brickwork were left open to allow water to percolate into the culvert from the river. The quantity of water extracted from the tunnel varied with the state of the river, being least when the river – containing much lime and some iron – was low, but on average it amounted to an estimated 3 mgd. This inadequate filtration system was the only one in use for about 30 years.[87]

In 1838 the Glasgow Company took over another water company which had been established by an Act in 1812 and had the entire supply of the city in their own hands. Although they continued to supply water for a number of years, the quality was poor and they completely failed to satisfy the general public. As a consequence many alternative schemes were proposed. One which reached the Statute Book was a scheme for taking water from Loch Lubnaig, situated approximately 80 miles north of Glasgow on a tributary of the Callander river, but when it was found that the prescribed compensation water was more than the storage could provide, it was abandoned. A scheme for exploiting Loch Katrine, about the same distance from Glasgow on another tributary of the Callander river, was also proposed but the promoters did not persevere with it. The only scheme which at that time came to fruition was one promoted in Parliament in 1846 by the Gorbals Gravitation Water Company for exploiting a catchment area of 2560 acres on the south-western outskirts of the city for supplying the district on the southern side of the Clyde.[88]

William Gale (?–1858), the able engineer of the Gorbals Gravitation Water Company, designed and supervised the execution of the works. The first stage came into operation in 1848 after two dams, Waulkmill Glen and Ryat Linn had been built and a second stage in 1854 after the Balgray dam had been built. Except that water could be drawn from several different levels instead of only from the bottom, the arrangements for drawing water from the Balgray and Waulkmill reservoirs were similar to the Harlaw reservoir (Fig. 6.2) which was under construction about the same time as the former. The total yield was some 5.5 mgd, of which 4 mgd was available for water supply, the remainder being compensation water.[89] Like Thom, Gale was a strong advocate of constant supply and 75 000 people were given a constant filtered supply of excellent quality.[90]

In 1852, after having, with Bateman's help, successfully opposed in Parliament an attempt to resurrect the Loch Lubnaig scheme, the Glasgow Council retained Bateman to advise them on water supply, and he recommended Loch Katrine where a supply of excellent water could be obtained in abundance.[91] The Council now engaged Messrs Stephenson and Brunel to reconsider the whole question, including various other sources and schemes which had been proposed, and they endorsed the Loch Katrine scheme. Thereupon the Council sought the necessary powers and the Loch Katrine Act was obtained in 1855. Work commenced in the spring of 1856.[92]

The top water level of the loch is 364 ft above sea level and the water is conveyed a distance of some 36 miles to Glasgow of which 13 miles are in tunnel, 8 ft wide by 8 ft high with an arched roof, 9 miles in open cut and bridges and the remainder in the form of pipelines. The built and tunnelled parts of the aqueduct were designed to pass 50 mgd but the pipelines were staged, only about half this quantity being passed in the first stage.[93]

The storage provided in the loch was given by a layer of water at the upper surface of the loch 7 ft deep, obtained by raising the natural water level by 4 ft and by drawing off the water so that the surface would sink to 3 ft lower than the original level. While 50 mgd was allowed to be extracted from Loch Katrine, 40.5 mgd had to be discharged from Loch Vennarchar, a neighbouring loch, as compensation water. The impounding works required at both lochs were modest.[94]

191

The main aqueduct is about 26 miles long and discharges into a reservoir of 548 million gallons capacity at Murdock 10 miles from the centre of the city. From this service reservoir, the water was conveyed to the city in two 36 in. diameter pipelines. In a speech Bateman said:

> It is impossible to convey to those who have not personally inspected it, an impression of the intricacy of the wild and beautiful district through which the aqueduct passes for the first ten or eleven miles after leaving Loch Katrine. After finding the narrowest point at which the ridge between Loch Katrine and Loch Chon could be pierced,[95] the country consists of successive ridges of the most obdurate rock, separated by deep wild valleys, in which it was very difficult in the first instance to find a way. There were no roads, no houses, no building materials, – nothing which would ordinarily be considered essential

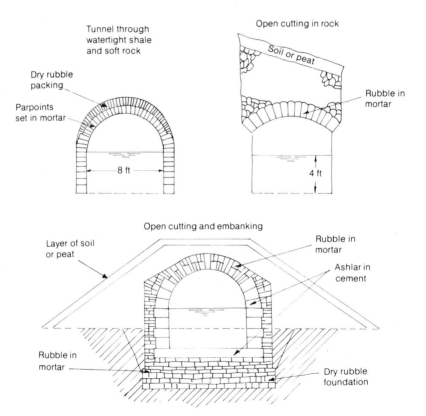

Figure 9.12a Loch Katrine aqueduct—typical cross-sections between loch and mile 10 (redrawn from Figs 12, 16 and 19 of reference 92)

Figure 9.12b Conduit bridges on Loch Katrine aqueduct, 1859

to the successful completion of a great engineering work for the conveyance of water; but it was a consideration of the geological character of the material which gave all the romantic wildness to the district that at once determined me to adopt that particular mode of construction which has been so successfully carried out. For the first ten miles the rock consists of mica schist and clay slate – close, retentive material, into which no water percolates, and in which consequently few springs are to be found. This rock when quarried was unfit for building purposes: there was no stone of a suitable description to be had at any reasonable cost or distance, no lime for mortar, no clay for puddle, and no roads to convey material. Ordinary surface construction was therefore out of the question; but I saw that if tunnelling were boldly resorted to, there would

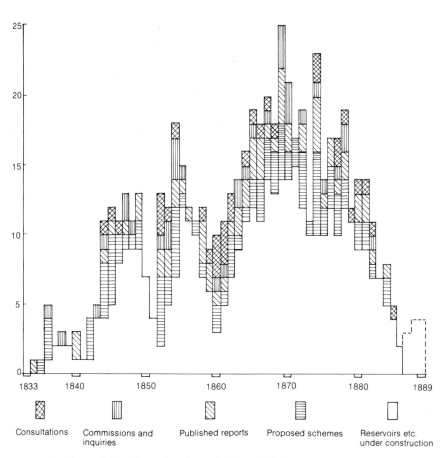

Figure 9.13 Chart showing activities of J. F. Bateman's practice

be no difficulty, beyond the cost and time required in blasting the rocks, in making a perfectly water-tight and all-enduring aqueduct; there would be no water to hamper and delay us in the shafts and tunnels, and little would require transporting through the country but gunpowder and drill iron. This course was therefore determined upon, and my expectations have been realized to the very letter. The aqueduct may be considered as one continuous tunnel. As long as the work continued in the primary geological measures, we had no water; and even after it entered the old red sandstone, and where it subsequently passed through trap rock, there was much less than I expected; so that our progress at no part of the work was very materially interfered with by those incidents which usually render mining operations costly and uncertain.[96] (Fig. 9.12a)

The aqueduct traverses the Duckray valley as three pipelines, one 42 in. and two 48 in. diameter, which cross the river on two pipe bridges. For three other crossings of streams flowing into the river Duckray Bateman used wrought-iron rectangular tubes 8 ft wide by 6 ft high spanning between piers at 50 ft centres and cast-iron open troughs 8 ft wide on the approach embankments (Fig. 9.12b). The Loch Katrine works, which are perhaps Bateman's most famous achievement, were completed in 1859 and were opened by Queen Victoria the same year.

Bateman was the first engineer to propose that water from Wales should be brought to London. To quote an account written at the time of his death:

> A pamphlet which Mr. Bateman wrote in 1865 'On the Supply of Water to London from the Sources of the River Severn', created some stir at the time. Nearly all his schemes had been conceived and designed on a large scale, but this was gigantic. It was designed and surveyed entirely at Mr. Bateman's own personal expense, and at a cost of some £4,000 to £5,000. It resulted in a Royal Commission being held, over which the Duke of Richmond presided, to consider, in conjunction with other minor schemes, the question of a better supply of water to London. The Commission reported in 1868 very much in favour of Mr. Bateman's project. It was a noticeable fact at the time that he gave nineteen hours' evidence before this Commission, hardly, if ever, referring to a note, and he placed at its disposal all the information he possessed, besides preparing many plans which illustrated the report and the evidence taken. It was a purely gravitation scheme, designed to convey to London 230,000,000 gallons of water per day, and the estimated total cost of the works was £11,400,023.[97]

No action followed and the scheme lay dormant until it was revived in principle again in 1894–95,[98] but it was rejected by another Royal Commission in 1902.

Besides waterworks in England, Bateman designed and executed water-supply

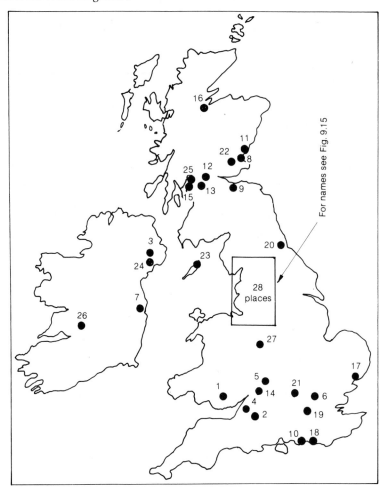

1. Aberdare	15. Greenock
2. Bath	16. Inverness
3. Belfast	17. Ipswich
4. Bristol	18. Littlehampton
5. Cheltenham	19. London
6. Colne Valley	20. Newcastle-on-Tyne
7. Dublin	21. Oxford
8. Dundee	22. Perth
9. Edinburgh	23. Ramsey
10. Felpham	24. River Bann
11. Forfar	25. River Clyde
12. Forth of Clyde Canal	26. River Shannon
13. Glasgow	27. Wolverhampton
14. Gloucester	

Figure 9.14 Location map of J. F. Bateman's projects in Great Britain

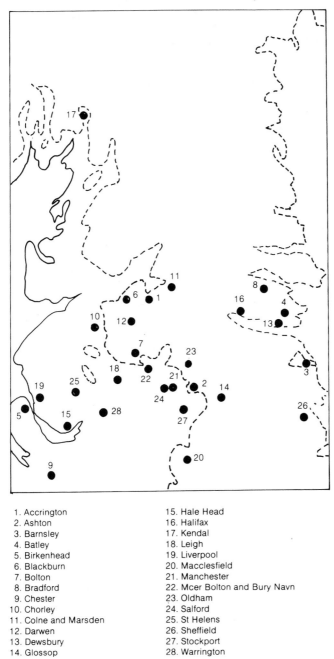

1. Accrington
2. Ashton
3. Barnsley
4. Batley
5. Birkenhead
6. Blackburn
7. Bolton
8. Bradford
9. Chester
10. Chorley
11. Colne and Marsden
12. Darwen
13. Dewsbury
14. Glossop

15. Hale Head
16. Halifax
17. Kendal
18. Leigh
19. Liverpool
20. Macclesfield
21. Manchester
22. Mcer Bolton and Bury Navn
23. Oldham
24. Salford
25. St Helens
26. Sheffield
27. Stockport
28. Warrington

Figure 9.15 Detailed map of J. F. Bateman's projects in North West England

schemes for Buenos Aires and Colombo and he also prepared water-supply schemes for Naples and Constantinople. Space does not permit any description of these works but a chart (Fig. 9.13) prepared by Russell shows the immense amount of work undertaken by him.[99] After 1860 Bateman had the able assistance of Hill. Maps prepared by Russell (Figs 9.14 and 9.15) show the localities in Great Britain where Bateman was called in to give advice or engineer schemes, also the concentration of work in the north of England.

It is believed that the approximate number of major dams for which leading dam designers in Great Britain were responsible are as follows:

The Leathers	14
James Simpson	6
James Leslie	13
Thomas Hawksley	18
The Bateman Office	43

The definition of a major dam used in this table is the official one of the International Commission on Large Dams (ICOLD) for inclusion in its Register, i.e.

All dams above 15 metres in height, measured from the lowest portion of the general foundation area to the crest, are to be included. Dams between 10 metres and 15 metres can also be included provided they comply with at least one of the following conditions:
(a) the length of crest not less than 500 metres
(b) the capacity of the reservoir formed by the dam not less than 1 million cubic metres
(c) the maximum flood discharge dealt with by the dam not less than 2000 cubic metres per second
(d) if the dam had specially difficult foundation problems; or
(e) is a dam of unusual design.
Dams less than 10 metres in height are not to be included.

Although during most of the time Hill was not a partner, nevertheless in at least one contract, namely for the Bollinhurst dam already referred to, his name only appears as the official Engineer and there were probably also other dams set against the Bateman Office above for which he was officially responsible. The outlet arrangements at Bollinhurst shown on Fig. 9.16, consisting of a valve shaft at the upstream end of a tunnel which passed some 20 ft below the dam foundations, were very advanced for the period.

Looking at Bateman's work as a designer of earth dams critically from today's standpoint, he had one blind-spot in that, for his reservoir outlets, he so frequently

Figure 9.16 (right)   Valve tower at Bollinhurst reservoir, 1872

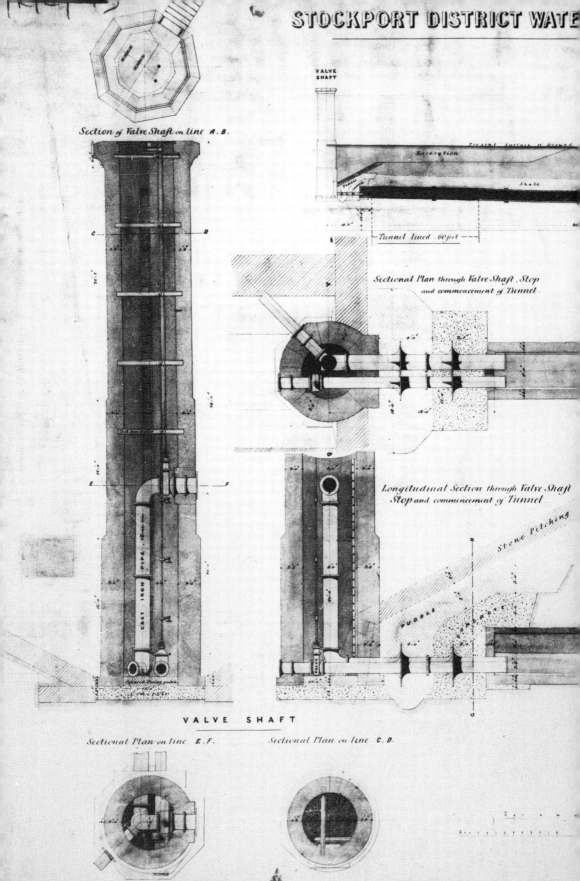

STOCKPORT DISTRICT WATE

Section of Valve Shaft on line A.B.

VALVE
SHAFT

Tunnel lined 60 feet

Sectional Plan through Valve Shaft, Stop
and commencement of Tunnel.

Longitudinal Section through Valve Shaft
Stop and commencement of Tunnel.

Stone Pitching

PUDDLE

VALVE SHAFT

Sectional Plan on line E.F.   Sectional Plan on line C.D.

used a pipeline buried beneath embankments with, to make matters worse, no control valve on the water side, the control valve being near the outer toe of the embankment.[100] Even long after this dangerous practice had been condemned by Robert Rawlinson in 1864,[101] he persisted in using it, one example being the East Hallington embankment for the Newcastle and Gateshead Water Company completed in 1871, a cross-section of which bears a close resemblance to that of the High Bullough dam (Fig. 9.3) designed 20 years earlier.

In the year 1866 an interesting accident occurred on the Vartry dam for Dublin's water supply. Here there was a tunnel under the embankment and through this tunnel a 48 in. and a 33 in. pipe were laid. About midway in this tunnel a stopping of brickwork was built through which the pipes passed. The 48 in. pipe, intended as a bottom outlet, commenced at the inner side of the plugging, was continued through the outer portion of the tunnel to a valve chamber at the downstream toe. There were two valves, one in the tunnel about 6 ft from the stopping and the other in the valve chamber.[102]

> On the 19th November 1866 the valve [in the tunnel] suddenly closed and cracked the pipe. What happened then? It was impossible to get inside the culvert; it was full of water and must so remain. Either the reservoir must be emptied, or divers would have to be sent down under 60 feet depth of water with a large wooden ball to put into the pipe. The latter course was adopted, and the ball, after great difficulty having been placed in the pipe, the valves were repaired; after the repair it was five days before the ball could be removed. Anchors were laid down, divers were employed, purchases were put on, and the pipe was subjected to hydrostatic pressure.[103]

Bateman was called in – not in connection with the cracked pipe but in connection with a leak which developed in the embankment a few weeks later – and he must have obtained detailed knowledge of this accident. However it does not seem in any way to have deterred him from having his control valves on the landward side of his embankments.

Bateman became President of the Institution of Civil Engineers from 1877 to 1879 and, during his term of office with himself in the chair, a discussion on reservoir outlets was held in which he said he:

> believed he had made as many large storage reservoirs as any man living, about seventy or eighty. . . . But as to the proper mode of discharging water from reservoirs, he was as uncertain as he was forty years ago. Every reservoir, as well as every reservoir embankment, should be constructed after a proper consideration of the particular conditions which applied to it. . . . There was no credit due to an engineer who, without reference to expense executed substantial works; the credit which an engineer ought to aim at was that of execut-

ing good, substantial work for, comparatively speaking, a small amount of money. . . . The means of discharge should be independent of the reservoir embankment – an entirely different and separate work – and access should be obtained to every part.

With the pipeline embedded in concrete in a trench beneath the dam, he regarded it as being sufficient to make it large enough for a man to be able to get inside it so as to be able to inspect or 'telescope' the pipeline.[104]

Bateman obviously took great care to secure 'a perfectly hard and uniform foundation'[105] for his pipelines, and he must also have taken great care with the caulking of the joints of his pipes for which he used lead. The pipelines were tested in place with water pressure before being surrounded with concrete and, as far as the author is aware, no trouble has been experienced with any of them. They were economical to construct and, on the grounds that 'the proof of the pudding is in the eating', it might be argued that Bateman has been vindicated. However, with the pipelines in most cases now more than 100 years old, they present problems to those engineers responsible under the Reservoir (Safety Provisions) Act 1930 for the continuing safety of the embankments and in at least one case, the cost of carrying out remedial works to bring the reservoir up to current standards of safety could not be justified with regard to its yield, with the result that the embankment (Daisy Green) has now been demolished.[106]

Why was it that, by and large, Bateman's reservoirs were reasonably watertight whereas about half of those built by his contemporary, J. Wignall Leather, were not? Initially Bateman was no more successful on the Longdendale Works than Leather was on the Bradford Works, but he retained the confidence of his clients and, by trial and error extending over several decades, he was able to develop methods of repair and construction which led to complete success. Wignall Leather, on the other hand, lost the confidence of his clients and was replaced by Gott who, by great audacity, succeeded in making one reservoir, Doe Park, watertight but left behind him two others, Leeming and Leeshaw,[107] where it was necessary to replace the culverts, already fractured during the construction period, with tunnels before the reservoirs could be used. Perhaps if Wignall Leather had not been so promptly dismissed in 1864 after it was discovered that the Barden and Doe Park reservoirs were not watertight, he would in time have become as versatile and successful an exponent of the art of dam-building as Bateman, but he was not given the opportunity.

Like any other structure, an earth dam needs to be maintained but, fortunately, those designed by Bateman are all owned by authorities or companies accustomed to and capable of ensuring that they receive regular inspection and adequate maintenance. Most of them are likely to be able to remain safely in existence for many more decades!

10 Sir Robert Rawlinson (1810–98) and the Swansea Corporation Waterworks

A notable harbour engineer of the period was Jesse Hartley (1780–1860) who during the last 36 years of his life altered or entirely reconstructed every dock in Liverpool. One of his young assistants was John Hawkshaw and another was Robert Rawlinson. Both became Presidents of the Institution of Civil Engineers and were knighted. Rawlinson was the son of a builder who, on coming of age, joined Hartley in Liverpool in 1831. After 5 years with Hartley, he worked for Robert Stephenson on a section of the London and Birmingham railway. On completion of the line in 1840 he then became Assistant Surveyor under the Corporation of Liverpool and from 1843 to 1847 he was employed as Chief Engineer under the Bridgewater Trust. It was during this period that he proposed a scheme for constructing an aqueduct for supplying water from Bala lake to Liverpool, a bold and imaginative project which, although not executed, earned him much kudos and on the strength of which in 1848 he was accepted as an Associate of the Institution of Civil Engineers. In 1866 he transferred to full membership.[1]

After the Public Health Act received the Royal Assent in 1848, Rawlinson was chosen by Chadwick to be one of his engineering inspectors and thus began a long career as a Government engineering inspector. He gave an amusing example of how an able and diplomatic inspector worked:

> On my arrival in Hexham, I found the town in a state of ferment as to the inquiry, the bell-man was perambulating the streets summonsing the rate-payers to a meeting to oppose the inquiry. This was repeated during the evening, one of the meetings being for the evening, the other for the morning. Several of the promoters called in upon me during the evening, evidently fearing the morning's meeting. I explained the Act to them, as the most absurd statements had been published and were believed. I learned that the leader of the opponents was a Local Solicitor. The promoters were most anxious to learn what course I should take, as they feared to come forward and support the measure in public. That is they would attend the meeting but wished to avoid taking an active part in the proceedings. I told them this was exactly the course

I desired they should take – namely – let the opposition have all the talking to
themselves, and so leave them to me as I was quite sure out of their own evidence I could convict, if not convince them. The inquiry had to be adjourned to
a large room as there was a full and rather formidable attendance. The day
being wet many workmen were there. I commenced the inquiry by a short
statement of the proceedings which had brought me down – and then glanced
rapidly over the powers contained in the Act – taking up one by one the objections which I had been informed the promoters of the opposition had made. I
then requested any persons having evidence to offer either for or against to
come forward and tender it. The opponents entered most resolutely into the
arena, declaring that Hexham was well supplied with water; and was, in all
other respects, a perfect town. I inquired for the return of the mortality, and
found that, for the last seven years, it was actually some 29½ in the thousand,
but with 'cooked' returns it was 24½ in the thousand. I then called the Medical
Officers and the Relieving Officers and soon got amongst causes of fever,
small-pox, and excessive money relief. I then traced disease to crowded room
tenements, undrained streets, lanes, courts and crowded yards, foul
middens, privies, and cesspools. The water I found was deficient in quantity
and most objectionable in quality, dead dogs having to be lifted out of the reservoir. And though the opposition fought stoutly they were obliged publicly
to acknowledge that improvement was needed – they, however, dreaded the
General Board, and the Expense. I then explained the constitution of the Board
and stated that their powers would be used to instruct, protect, and to check
extravagant expenditure. By this time the eagerness of the opponents had
somewhat subsided, the body of the meeting had come partially round, and so
I entered into an examination of the promoters who came willingly forward.
At the termination of the inquiry several of the opponents came forward and
stated that I had removed their objections and they wished the Act could be
applied immediately. Today I have inspected the town – and have found it as
bad as any place I ever saw. I have had about twenty gentlemen with me all day
although it has rained most of the time. The town is old, and in as bad a condition as Whitehaven, and I don't know that I can say anything worse of it. I am
staying at the best Hotel in the town, but there is no watercloset, only a filthy
privy at some distance, – the way to it being past the kitchen. I have just been
out in the dark and rain blundering and found some one in the place. I have inspected the sources of the present water supply, and find that the water is
taken from an open brook, filthy and muddy in wet weather, and filthy and
bright in dry weather. In the same districts I have found – or rather, been
shown, springs – pure and soft – and at a sufficient elevation, to give 150 foot
pressure in the town – and in abundance for the whole population. The existing springs will be added to if requisite by deep drainage. Most complete water

works might be formed at a cheap cost. And the town may be sewered and drained for nothing, as a Nursery Man adjoining has stated that he will give £100 a year for the refuse, if it is all collected by drains. There are many acres of market gardens and nursery grounds within reach of the outlet sewer and more than £100 a year will be obtained. Since the inspection today I have had parties from both sides with me, the opponents trying to explain away their opposition; the promoters to furnish information; and, at times, I have had nine or ten gentlemen at once, belonging to both parties. The leader of the opposition has made me a present of some Anglo-Saxon coins – called Stycus, which were found in Hexham Church Yard.[2]

In 1852 Robert Rawlinson contributed his classical paper 'On the Drainage of Towns'[3] to the Institution of Civil Engineers in which he advocated the use of pipe sewers. He described the system, since universally adopted, of laying the sewers in straight lines from point to point and leaving a manhole at each change of direction or gradient. The paper gave rise to a very heated discussion extending over four evenings in which all the prejudices against the Board of Health and pipe sewers were ventilated but, as one speaker declared:

the new system was making rapid progress, and many of those who had opposed it, and appeared still to oppose it, were now using certain portions of the system. This improvement had been, like every other great innovation, at first disregarded, and despised – next abused as quackery, – and at length gradually adopted, whilst the proposers were abused; eventually it would be discovered that the invention was a good one, and that its proposers should have been praised and its opponents censured.[4]

In 1884 the Institution elected as their president Joseph Bazalgette, who had been the main opponent against pipe sewers, but made amends by electing Rawlinson president in 1894.

In 1854 Parliament altered the character of the Central Board and in 1858 distributed its duties amongst other departments. Rawlinson was then attached to the Home Office. An Act of 1866 compelled local authorities to employ sanitary inspectors and for the first time allowed the central government to insist upon the removal of nuisances, the provision of sewers and a good water supply. A strong royal commission, appointed in 1869, laid down a number of requirements necessary for civilized social life, including a good water supply, a proper drainage system, the prevention and removal of nuisances, healthy houses in healthy streets, the inspection of food, proper provision for burial and the suppression of the causes of disease. On the administration side, the commissioners recommended the creation of a new department responsible for services connected with public health.

The Local Government Board was established in 1871 to be responsible for public health services and Rawlinson became its first Chief Engineering Inspector, a position he held for the next 17 years.

During the period 1855–76 he served on several Government Commissions, including one which was sent by the Government to the seat of war in the Crimea in 1855, and at the time of the cotton famine in Lancashire in 1863 he organized relief works for the thousands thrown idle. His services were recognized by a knighthood in 1883 and by a KCB in 1888.

In Chapter 13 a brief description is given of the coroner's inquest on the failure of the Dale Dyke dam in 1864 which Rawlinson attended as the Government's representative. After the collapse of this dam nervousness arose as to the safety of other dams and, at the request of the authorities concerned, Rawlinson inspected and reported on the dams of the Bradford Corporation,[5] the Rochdale Waterworks Company, the Rochdale Canal Company and the Oldham Corporation.[6] He strongly condemned pipes embedded in embankments, particularly those controlled by valves at the downstream end.

Rawlinson completed a dam for Lancaster's water supply at Abbeystead in 1852 which, after having been raised once, was demolished and replaced in 1881 by another higher dam designed by James Mansergh which still exists.[7] However, Rawlinson's most ambitious undertaking in the waterworks field was the design of the Lliw dam, afterwards known as the Lower Lliw dam, for the Swansea Corporation, which was demolished and reconstructed to a modern design during 1976–78. This narrative is based partly on contemporary records[8] and partly on what was found during demolition of the old dam.

To appreciate fully the importance of the Lliw reservoir at this time it is necessary to go a little further back in the history of the town's water supply, starting in the year 1837 with the formation of the Swansea Waterworks Company by Act of Parliament. At this time very few houses had any kind of water supply and the sewerage arrangements were primitive to say the least. Due to lack of funds very little was achieved and in 1852 a further Act of Parliament was passed giving the local Board of Health powers to construct their own works for supplying the town and port of Swansea with water. Specifically the Act was for the construction of a reservoir at Cwmgelli but this turned out to be a particularly inappropriate site as it had such a small catchment area and nothing ever became of this plan. However, the local Board of Health did buy the existing Brynmill and Cwmdonkin reservoirs, at great expense, to incorporate into their supply but both these were fairly small. Later, the former proved to be too low to be of much use other than for flushing the sewers, and the latter too small for anything other than a service reservoir.

It was about this time that the Board realized their own lack of expertise and decided to call in outside professional help. The man they decided to appoint as Consulting Engineer for this purpose was Robert Rawlinson. At this time the

General Board of Health's inspectors were paid by the day and were free, once they had completed an engagement for the Board, to undertake private commissions.

Rawlinson's first proposals as Consultant to the Board were to abandon the Cwmgelli scheme, improve the efficiency of the Brynmill and Cwmdonkin reservoirs and to dam the Clydach river to provide a greater water supply to the town. However, the story seems to have been much the same as before; through procrastination and lack of money the scheme for impounding water in the Clydach valley was never implemented and only minor works were done to the other two reservoirs. In 1859, however, when water shortage was becoming a desperate problem, new proposals were put forward for constructing three new dams on the Llan, Lliw and Blaenant-Ddu streams together with four service reservoirs in the town and the necessary connecting conduits. After much opposition and expense this ambitious scheme was approved by Parliament and received the Royal Assent in 1860.

The main opponents to this scheme were the millers on the three streams and local landowners, given considerable muscle by the support of the Duke of Beaufort who owned many mines in the area. Both parties fought their cause hard, and as a result the Act included clauses specifically protecting the rights of both the Duke and the millers. A minimum flow from the proposed reservoirs was stipulated, and in the event of this not being maintained the millers and other parties with interests in the water were entitled to compensation of £10 per day together with the amount of damage or loss sustained. This was a very large sum of money, considering the average wage for a labourer was about £1 per week and the salary for a professional man might be of the order of £400 per annum. It was this clause that was later to prove a very expensive liability to the Local Board.

After this Act had passed through Parliament, Rawlinson was appointed Engineer-in-Chief for the project, as it was considered that for the construction of these embankments – which would then be some of the highest earth dams in Britain – it was necessary to have an eminent and experienced civil engineer to superintend the works. His commission was to be 5 per cent of the capital cost but he was also to appoint his own Resident Engineer and to pay him for the first 2 years of the contract. In his newly appointed capacity Rawlinson was asked to make recommendations to the Board on which works should be carried out first, to which he replied:

> Twenty gallons per head are found to be required for domestic and sanitary uses, and thirty gallons to include trade purposes. The two reservoirs, Lliw and Blaenant-Ddu, if constructed, will therefore ensure to a population of 50,000 some 32 gallons per head under the conditions of rainfall named and compensation provided in the Act. This will be in addition to the existing water supply.

The increase of Swansea in population and in trade is a question for local speculation. I cannot enter into this portion of the subject. I can, however, say from experience that it is a very wise provision to have ample means for water supply at command. There are few large towns in Great Britain in which the supply of water has not, in use, been found to run below preliminary calculations. This has been especially the case in Liverpool and in Manchester. In both these towns a much less volume can be supplied than was promised in the respective Bills.

Water so pure and so good as that about to be supplied to Swansea will create a desire for its use in washing, in bathing, and in trade. The results will be increase of comfort and health. To cripple such supply by any falling off in volume, or by any diminution to individuals, in consequence of increased population, or otherwise, will be an acknowledged evil all will regret.[9]

The Local Board decided that Rawlinson's rainfall figures were conservative and reasoned that the Lliw reservoir alone would supply their needs at a cost that they could afford. The Board's decision later proved to be an expensive mistake, although neither they nor Rawlinson could have foreseen the crisis that was to overtake them 13 years later.

Subsequently, in 1861, after Rawlinson had produced detailed drawings, tenders were invited for the necessary works but when these were examined they were found to be much higher than expected.

Rawlinson, therefore, prepared another plan for a reservoir at the Lliw, and altered his previous plan by substituting an earthenware pipe instead of the brick conduit, which would materially lessen the cost of the work; and the Committee now recommended the Board to accept the suggestion of Mr Rawlinson for the pipe from the Lliw.[10]

The revised tenders for these works produced a saving of some £10 000 and the contract for the dam itself (contract No.1) was awarded to Mr William Williams of Swansea for £27 449 5s. 8d.

Construction started in March 1862 and Rawlinson appointed Hugh Unsworth as the Resident Engineer at a salary of £300 per annum. The Town Surveyor, Edward Cousins, who had been involved in drawing up the original scheme, represented the Local Board of Health and kept them informed of progess on the various contracts. By November 1863 the pipeline from the dam to Morriston was completed and the first of the new water passed into supply.

In the spring of 1864 news of the catastrophic failure of Dale Dyke dam near Sheffield, in which nearly 250 people lost their lives, disturbed the Local Board who called on Rawlinson to set their minds at rest concerning the safety of the Lliw

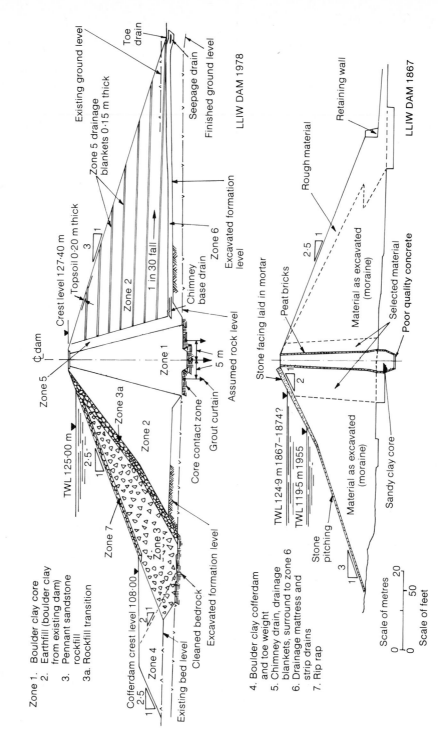

Figure 10.1 Lliw dam – cross-sections of old embankment, 1867–1976, and new embankment, 1978

embankment. This had by then reached a height of 40 ft out of the ultimate 70 ft. He reassured them that the Lliw dam was far more substantial and had a much wider base for its height than Dale Dyke but recommended that a second outlet culvert some 6 ft in diameter be constructed at the existing level of the embankment as an additional means of lowering the reservoir in an emergency. He also said that at a cost of some £3900 it would be possible to increase the height of the dam by 12 ft to 82 ft giving what already looked like being a much-needed increase in storage capacity from 200 to nearly 300 million gallons. Both recommendations were accepted by the Board and the plans altered. Rawlinson's further advice to buy up the land that would be required for the Blaenant-Ddu reservoir in the next valley was not taken until just before the Parliamentary powers of compulsory purchase lapsed, the following year.

Later during the construction of the Lliw reservoir Rawlinson re-entered Government service but was able to remain the Consulting Engineer by special permission of the then Home Secretary.

After the first 2 years of the contract had elapsed the payment of the Resident Engineer's salary fell from the hands of Rawlinson to the Board and the Board wished to obtain the agreement of Rawlinson to termination of his services. The minutes of a meeting in January 1867 record that:

> Mr Rawlinson's answer had been that, looking at the fact that the embankment was being raised higher than any other in England, and to the very ticklish nature of the works he (Mr Rawlinson) would not be responsible for the works unless he had some person constantly there, who should be responsible to him (Mr Rawlinson) that the materials used were the very best quality. The present was the time when such supervision was most urgently required, and as the works would be completed in a few months, it would be very bad policy to remove the responsibility from the Engineer by dispensing with the supervision of the Resident Engineer.[11]

The Resident Engineer was later accused of spending his time 'hunting and fishing' instead of carrying out his proper duties, so perhaps the Board had been justified in trying to remove him.

Cross sections of the original Lliw earth dam and the new embankment built in 1976–78 are shown in Fig. 10.1. Referring to the original embankment (Fig. 10.2) the centre consisted of a core trench excavated down to bedrock, a relatively thin layer of lime concrete on the bedrock with the remainder of the trench filled with puddle clay and a clay corewall 20 ft to 13 ft wide above. On either side of this core was selected material, then coarser boulder-clay shoulders, the upstream face being pitched with stone. The embankment had a height of 80 ft above the original ground level, a base width of 425 ft in the direction of the valley and was 195 yd along its crest. The spillway located on the left bank was a side-channel masonry weir discharging into a masonry open conduit with steps. There were two masonry outlet culverts at different levels extending right through the dam foundations. Beneath the clay core in the 8 ft diameter lower culvert there was a concrete plug from which emerged twin 24 in. cast-iron pipelines, one being for water supply, the other – which discharged into the river bed – being for compensation flow and flood releases. These were controlled by valves in a valve house situated near the toe of the dam (Fig. 10.3). A screening chamber (Fig. 10.4) built up the slope against the adjacent abutment of the dam protected the inlet to the water supply main from trash.

Higher up on the upstream face of the dam there was a masonry forebay leading via the main valve tower to the 6 ft diameter upper culvert. The valve tower was divided by a vertical cast-iron midfeather; water passed from the wet to the dry side and into the culvert by means of three gate valves in the midfeather, the quantity released being controlled by the number of valves open. This culvert then joined the stepped masonry overflow channel and any water issuing from either flowed into the old streambed downstream of the dam.

The presence of springs under the embankment had been appreciated at the time of construction, as demonstrated by the inclusion of lime concrete in the bottom of the core trench and the construction of stone drains under the downstream shoulder of the dam. In service the volume of water issuing from these drains varied from 27 360 to 54 270 gallons per day after much rain, and this water went towards providing the compensation flow. The nature of these springs is best described by a paragraph from a paper read by Cousins to the British Association in 1880 about the Lliw and Blaenant-Ddu dams:

> The reservoirs are constructed in valleys of denudation in the coal measures, the strata consisting of alternating beds of rock and shale. The workable seams of coal beneath the reservoir site being at a depth of about 500 feet. The surface of the valley being covered with alluvium, but only to a moderate depth. Through the whole length of these valleys there are springs of water, some permanent but others which only flow after long-continued rain, the surface water entering fissures in the exposed joints of rock, and finding an outlet at lower points.[12]

At the date of completion of the dam in 1867 the total expenditure on the reservoir, pipeline and arrangements for supply was £76 600, just a little over the £75 000 that the Board had been authorized to borrow by the 1860 Act; about £32 000 of this had been spent on the reservoir.

The reservoir itself gave virtually a trouble-free service for nearly 6 years, although the earthenware pipe seemed to need considerable repair and maintenance.

During this time the Swansea Corporation was finding it more and more difficult to meet the repayments on this and other loans, even though the new waterworks were bringing in an annual revenue of some £5000 – £6000 per annum. Although it was becoming apparent that a further supply of water was necessary, as highlighted in the dry year of 1870 when restrictions were imposed from as early in the year as March, the Corporation could not afford any further large expenditure. However, Swansea could deservedly congratulate itself on what it had already achieved as illustrated in an article from the *Builder* reprinted in *The Cambrian*:

> This town [Swansea] now contains a population of 66,000 inhabitants, and it is
> well known as the seat of the largest copper smelting works in the Kingdom,
> something like two thirds of the whole of the copper ores of the country being
> smelted in its immediate vicinity. Then, adjacent, there are gigantic iron-
> works, tin plate works, and other manufactories, which emit dense volumes
> of smoke, so much so, indeed, that the inhabitants of some of the outlying
> districts of the borough may be said always to live in smoke, and the surround-
> ing hills and districts are entirely denuded of vegetation. The inhabitants,

Figure 10.2   Old Lliw dam during draw down – flume just beginning to appear on far bank

however, and their representatives felt that if they lived in smoke they also lived upon or by smoke – that is, that the stability of their trade and commerce depended upon the prosperity of their large works. Impressed with this opinion, they did not make a crusade upon the proprietors of the works, compelling them to put the provisions of the 'Smoke Nuisances Act' into operation. It was, however, felt on the other hand that the rate of mortality was higher than should be reasonably expected, notwithstanding the adverse conditions to be contended with. It was determined, after much controversy in the local Board of Health, that a perfect system of drainage should be carried out, and that an abundant supply of pure water should be obtained at whatever cost.

The combined effect of these two important works has had the most satisfactory, and we may say, extraordinary result upon the public health, and has enabled the Registrar-General to place Swansea in its present proud position of the third healthiest of the forty-six towns he has enumerated. Prior to the carrying out of the drainage and water supply, the rate of mortality in Swansea was about 26 per 1000. The last return of the Registrar-General now shows it only 18.4 per 1000.

We can scarcely be wrong in attributing much of this good result to the improved sewerage and abundant water supply provided for the town.[13]

The first dam crisis came in the spring of 1873. It had been a very wet winter and according to one account 30 in. of rain had fallen in 3 months, when the Lliw embankment suddenly sprang a leak. Water started flowing from the downstream drains at a far greater rate than had ever been observed before (about 500 000 gallons a day) and the water was turbid, indicating that material was being washed out of the embankment. The water level in the reservoir was immediately drawn right down, on the instructions of Cousins, and Rawlinson was informed. Both he and Major Tulloch, a government engineer,[14] believed the embankment was sound and that the water was issuing from a newly formed spring actually under the dam, caused by the heavy rainfall. Rawlinson said this theory could easily be tested by seeing if the leakage rate was independent of the reservoir level. However, when this was tried by Cousins, it was found that the leakage did depend on the amount of water impounded, seemingly disproving this theory.

Rawlinson was, however, later proved to be correct; a spring had burst through the fissured rock below the puddle clay core but subsequent erosion of the clay caused subsidence of the embankment and further fractures of the core developed. This subsidence was visible and increased with time. The pressure of the impounded water then washed selected material upstream of the core into these fissures leaving leakage paths through which the impounded water could escape.

Some of the Swansea Council members seemed to think that the blame for what

212

Figure 10.3   Valve house at old Lliw dam

had occurred should be attributed to someone, but it was not clear whether the responsibility lay with Rawlinson or Cousins. A particularly outspoken member of the Council, John Glasbrook, was prepared to blame both men and in a letter to *The Cambrian* started what was to be a 10-year feud with Cousins that ended in a libel suit and the removal of the latter from office in 1883. Glasbrook wrote:

> It will take but little trouble to prove that what Mr Phillips said as to Mr Cousins' doings with the Waterworks, spending most of his time at it, and neglecting his proper duties in the town as Town Surveyor; and Mr Rawlinson behaved very badly to the Board by taking the enormous sum he had for commission while their paid officer did the work. Mr Rawlinson and Mr Cousins are like the old man and the old woman in the portable barometer—when all is fine and smooth the old woman comes out; when a storm is brewing the old man must weather it.
>
> The ratepayers will now understand by Mr Phillips' speech that our Surveyor has been doing other people's work and neglecting his own, and takes credit for it when it suits him, and throws the burden on others when it doesn't. [15]

Two immediate problems now lay before the Swansea Corporation. First, with the water level in the reservoir so low they could no longer provide a supply to the town and maintain the statutory minimum flow down the river. Second, the town had to face the coming summer with a seriously diminished water supply and it was imperative to construct another reservoir as soon as possible.

Compensation for the millers was negotiated at a rate below £10 per day, a total payment of £1900 being made for a 6-month period, but this was still a crippling extra expenditure that was to drain severely the resources of the already financially shaky Corporation for the next 7 years. As for the second matter, application was made to Parliament for powers to construct the Blaenant-Ddu reservoir and to repair the Lliw. Although the compulsory purchase of the millers' rights had been suggested, it was thought prudent to omit this clause as, however desirable, this would lead to considerable opposition and delay. So in the same year, 1873, the Bill was rushed through Parliament unopposed, authorizing the borrowing of a further £80 000 for these works.

Meanwhile Cousins arranged that hourly checks should be kept of the leak at Lliw so that the reservoir could be maintained as full as was safe, but urged that plans for the Blaenant-Ddu reservoir should be drawn up in readiness of the Act passing, and that repairs to the Lliw embankment should be left until the new reservoir was completed.

In the midst of this disorder Rawlinson resigned as Consulting Engineer on the grounds of ill-health and because his new authority under a Government reshuffle

214

Figure 10.4 Screening chamber at old Lliw dam

prohibited him from either advising for payment or undertaking works on any conditions.[16]

So the design and supervision of all works at Blaenant-Ddu fell to Cousins, who was paid, at his own request, 2 per cent of the capital cost of the works on top of his annual salary of £500.

Before tenders were invited for this work a Local Government Board inquiry was held before Major Tulloch so that the opponents of the new scheme could voice their opinions. The principal objections were that, on account of mine workings, the reservoir would not hold water, and it would also interfere with further mining below the reservoir.[17]

It is interesting to comment here that after it was put into service it was described as having 'a miserable gathering ground for while the water level in Blaenant-Ddu rose by inches the water level at Lliw rose by feet.' Also, much later in 1919, Blaenant-Ddu was taken out of service as the seepage into the mineworkings below had reached a quantity that had become unacceptable.

In 1874, while subsidence at Lliw was becoming even more noticeable, the contract for Blaenant-Ddu was let to Messrs. Green and Dickon of Birmingham for £43 700. This was finished in 1878, having taken longer than anticipated and at the cost of twice the original contract sum. This in the main part was due to the depth to which it was necessary to go in the core trench (up to 90 ft in places) and the subsequent pumping of water from it, as well as difficulties with springs encountered in the draw-off tunnel. It seems that in the light of what had happened at Lliw, Cousins was not taking any chances of a similar failure here. He also allowed some time to elapse between completion of the dam and filling the reservoir for the embankment to consolidate and settle. We know also that the source of clay for the puddle core of this dam was almost certainly the Abergelli clay pits, from where a tramway of some 2½ miles was constructed by the contractor for importing this material. This, too, must have been a costly undertaking.

Having now provided an alternative source of supply it was possible to turn to the repairs of the Lliw embankment which had by now suffered considerable subsidence. Despite Rawlinson's resignation 6 years earlier, it was considered desirable by what had then become Swansea's Town Council that the engineer who had designed and executed the works that had failed should be responsible for their restoration, and he was again appointed the Consulting Engineer for the duration of the repairs with the sanction of the President of the Local Government Board. Cousins was appointed as the Acting Engineer.

Before any work could begin on the repairs, the reservoir water level had to be lowered and the river had to be diverted through the dam. One can conjecture that the reservoir water level was first lowered as much as possible by discharging water through the compensation water outlet and the supply pipeline converted to a second outlet. The plug and the pipelines inside the bottom culvert were then

216

removed and, with the aid of a coffer dam and the timber flume shown on Fig 10.5, the river was then diverted through the dam. This flume, 240 yd long, 7 ft wide and 6 ft high, carried on 12 in. square timber piles, was probably constructed by Swansea shipwrights. It was found by the contractor in 1974 and was used again for diverting the stream during demolitions of the old dam.

In addition, there is a platform supported on timber piles (not visible on the photographs) adjacent to the flume. Cinders in the mud beneath this platform established that it had been used to support a steam-driven pump. By pumping, the reservoir water level could be lowered below the invert level of the bottom culvert and this was presumably done when it was necessary to work inside it.

Quoting Cousins, the method adopted in repairing the embankment was as follows:

> An open cutting was made transversely through the embankment 160 feet wide at the top, and 50 feet wide at the bottom, to a depth of 36 feet below the

Figure 10.5   Timber flume in Lliw reservoir

top of the embankment. A trench 30 feet long and 20 feet wide was then sunk from the bottom of this cutting through the puddle wall to the rock, a depth of 70 feet, or a total depth of 106 feet from the top of the embankment.

In sinking this trench, indications were soon observed that the puddle wall was fractured. The fractures as at first discovered were small and branching, and were filled with sand formed by the washing of the selected material from the inside slope of the embankment.

At a depth of 24 feet in the trench, the puddle wall was found completely punched through, and the fissure (which was about 2 feet wide) was filled up with the coarser parts of the selected material of the embankment.

This fissure extended down to the face of the rock where a spring was discovered that had evidently, during the extra-ordinary rainfall in 1873, burst through the layer of concrete on the rock at the bottom of the puddle trench. The spring must then have acted directly upon the base of the clay puddle wall

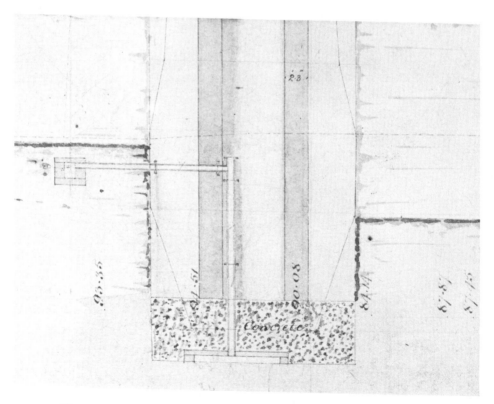

Figure 10.6 Bottom of repair shaft for old Lliw dam (as originally designed)

until it formed a passage across the bottom of the puddle trench, thus allowing the water in the reservoir to find its way through the puddle wall into the drains underneath the outer slope of the embankment, the outlet of which is at the base of the bank.

This continual wearing and washing away process of the clay puddle caused it to settle down from time to time, resulting in the puddle becoming fractured, and the pressure of the water in the reservoir caused the material from the inside slope of the embankment to wash into and fill up these fractures in the clay wall.

Having proved that the defect was confined well within the extent of the trench, it afterwards became necessary before commencing to refill the trench to make provision for relieving the pressure of water arising from the spring, and for this purpose the rock at the bottom of the trench was excavated to sufficient depth, and drains were constructed over the several fissures conveying the water to one point, from which an iron pipe was laid, passing up the shaft to a height of 17 feet, and passing thence through a heading to the drains underneath the outer slope of the embankment (Fig. 10.6).

The brick drains and the whole area of the bottom of the shaft were then covered with a layer of Portland cement and afterwards with Portland cement concrete, which was carried up to the level of the old concrete.

After this was completed, the drains and pipes were tested, when it was found that the spring water rose to a height of 17 feet through the iron pipes, and then discharged itself into the old drains underneath the embankment without the slightest indication of any escape of water at the bottom of the shaft.

The trench was then filled with fresh pugged clay puddle, and well rammed by means of hand rammers and a monkey, weighing 1½ cwt, with a fall of about 6 feet.[18]

At one time, as indicated on Fig 10.6, there was a proposal to build an 80 ft high circular brickshaft on top of the platform to enable access to be obtained to it, but this shaft was omitted. However, an opportunity to examine this work was given during demolition of the dam and it was found that it had been well executed as described by Cousins, the puddle clay and concrete used for the repairs being of much better quality than that used for the original construction. The 17 ft high vertical pipe with a 90° bend at the top leading to the old drains was found embedded in masonry.

Rawlinson visited the site while these remedial works were under way, and after going down the shaft stated that he was very satisfied with what they had found and the works to remedy it. However, the cost of the repair was rather greater than the contract sum and more money had to be borrowed.

> The Committee recommended the borrowing of £3070 for the completion of the repairs to the Lliw reservoir and for the discharge of all expenses connected therewith. When the estimates were made up for the repairs the surveyor was not in a position to ascertain what would be necessary to complete it. Upon going down into the dam it was found necessary to hollow out and fill up certain fissures in the rock beneath; it had also been necessary to construct of wood and iron at considerable expense a chute or aqueduct [see Fig. 10.5] to carry off the water which was continually gathering upon the watershed above. There now remained the repair of some masonry underneath the embankment, and this would be done as soon as a succession of a few days enabled them to pump the water out of the reservoir. The pumping had also considerably added to the expense.[19]

The final cost of these repairs was about £12 000.

After the water was again impounded behind the dam the Lliw reservoir gave good service for another 2 years but the earthenware pipe from the two reservoirs to Morriston seems to have been in considerable trouble from tree and other roots growing through the joints, causing large leakages and water loss.

In January 1883 a considerably increased turbid flow of water was again observed issuing from the Lliw embankment drains, quickly followed by subsidence in the embankment itself at the location of the remedial works. The water level in the reservoir was immediately lowered by 30 ft and this greatly reduced the leakage flow.

Many theories as to the cause of this second major leak were put forward. One was that the clay puddled in the shaft during the repairs had settled, leaving a void between that and the clay backfill in the sloping-sided cutting above. The evidence above seemed to support this, as the shaft had started 36 ft below the crest of the dam.

It was decided by the Town Council to call in Thomas Hawksley to inspect the leaks, both in the Lliw embankment and the earthenware pipe – which had then become much worse – and to report on what could be done.

During the discussions in the Council about the possible works that could be undertaken to improve the water-supply situation much curiosity was aroused by the route of the earthenware pipe chosen by Rawlinson. Perhaps Rawlinson's boast in 1863 that 'the Lliw Reservoir should last as long as the pyramids of Egypt, and it would be found intact when the last trump shall sound' prompted the following observation on that route from a Council member:

> He had followed for some distance the route of the conduit and could not understand why that route had been followed. Had it been an open water course it was conceivable, but not under the present circumstances. He sup-

posed Mr. Rawlinson, the Engineer, had been at that time studying the way the Israelites had wandered between Egypt and Canaan when he decided that route of the Conduit, it was so tortuous.[20]

As the pipes were only earthenware, Rawlinson no doubt followed the hydraulic gradient to avoid high pressures.

Hawksley later visited Swansea and approved the Council's plan to replace the earthenware pipe by a 24 in. cast-iron main laid along a more direct route. As far as the embankment was concerned he was not so conclusive in his answers to the Council's questions.

> What is the cause of the leak? To answer these questions in a satisfactory manner is really impossible. At best I can offer only a speculative opinion. I think the recent leakage commenced at or near the bottom of the trench, and at or near the seat of the former failure.
>
> Whether the materials found in the embankment and puddle trench are sufficient for the purposes for which they are used? I think the materials were sufficient.
>
> What course do you recommend for remedying the defect and preventing a recurrence of the same? The method in the former instance was, in my judgement, unexceptionable, and nothing better than a repetition of the same method can now be suggested.
>
> What will be the cost, roughly, of carrying out your scheme of repairs? The cost may be from £25,000 to £30,000 and not less than two years will be occupied in the operations.

This unfortunately did not greatly assist the Swansea Council in their deliberations.

> Alderman Ford said that the report of Mr. Hawksley had been read by all. The only point it had established was the desirability of the new iron conduit. As to the cause of the leak, or the particular place of the leak, that was left in as much doubt as ever.[21]

Hawksley's rather inconclusive report caused disillusionment amongst Council members who had already seen a large sum of money spent on what had apparently been a short-lived repair on the Lliw dam. Glasbrook saw this as a suitable opportunity to revive his feud with Cousins and issued a printed circular strongly criticizing the former Town Surveyor for the part he had played in squandering this public money. Cousins put the matter in the hands of his solicitors.[22]

Only a month later the Council proposed that Cousins should be given 3 months' notice and after some dispute this was passed.[23]

221

What reflection this had on Cousins' conduct we do not know. It is possible that the Council was under considerable pressure to remove so controversial a figure from their employment, but it is interesting to note that it was he, not Glasbrook, who was forced to stand down. Perhaps there really was some foundation to Glasbrook's allegations.

Meanwhile in Council there was talk of abandoning the Lliw reservoir for other sources of supply, and there existed a strong contingent who advocated building a reservoir in the Cennen valley which, being on the Old Red Sandstone, had none of the geological problems associated with the coal measures. The main drawback to this scheme was the distance, some 20 miles from Swansea. Eventually, having obtained a report on the coal measures in the Lliw valley from John Roberts, a mining engineer, the Council decided on building an additional reservoir in the Lliw valley above the site of the existing reservoir and an application was made to Parliament for this, together with plans for reconstructing a slightly higher embankment 66 yd upstream of the existing Lliw embankment. At the same time the compulsory purchase, or at least a reduction, of the millers' rights, which at that time had cost the Council more than £9000, was felt to be long overdue.

So in 1884 the Act was passed giving Swansea Corporation the necessary powers for construction as well as permitting them to reduce the required compensation flow from the reservoirs to a third of that set out in the 1860 Act if 3 months' notice were given. The millers' compensation was also reduced from £10 to £5 per day, and further to £4 per day after the reconstruction of Lower Lliw.

The upper reservoir was duly constructed and finished in 1894, but the scheme for additional work at Lower Lliw was not implemented, probably due to larger water schemes being developed elsewhere. Instead the Lower Lliw reservoir continued to be used from 1883 to 1975 with a top water level reduced by 18 ft, thus reducing the storage to a third, some 100 million gallons. It seems that there was no further subsidence in the embankment and that while the water level was kept down the water from the under-drains remained clear.

From this evidence one can conclude that, in so far as leakage in the cut-off trench was concerned, the remedial measures undertaken during 1878–80 achieved their object but that unfortunately either the subsidence that had occurred during 1873–78 or the execution of the work damaged the corewall elsewhere, causing cracks in it to a relatively shallow depth below top water level. If the close-timbered shaft had been sunk from the bottom of an open cut 10 ft deep instead of 36 ft deep, the repairs might have been completely successful.

222

11 Henry Conybeare (? –1884) and the Bombay Waterworks

Henry Conybeare was one of the sons of the eminent geologist, William Daniel Conybeare (1787–1857). Nothing is known by the author about his education or training but he came under the influence of the Scottish water engineer James Leslie, and he appears to have acquired a good geological engineering background. He became a Fellow of the Geological Society in December 1855 and a member of the Institution of Civil Engineers a year later. After his return from India, Conybeare took up railway engineering. During 1857–58 he was responsible for the construction of a bridge over the river Swale for the Sittingbourne and Sheerness Railway,[1] in 1864 he was 'engineer to various railways and at present engineer to upwards of 200 miles of railway in course of construction';[2] and in 1871 he was the Chief Engineer of the Welsh Coast Railway.[3] He emigrated to Caracas in 1878 and died out there in 1884.

In the preamble to his report for the Sheffield Corporation (see Chapter 13, p.270 Conybeare claimed that he had been engineer 'to various works of water supply and reclamation of land'. His biggest claim, however, and the only one for which he gave a place-name, was that he had 'designed and constructed for the Government of India the waterworks for the supply of Bombay in the East Indies',[4] which are the subject of this chapter.

As part of the dowry of Catharine of Braganza, the island of Bombay was ceded to Charles II in 1661 and he, in his turn, handed over Bombay on payment of a quit rent to the Honourable East India Company, who in 1684 fortified Bombay, having 4 years previously established it with its own governor as one of their three presidencies. Whilst on military matters the Governor of Bombay came under the Governor-General in Calcutta, in all other matters, such as commerce, he was independent and dealt directly with the Court of Directors of the Company in London. For more than 100 years the Company with their trade monopoly and their royal charter enjoyed autonomy, but William Pitt's India Act of 1784 set up an India Board which, in course of time, was given complete authority over the Court of Directors of the Company. Nevertheless the latter remained the channel through which most government business with the Indian sub-continent was conducted until 1858 when the Company reluctantly transferred its possessions to the Crown.

On the island of Bombay the rain falls only during the monsoon, and prior to 1860 the population was mainly dependent for water, for 9 months out of 12, on the rain caught in shallow tanks during the monsoon. During the eighteenth century when the population did not exceed 150 000 such a supply was barely sufficient, but with the turn of the century when there was a rapid increase in population to 250 000 in 1833, more than 400 000 in 1845 and nearly 700 000 in 1856, it became totally inadequate. The *Bombay Times* wrote:

> Water famines occur with great regularity on average every five years, or whenever the fall of rain is under fifty inches, above ten of which fall in June. When we have a good fall in August, it mitigates the results of drought even when the total is below the average. It is when two dry seasons occur in succession, as happens on an average every ten or fifteen years, that our sufferings are most severe. . . . Glancing at the Register from 1817 to the present date we find that on ten occasions the Bombay fall has been short of sixty five inches, and that in all of them there was scarcity – in five it has been short of sixty and twice only it has been under fifty. In 1824 it was thirty four inches, last year (1854) it was forty-two inches. In 1850, fifty one inches fell, and the sufferings of the population were very great, but they were limited to a single season; in 1849 and 1851 we had nearly a third over our average fall. In 1823 and 1824, in 1838 and 1839, and in 1844 and 1845, we had two dry seasons on end; on the first two occasions India experienced the most frightful famines on record.[5]

India was, and still is, renowned for its religious festivals; but it was at the festival held every sixth year, and above all every twelfth year, at Hardwar on the Ganges that particular merit could be acquired, and the story of this twelfth-year fair was largely the story of cholera in its homeland. Quoting from a contemporary account, Longmate has written:

> Dr. Charles Macnamara of the Indian Medical Service described the Fair in 1867. Its key moment was twelve noon on the twelfth of April and for weeks beforehand crowds of men, women and children had been pouring into Hardwar, until eventually there were three millions of them scattered in encampments over an area of twenty-two square miles. On the night of the 11th April there was a heavy thunderstorm. 'Those only who have been exposed to these hill storms in the tropics', wrote Macnamara compassionately, 'can realise what a night of misery these three million pilgrims must have passed on the open plain of Hardwar, cold and drenched to the skin; the water running in streams off their half-naked bodies over the rocky ground into the river.'

Next day, from early morning onwards, the unfortunate pilgrims pushed their way into the river, while the rain beat mercilessly down upon them. A space two hundred yards long by ten yards wide had been railed off for them and here whole families crowded in side by side, dutifully dipping their heads under the water three times while saying their prayers and, in accordance with the traditional ritual, helping each other to water with their hands. Some sick and elderly people were so frail that they could barely enter the river unaided, and when their ritual ablutions were completed had to be lifted out. Soon the river was black from the bodies of the millions who had washed in its sacred waters and from the ashes of the dead, which their relatives had brought hundreds of miles to deposit there.

By the 15th April the pilgrims had dispersed, shuffling off in all directions at a rate of about fifteen miles a day, so that they choked the roads through Meerut for a week. And soon the familiar signs were mapping their course all along their route: the funeral pyres dotting the fields as the more pious families burned their dead; the canals and irrigation dykes choked with corpses, dumped there by the less devout. Soon cholera was in Peshawar and Kabul more than 500 miles away, where it killed its thousands before spreading all over the sub-continent and into Europe and Asia.[6]

Thus originated the dire visitations which finally reached Great Britain in 1831, 1849, 1853 and 1866.

In Bombay the water caught, during the monsoon, in old quarries and other shallow excavations situated in the midst of a very dense population became so thoroughly contaminated as the dry season advanced that a charge 'for clearing dead fish from the tanks' was an item of annual recurrence in the accounts of the municipality and there was also an annual prevalence of cholera towards the close of the dry season due to the extreme pollution of the only water the lower classes could then obtain.[7] After 1840, in addition to the annually recurring threat of cholera, it was evident that a total failure in the supply, and the consequential death of tens of thousands by absolute thirst, was likely after any failure of periodic rains as severe as some that had occurred when the population of Bombay was much smaller. This was the situation – even worse than that of the overcrowded towns in England – that faced the Government of Bombay.

On 2 June, 1845, Government was so alarmed at the deficiency of water in the town that they passed a Resolution appointing a Committee of two doctors to report with the least possible delay on the state of the wells in the island, the quality of the water in them, and the quantity remaining for consumption. Such was the urgency that the doctors reported the very next day, but the remedies proposed by them and others were all too limited in scope to offer any real solution.

There now appeared on the scene Captain (afterwards Colonel) J. H. G.

225

Crawford, of the Engineers, who took a very different view of the state of things and made a proposition in 1846 which ultimately grew into the first water supply scheme for Bombay – leaving the tanks in the town to take care of themselves, he

> proceeded out of the Island and following the course of the stream [the Goper] which formerly took its rise near the village of Vehar, proposed to intercept it at a point not far from Koorla. Here the water was to be pumped up and brought under pressure into Bombay by iron pipes. The dam was not to be built to retain any large quantity of water but merely to give sufficient depth to pump from. This supply every year could, of course, last so long only as the stream continued to flow or from the setting in of the monsoon up to about December. For the supply of the town during the other months a series of reservoirs were to be formed along the course of the stream above the dam and as the stream dried up, the water in these reservoirs was to be led down to the lowest one where the pumps were to be placed.[8]

The Gopur scheme lay dormant until the water famine of 1851

> and now we find associated with the originator of the (first) water supply of Bombay another able man to whom Captain Crawford entrusted the working out of his ideas. So satisfactory indeed was the manner in which Lieutenant [afterwards General] De Lisle prepared the scheme that not only did Colonel Crawford speak of him in high terms but, finding his own original idea open to objection, he at once and finally abandoned the pumping of water at Koorla. It is in Lieutenant De Lisle's Report, submitted so far back as March 1851 that we first meet the proposition distinctly put forward to construct a reservoir at Vehar.'[9]

His reservoir with a dam 50 ft high was to impound 1000 million gallons.

Henry Conybeare now came on the scene. He 'appears to have succeeded Captain Crawford in the anomalous appointment of Superintendent of Repairs, the duties of which in some extraordinary way seem to have been the investigation of original projects.'[10] De Lisle's papers were forwarded to Conybeare who, in December 1852, submitted a carefully prepared memorandum in which on the subject of evaporation he wrote:

> The mean annual evaporation of even the neighbourhood of London (as ascertained at the Royal Observatory of Greenwich) amounts to as much as 5 feet; that of Calcutta is stated in the *Journal of the Asiatic Society of Bengal*, Part 1 Vol. XVII, to be 15 feet per annum; and as the mean annual temperature of Bombay is higher than that of Calcutta, there is every reason for supposing

that the evaporation of the former locality would at least equal that of the latter.

The adoption of the Calcutta standard of annual evaporation (15 feet) would reduce the maximum depth of the Vehar lake from 50 feet to 35 feet, and would consequently diminish its available contents from 157,100,000 cubic feet to 53,886,300, or nearly two thirds and, were an annual evaporation of only two thirds of the Calcutta standard allowed, the supply would still be diminished from 157,100,000 to 60,436,200, or very nearly a half, or in round numbers to 500,000,000 gallons. This is only an eighth of the quantity (4,000,000,000 gallons) I have shown to be requisite for the supply of Bombay, according to what is considered in England the minimum scale on which town populations should be supplied with water.[11]

Conybeare proposed instead that efforts should be made to increase the local water resources. Fortunately, the Board of Conservancy, in forwarding Conybeare's Report to Government, in 1853 took an altogether different view of the subject. They expressed doubts whether a sufficient quantity of water could be obtained in the island in the manner proposed by Conybeare. They believed 'that none of the water in the public tanks except only one could be considered wholesome – that they were all more or less filled by drainage, at the best of times impure and subject to the taint of a large town.' They were 'of opinion that a great additional supply of water was required for the health and comfort of the inhabitants and that such supply could be best obtained from the valley of Gopur, and in the manner proposed by Captain Crawford and Lieutenant De Lisle.'[12]

In 1854 the monsoon failed, the rainfall being only 42 in. and there was such scarcity of water that the Great Indian Peninsula Railway (presently known as Central Railway) was requisitioned for bringing in water from the mainland; water was also imported to Bombay in boats and by steamers from the island of Elephanta.

Both the letter from the Board of Conservancy and this water famine had their effect. In December 1854 the Government, setting aside altogether the idea of collecting more water on the island, directed Conybeare to investigate thoroughly the project of obtaining water from the Goper. At about this time also, a copy of the General Board of Health's Report on the Water Supply of the Metropolis published in 1850 came to the notice of Conybeare, and in his next report dated March 1855 he wrote, on evaporation:

In my former report on the subject of Water Supply, I assumed that the Observatory experiments . . . would indicate with tolerable correctness the loss of the proposed reservoir from evaporation; but I found that hydraulic engineers in England are generally of opinion, that the small scale experiments on evaporation carried on at Observatories give results considerably in excess of the actual loss of large reservoirs from the same cause. Thus while it is stated that the evaporation of Greenwich Observatory is equal to 5 feet a year, Mr Hawksley gives a rule for calculating the loss from evaporation, in which he states that it varies from 9 to 16 inches per annum only. Another hydraulic engineer of experience, Mr Stirrat, states that there is no evaporation at all in the large reservoirs.

This last opinion is of course erroneous, but it is probable that, especially in hot climates, the impossibility of keeping the water in a small evaporating dish below the temperature of the air (which often exceeds 90°) may give results much in excess of the actual loss from evaporation in a reservoir from 60 to 80 feet deep, containing nearly 10,000,000,000 gallons, and sheltered from the wind on all sides by precipitous wooded hills.

The evaporation from the reservoir, while the rains are falling, may be neglected; and as the Goper continues to run till the end of January, there is reason to expect that its flow will be sufficient to repair the waste from evaporation during October and November, or at any rate to make up for the evaporation of October.

I shall, however, assume the evaporation to which the lake will be exposed at 60 inches, or 5 feet per annum. At such rate, the loss from this cause will be represented by a layer of water 5 feet in thickness, having its upper surface equal to the high-water surface of the lake and its lower surface equal to the low-water surface of the lake.[13]

In the light of what is now known on evaporation, Conybeare's revised assumption of 5 ft per annum from Vehar lake was close to the truth.

By means of a main dam higher than proposed by Lieutenant De Lisle, and two saddle dams, Conybeare very substantially increased the storage capacity of the reservoir from 1000 to 10 800 million gallons. The area draining into the Vehar basin is 3950 acres, of which about 1400 acres is the area of the surface of the water in the reservoir and the yield was about 8 mgd.

Conybeare recommended that the water should be filtered and he proposed that it should be passed through the wall of a filter well 50 ft in diameter located inside the reservoir at the foot of the inner slope of the dam and rising to the same height as the latter, the circular filter wall being built of a highly porous littoral concrete found locally. However, the idea was not practical, because the pores in the stone would soon have choked up, and fortunately it was not executed.

Including a cast-iron pipeline 14 miles long and 48 in. diameter from Vehar to Bombay and a constant supply distribution system in the town, Conybeare estimated that the total cost of the scheme would be nearly a quarter of a million pounds. His proposals and estimate were submitted to Major Crawford who, on 20 April, 1855, gave his general approval to the proposed works. Conybeare was then despatched by the Government to England where the designs for the Outlet Works were altered and some modifications were made in the plans. The pipes were selected and sent out under his direction. *He never returned to India again.* The contract was drawn out in England by the Honourable the Court of Directors and was given by them to Messrs. Bray, Son and Champney of Leeds. Mr. Walker was appointed Resident Engineer and Mr. Conybeare was made the referee for all disputes between the Government and the Contractors.[14]

On the occasion of turning the first sod, Lord Elphinstone referred to Conybeare's estimate for the cost of the works and said:

> When we consider that for New York, a town of about the same population as Bombay, with a large river flowing past it, about a million sterling had been expended in bringing water from a distance of forty miles by aqueduct, and that London, whose population was not four times as great, and whose water supply was notoriously insufficient, pays annually nearly double the prime cost of our projected works, the estimate could not be thought otherwise than extremely low'.[15]

To quote Conybeare:

> The conditions under which the work had to be executed were somewhat peculiar. The want of water was so grievously felt at Bombay that the Government and the public were impatient for the immediate completion of the works. But all the pipes and machinery had to be manufactured at a distance of 15,000 miles from Bombay and it was a difficult matter to provide shipping to a single port for so large an amount of dead weight within so short an interval.[16]

Moreover, on account of the very heavy monsoon rains, it was only during the eight months of the fair season, from 1 October to 1 June, that work could to any extent be carried out on the mainland. When the Indian Mutiny broke out, in 1857, all the other public works in course of construction were ordered to be stopped and the solitary exception was the Bombay waterworks.

A section of the main dam and of the inlet tower as designed in England is shown in Fig. 11.1. The dam was of conventional design with a clay puddle corewall, the exterior slope being 2½ to 1 and the interior slope 3 to 1. Because the duration of the intervening dry season was too long to allow protection by means of turfing or vegetation against heavy downpour during the monsoons, both the upstream and downstream slopes of the dam were protected by pitching stone laid on broken stone.

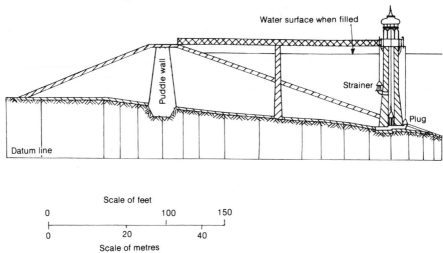

Figure 11.1 Vehar dam, 1858 (redrawn from plate XIX of reference 6a)

The water was drawn from the reservoir through the tower provided with four inlets at different levels, the one in use being surmounted by a wrought-iron straining cage covered with extremely fine copper gauze and presenting a surface of 54 sq. ft, while the three not in use were closed by conical plugs. At the bottom of the inlet well, and exactly over the orifice of a 41 in. diameter outlet pipe, there was a similar straining cage with a surface of 90 sq. ft. The water thus passed through two strainers before it started for Bombay. Conybeare stated that 'the primary object of this arrangement was to obtain in the town distribution the benefit of the additional head of water – due to the depth of the lake which would have been lost had the

Table 11.1 Conybeare's measurements for the three dams at Bombay

Dam	Height (ft)	Length (ft)	Earthwork (cu. yd)	Puddle (cu. yd)	Total Earthwork and Puddle (cu. yd)
No. 1	84	835	255 706	30 910	286 616
No. 2	42	555	46 617	10 332	53 949
No. 3	49	936	106 743	14 717	121 460
		TOTALS	409 066	55 959	462 025

230

water been strained (as in the more usual arrangement) at the outside foot of the dam.'[17]

The waste weir was 358 ft long, had a top width of 20 ft and was faced throughout in chisel-dressed ashlar set in cement.

The outlet pipe (1¾ in. thick) under the embankment rested on a firm foundation of rock or masonry. On issuing from the dam it bifurcated into two branches each 32 in. diameter, only one of which was used in the first stage, the other being provided to allow for future extension of the waterworks. The 14 mile long cast-iron pipeline to Bombay was 32 in. diameter and, except where it crossed streams, it was placed underground a few feet from the surface.

The two saddle dams were of similar design to the main dam and Conybeare's estimated particulars for the three dams were as shown in Table 11.1. It was specified that the embankments were to be formed in regular layers of not more than 6 in. thickness, each properly watered, punned and consolidated.

Conybeare wrote:

> Much difficulty was experienced in raising the principal dam to the height required to ensure safety before the setting in of the first monsoon, June 1857. The Contractor had arrived at Bombay at the commencement of the fair season of 1856–57 but the locality and the season were so unhealthy that the works at the reservoir could not be commenced in earnest before the beginning of December 1856. On the 15th of that month, there were however upwards of two thousand men employed in the excavation of the trench for the conduit pipe and fifteen hundred men and one hundred and seventy carts on the principal dam at Vehar. The excavation for the puddle wall already occasioned much anxiety from the hardness of the rock and the volume of the surface springs which were formidable obstacles to the progress of the work. These difficulties increased as the excavation proceeded until the engine power employed was barely sufficient to keep down the water. A thoroughly impermeable foundation for the puddle wall was not attained, throughout its entire length, until the commencement of March or very close upon the rainy season; so that the Resident Engineer's bi-monthly progress reports were most anxiously looked for by the Author. All difficulties were, however, surmounted by the ability of the engineering staff and by the energy of the Contractor. On the 16th of June 1857 the dam had reached the height required to ensure safety.[18]

After the water level in the reservoir attained the 56 ft contour, the water escaped over the virgin site of one of the saddle dams which served as a temporary weir.

As soon as construction of the saddle dams started there was no safe outlet for monsoon floods until the tops of these dams started coming above the crest level of

231

the waste weir, the discharging capacity of the 41 in. diameter outlet main being negligible. The main dam was constructed in accordance with Conybeare's design and, it is believed, also in compliance with his specifications but, unknown to him at the time, the clay corewalls were omitted from the saddle dams. As communications between London and Bombay took 90 days each way, Conybeare was unable to give directions on site during the construction period and the bold decision to omit these clay corewalls was probably taken on his own responsibility by Walker, to enable construction to be speeded up and to ensure that the saddle dams would be completed in time. Even so, whilst the main dam was completed in May 1858 the saddle dams were not completed until August 1858 after the monsoon must have already begun and the omission of the clay corewalls would appear, in the circumstances, to have been justified by necessity. By October 1859 the reservoir was filled to about 9 ft below the top of the waste weir and delivery of water into the town commenced in March 1860. As mentioned below, clay puddle corewalls were subsequently put down at both saddle dams during 1870/71.

Since the end of the nineteenth century, the main dam has performed extremely well but the two saddle dams have spread and today (1980) there is definite bulging to be seen on the downstream slope of both of them.

Major Hector Tulloch[19] arrived in Bombay to take up the appointment of Executive Engineer to the Municipality during June 1870. Soon after Tulloch arrived, it was reported to him that one of the saddle dams was leaking and on examination he found both were leaking. By sinking hit-and-miss shafts on the downstream side of where the alleged corewalls should have been, filling them with puddle clay taken down into the underlying rock and subsequently closing the gaps with puddle clay in a similar manner, Tulloch constructed continuous clay corewalls at both the saddle dams. Without perhaps fully appreciating that the saddle dams had had to be built in remote fever-ridden localities in great haste, he was very critical of the manner in which they had been constructed.[20]

A sudden and severe illness contracted whilst carrying out his duties compelled Tulloch to depart for England in October 1871. However, immediately after his return to England he completed, on behalf of the Municipality, an outstanding report on 'The water supply of Bombay' which was printed in 1872. This report includes extracts from his earlier 'Report on the Vehar Lake dams' from which is quoted the following:

> A time must come when the 41 inch iron main running through it [No. 1 Dam] must be worn away. No arrangements were made in the construction of the dam to enable the engineer to put down another main when this one became useless. Should a leak ever occur in this main under No. 1 Dam, it will be a most serious matter for the town, and the very worst consequences may be expected.

The pipe lies about seventy feet from the top of the dam, and there is a pressure of from 63 to 50 feet of water on it, dependent on the lake being full or otherwise. Suppose there is a burst in the main (and this supposition is no extraordinary one), water will issue from the pipe with a pressure of say 25lbs, on the square inch. What the effect of a stream passing with a velocity due to this pressure will be on the surrounding earth it is hardly necessary for me to explain. Material must be washed out from the dam by the water in its course, and after this has continued for a short time the stability of the work must be destroyed. To repair a leak of this nature in the manner which I have adopted to render Nos. 2 and 3 Dams secure (that is, by dropping a vertical puddle wall down into the natural soil through the exterior slope of the dam) will be not only attended with great risk, but impossible, unless the supply to the town is stopped for several consecutive weeks. This fact, therefore, must be looked in the face – viz., that a time must come, sooner or later, when from the pipe under the embankment being worn away (as all iron ultimately wears away) and from there being no means of substituting another pipe in its stead, the inhabitants of Bombay, unless they furnish themselves with some other source of supply, will have to pass through a water famine.

The question is really a very serious one for the community. The arrangements for drawing water from the Vehar Lake are most imperfect, the masonry of the tower leaks so badly that I am told an attempt which was once made to examine the mouth of the outlet pipe at the bottom, nearly resulted in the death of the diver, who was almost forced into the pipe by the quantity of water falling on him from above. It will thus be seen that to close the mouths of the strainers, does not render the tower dry. It follows, therefore, that if a pipe bursts under the embankment it will be impossible to discover the point of fracture by sending a man down the tower. The only thing to be done in this case will be to block up the mouth of the outlet pipe so as to prevent any water entering it. Even this may be attended with difficulty, but if it is successful, the next thing will be to send a man into the pipe through the sluice valve at the outer foot of the embankment. If a real fracture of the pipe has taken place, it will not perhaps be difficult for the man to discover its position, but if the leak were due to an imperfect joint, no examination of the pipes from the inside could enable a man to discover its locality.

Under these circumstances, I cannot but draw the attention of the Bench to the risk they are running in delaying to construct proper outlet works for the Vehar Lake – works which should have no connection with any of the dams, and be so arranged that any defective portion may be repaired without difficulty or danger.

But in either case, whether the iron is fractured or whether the joints have separated, it will be impossible to repair the pipes from the inside. And let the

233

pipes be repaired in any way whatsoever, the supply to the town must be shut off for weeks.[21]

A leak in the pipeline seems to have developed at the time or very soon after Major Tulloch wrote these words, because A. R. Binnie, who left India in 1873, recorded that he was consulted about a serious leak of this nature at the Vehar reservoir but as the water could not be shut off, 'it could not be discovered whether it was caused by leakage from the reservoir, a broken pipe, a drawn joint or a land spring'.[22]

In accordance with Major Tulloch's recommendation another outlet, with a pipe outlet in tunnel adjacent to the main dam, was constructed at some time during the latter part of the nineteenth century. When the new valve shaft was constructed the cast-iron superstructure of the old valve shaft was salvaged and reconstructed on it (Fig. 11.2), a fine example of ornamental detail based on Indian architecture.

Referring to the 14 mile long pipeline, Major Tulloch reported that it was being corroded by the soil and that layers of oxide of iron ⅜ in. thick could often be removed from the surface. 'Occasionally pipes are taken up in the town reduced to a state of graphite. The iron can be cut like the softest lead pencil with an ordinary pen knife. This state of things is no doubt due to the action of saline matter. Some of the soils about Bombay are impregnated with salt.'[23] After these experiences, it became the practice as recommended by Major Tulloch to place the pipelines above ground.

Still on the subject of the cast-iron pipeline, Major Tulloch wrote:

> the thickness of the iron was intended to be from one to one and one-eighth of an inch thick but there are many pipes not even three-quarters of an inch thick. The consequence is that we have numerous bursts of the main when the town has sometimes to go without water for hours together.[24]

He also wrote:

> Every now and then the water delivered through some particular pipe becomes exceedingly foul and, when this is the case, the cause generally turns out to be some dead animal matter in the pipe. Fishes and eels often pass into the pipes and dying there, poison the supply. Whether they escape in the form of spawn through the strainers and subsequently develop to full size in the distributing pipes or whether they escape after development in the lake through crevices in the tower I cannot say, but at times they are found of a great size. Fishes have been found 4 feet long and 12 inches round the body.'[25]

Nevertheless, in spite of these and other defects, Major Tulloch wrote:

234

Figure 11.2   Superstructure of Vehar valve shaft

It is impossible to gainsay the beneficial results to the town that have followed the introduction of Vehar water. The best proof, perhaps, of its superiority to all other sources of supply in the island, such as tanks and wells, lies in the fact that, although the strongest prejudices existed in the native mind against its use, these prejudices have now all disappeared and the native who cannot obtain Vehar water considers he has a just complaint against the Muncipality.[26]

Before leaving the subject of Major Tulloch's report, it is interesting to mention that he indicated with remarkable insight the future sources of water supply for Bombay, including the Tansa gravity dam built during 1886–92 and the Batsai gravity dam at present (1980) under construction by the Maharashtra State Government. It was in correspondence with Major Tulloch on the former that Professor Rankine propounded in 1871 his famous 'inner third' rule for gravity dams.

The Vehar water supply scheme was not comparable in size with the water-supply schemes for Manchester, Liverpool and Glasgow all under construction at the same time but the construction of the Vehar project 15 000 miles away had far greater logistic problems. Probably because the Court of Directors of the East India Company had had considerable experience of shipping, the pipes manufactured by Messrs D. Y. Stewart of Glasgow, and the sluice valves, also other special castings, manufactured by James Simpson at his Pimlico Iron Works, were shipped to Bombay with remarkable speed and efficiency for which Conybeare, no doubt, deserves some of the credit. While one can criticize him for burying the outlet pipe beneath the dam, in most other respects his designs were competent and his specifications were evidently sound. His mistake in burying the pipelines in saline ground was due to the general ignorance of its effect on cast-iron pipes at that time. The inspection of pipes before they were shipped evidently left a good deal to be desired but can probably be excused on grounds of urgency. However, Conybeare overstated the case when he claimed that he had also constructed these works which he never saw! The main credit or blame for construction rests with Walker, whose initials were either J. D. or H., and with Messrs Bray, Son and Champney of Leeds, who seem to have been an *ad hoc* partnership formed specially and solely to execute the Bombay waterworks. The author has not been able to find out anything more about Walker but Bray, in partnership with someone else, had previously carried out work on the Great Indian Peninsula Railway.

12 *Matthew B. Jackson (1825–?) and the Melbourne Waterworks*

Early in February 1861 the advertising columns of the *Argus* published in Melbourne contained the following:

> Mr. Matthew Bullock Jackson (late engineer to the Melbourne Water Commission) to John Millar (engineer-in-chief to the late Geelong Water Commission).

> Ship, Empress of the Sea
Hobson's Bay
Port Philip
Melbourne.   February 2, 1861

> Mr. John Millar,

> Sir,
>   Before leaving the colony, which I propose doing by the *Empress of the Sea*, on this day I desire as an act of justice towards you, to retract, in the most unqualified manner, every assertion which I have ever made, publicly or privately, against your character as a professional man and a gentleman.
>   In addition, I desire to put on record that my statements concerning you at page 26, in the Appendices to the Report of the Yan Yean Committee – Session 1860 – are without foundation, and were made by me to serve a purpose at the time.
>   Hoping that you will forgive, even if you cannot forget, the deep injuries which I have temporarily inflicted upon you, and the consequent mental anxiety I pledge myself, for all time, to abstain from pursuing this line of conduct to your disparagement, and which I now so deeply deplore.

> (signed) M. B. JACKSON

> Witness – John Slater, Alexander Kennedy Smith.

A few days later an editorial appeared in the *Argus* as follows:

> The *Empress of the Seas* has carried away from Victoria – it would be presump-

237

tuous to hope for good – a very extraordinary and destructive biped. It was for a long while much debated amongst naturalists to what department of the animal kingdom this strange creature should be attached; and one celebrated savant, more learned in phonography than orthography, pronounced it a lyre-bird, or liar, as the savant himself used to spell the word. It has now, however, been ascertained, beyond doubt, to belong to the order 'Raptores', or predaceous birds of passage, which are common in all parts of the civilised world. The individual is unique, and a giant of its kind. Its original habitat was in England, whence it migrated to this country about the time of the gold discovery, and located itself in the neighbourhood of Melbourne. It is well known to all the labourers who were engaged in the construction of the reservoir which supplies this city with water. Indeed, the fondness which the animal exhibited for the poisonous Yan Yean was very curious, and not less so the ingenuity with which it lined its nest.

It must be allowed that Mr. Matthew Bullock Jackson, to drop the scientific style, is as great a curiosity as ever was placed in a museum. Matchless in impudence, in fertility of imagination unsurpassed, he has impersonated more characters successfully than Mr. G. V. Brooks or Sir William Don. His invention is unparalleled by that of any professional puffers. The invention of auctioneers, of corn and bunnion cutters, even of quack doctors, dwindles into insignificance beside his. According to his own report, he was capable of designing and accomplishing the most difficult engineering enterprises, and had achieved as high distinction as his masters the Stephensons. He had 'personally superintended, constructed, or erected', to use his favourite form of words, the Lambeth, Leicester, and Durham Waterworks, and extensions at Stockton and Darlington. He had been employed by the Home Government 'to report on the bursting of the far-famed Holmfirth Reservoir, a terrible catastrophe, by which upwards of one hundred lives were lost, besides property destroyed of immense value'. The dock gates at Sunderland and West Hartlepool, and others of less importance, were erected by him; and his fame in this line of business was so widely spread that the Prussians brought him over to Bremen to erect the dock gates there. With the sewerage commissioners, or their engineers, he was in high repute, and several miles of tubular and brick sewers were laid under his supervision. But next to waterworks, bridges were his great forte. The tubular bridge over the Aire, in Yorkshire, he was kind enough to undertake for Mr. Robert Stephenson, and it was to his ingenious industry that the men of Lincolnshire and the boys of Derry owed the bridges across the Nene and the Foyle. About a dozen different engineers, eminent in every branch of their profession, including Simpson, Hawksley, Rendel, Frank Foster, George and Robert Stephenson, and Sir William Cubitt, had secured the valuable assistance of our great Bullock in undertakings the most arduous, and the labour which rumour has distributed amongst a score of sub-engineers, inspectors, draughtsmen, and contractors, was all accumulated on his shoulders. So at least said Mr. Jackson, without, as it is refreshing to discover, one word of truth. Of all the grandees whose intimate acquaintance he enjoyed, none but the Stephensons, with whom he served four years' apprenticeship in mechanical engineering, has ever heard his name. As for professional accomplishments, he had none. The late secretary to the Sewerage and Water Commission describes his drawing as the comical crawlings of a spider just escaped from an ink bottle; and we are assured by the same authority, that to this prince of engineers a theodolite was an inexplicable mystery, and that by a dumpy level he was floored. He has been charged, too, on strong evidence, with offences of the most serious nature – not extravagance and mismanagement only, but collusion with contractors and misappropriation of public moneys. His last act before quitting the colony was consistent with his previous character. Under the threat of an arrest, when the *Empress* was on the point of sailing, he put his name to the letter of apology which has appeared in our advertising columns. The document is a very masterpiece of brazen effrontery. The coolness with which the author acknowledges himself guilty of systematic lying and traduction is really astounding; and he has evidently been a student of the euphonies of Parliamentary debate. With him 'to tell a lie' is 'to make a statement, which is without foundation'; and 'to swear away a man's character' is 'to pursue a line of conduct'.

It is not a little singular that a person with no other qualifications than unblushing impudence and audacity should ever have been appointed engineer to the commission, notwithstanding the assistance of forged testimonials. He deceived, indeed, we cannot tell how, the Institution of Civil Engineers at home; but the stringency of their rules must have been a good deal relaxed, or he never could have been admitted a member. This will hardly happen again out of compliment to Victoria. But how comes it, we should be glad to know, that Mr. Jackson could deceive for so long a period the members of the commission, and that his ignorance and peculations were not sooner discovered and reported by his fellow officers? And why has he been suffered to retire from our shores unmolested, to enjoy in some Sicilian retreat the fruits of his fraud and depredations? The report of the famous Yan Yean Committee has for months remained uncontradicted, and the replies to the queries sent home must all have been received in Victoria before Christmas Day. On whom the blame rests we cannot positively say; but it is culpable neglect in some one to have allowed this scoundrel to get off with his booty scot-free. Nor can we by any means exonerate Mr. Millar, who was perfectly acquainted with the whole matter, and appears to have used the information he possessed solely for his own purposes, but with a total disregard to the public benefit.

Who was this Matthew Bullock Jackson whose departure in certain quarters was so little lamented?

According to Jackson himself, in his letter of application for the appointment of Chief Engineer,[1] his near relations had for many years an interest in an engineering establishment at Leeds and his uncle Thos. Jeffcock of Sheffield had an extensive practice as 'coal viewer and mining engineer' in the Yorkshire coalfields. He was brought up as a surveyor until in 1845 he was apprenticed to Robert Stephenson at his works at Forth Street in Newcastle.[2] Jackson appears to have started his career as a draughtsman and he was engaged under various engineers named by him in his letter on the designs for five bridges, also on the manufacture of dock gates for the Keyham Yard at Devonport. Curiously enough Jackson made no mention in his letter of having been employed on the colossal high-level bridge at Newcastle under construction at that time but he was seconded by Stephenson to Hosking, a Cornish engineer, who was the contractor's agent on this bridge and who evidently needed someone with dock gate experience. Jackson wrote that he was employed under Hosking as a designer on dock gates at Sunderland harbour and Bremen, the designs for the latter being approved by Rendel, and as outdoor superintendent in charge of the erection of dock gates for Hartlepool harbour. He named two people in the colony who had called on him while he was engaged on the Hartlepool works. He was also employed by Hosking on some work, probably the installation of pumping machinery, at the Lambeth waterworks. Having visited the site of the Bilberry dam, he wrote a report on the failure of this dam for Rendel.

In 1851 he was employed by Chapman of No. 3 Cannon Row, Westminster, on drawings and designs for the Durham Waterworks, which designs were got up under and for Thomas Hawksley. He was further employed, at the same establishment, in getting up designs for a tubular girder bridge across the river Foyle at Londonderry with a lifting span operated by Armstrong's hydraulic machinery. These designs were done on behalf of Hawksley's partner, Charles May, and were approved by Rendel.[3]

While Hosking appears to have delegated a fair amount of responsibility to Jackson, in no case did the latter claim in his letter that he was a principal, nor is there any record of him ever having done so to substantiate the allegations made in the *Argus* against him.

The circumstance which brought him to Melbourne was that he was further employed, probably on behalf of Rendel, on designs for the South Australian Railway from the city to the port and he emigrated with a view to being employed on the construction of this railway.[4] He arrived (aged 27) in Melbourne in December 1852, when gold had been discovered in Victoria and there was almost a complete exodus of the male population to the goldfields.[5]

Due to scarcity of labour, construction of the railway was postponed and as a consequence when the Board of the Commissioners of Sewers and Water Supply called for applications for the appointment of Chief Engineer for Waterworks, Jackson applied. He enclosed with his application particulars of his career as already briefly described and two testimonials, one from George Stephenson and the other from Charles May. Seventeen persons applied for the post, of whom five, including Jackson, were selected for interview; on 20 June, 1853, he was appointed.

It is now necessary to go back in time to the year 1835.[6] In that year the earliest settlers in the locality, which 2 years later was named Melbourne, obtained their water above a ledge of rocks across the river Yarra, the ledge being high enough to prevent the fresh water from mingling with the saline water of Hobson's Bay except at high tide. However, the Yarra soon became very polluted and this caused a great deal of discontent.

The Melbourne City Council was formally constituted in 1842 and a few years afterwards the City Surveyor propounded a scheme for conveying the river water to a large filter in the city for public sale, but this scheme was not properly carried into effect until the arrival from Tasmania in 1849 of James Blackburn. A civil engineer and architect who had been sent to Tasmania after his conviction for embezzlement in England, Blackburn came to Melbourne as a 'ticket-of-leave' man and was immediately appalled by the lack of good water. Wasting no time, Blackburn persuaded four other men to join him in a private venture and filtered water was shortly on sale. His ability soon led to his appointment as City Surveyor.

In 1850 Blackburn, in a report to the Council, pointed out that an abundant source of supply of water could be obtained from the streams flowing from Mount Disappointment which when united formed the river Plenty (Fig. 12.1). Subsequently, after careful exploration, he submitted a full report with plans in August 1851 confirming his earlier conclusions.

The Melbourne City Council applied to the Government of the day for funds to carry out Blackburn's scheme but control of water supply and sewerage was given to a Board nominated by the Government in April 1853 and vested with power to levy rates. John Lanktree was appointed Secretary and Treasurer of the Board at a salary of £600 per annum, a disastrous choice which was to have bad consequences later.

The newly created Board at first rejected Blackburn's scheme and adopted one which involved lifting water from a site some way upstream on the Yarra river, where there were some falls, by waterwheel, piping it to a reservoir to the north of the city and reticulating it from there. However, after he was appointed Chief Engineer Jackson soon persuaded the Board to adopt, with some alterations, Blackburn's scheme. In October 1853 Blackburn was appointed Consulting Engineer to the Board at £300 per annum, but he was killed in a riding accident in March 1854.

Blackburn had devised a scheme for supplying a population of 70 000 at 40 gallons per head.

Jackson recommended various alterations to Blackburn's scheme so as to provide water for 200 000 persons at 30 gallons per head per day, also water for flushing sewers and supplying public fountains. The project consisted of tapping the Plenty river below its confluence with Bruce's Creek and diverting the water into a large artificial reservoir formed by the construction of an earth embankment 1053 yd long and with a height of 30 ft across a valley east of the Plenty river at Yan Yean. The reservoir covered an area of about 1200 acres and had a capacity of 6400 million gallons when full, of which 1000 million gallons was dead storage. The embankment had side-slopes of 3 to 1 and 2 to 1 on the inner and outer slopes respectively, also a central clay corewall of great width comparable to that of a rolled clay core, and a cut-off trench which was also very wide. In addition, an inner apron and check trench was constructed. To reach the Plenty river, a tunnel 440 yd long was driven through a ridge of hills and a dish-shaped canal 3000 yd long was excavated. As the ground, a hard clay slate, was erodible both the tunnel and the canal were stone-lined, a hard basaltic rock (bluestone) being used. To enable the entry of the Plenty river into the reservoir to be controlled, gates were constructed at the entrance to the canal. At the foot of the inner slope of the embankment a hexagonal-shaped stone well-tower, with three outlets at different levels and with an 18 in. diameter compensation water pipeline passing through the base, was constructed (Fig. 12.2). From the well-tower, two 33 in. diameter pipelines and the 18 in. diameter pipeline were laid on flagstones in trenches excavated in the solid ground and backfilled with puddle clay up to the edges of the cut-off trench and on ashlar pillars at 6 ft centres (the length of a pipe) across the cut-off trench where the pipelines were embedded in the puddle clay at the base of the corewall.

All three inlets to the valve well were controlled by valves. The pipelines were also controlled by valves on the upstream side in the valve-well and on the downstream side of the dam. For the smaller compensation water supply pipeline no easy means of repairing or replacing the upstream valve was provided, but for the other two large-diameter domestic water supply valves, access for repairs and maintenance could be obtained by closing all three inlet valves.

There is a contemporary drawing showing an outlet tunnel at one end of the dam with the valve well at the entrance to it, which would seem to indicate that Jackson originally intended his pipelines to bypass the embankment in a tunnel. Perhaps on account of the difficulty in getting a tunnel excavated, or for reasons of economy, it would appear that, possibly against his better judgement, he subsequently allowed them to be buried in the embankment.

The water was brought to Melbourne by means of a pipeline 19 miles long varying in diameter from 30 to 24 in. Probably due to unequal settlement on foundations stated to have been clay and sand, two pipes on each of the 33 in. pipelines through the embankment were cracked. Jackson was not informed about the cracks until there was already 21 ft of water in the reservoir but before any water had been passed through the pipelines. With the upstream valves kept shut, these cracks were successfully repaired by installing tubes of boiler plate inside the pipelines and rusting up the space between the pipelines and the tubes with iron cement.[7] As there was a very large volume of water in the reservoir which could not have been run off quickly, the situation could have been disastrous if Jackson had depended on valves on the downstream side of the dam only. For its period the valve well was a good feature of the design which saved him from a potentially

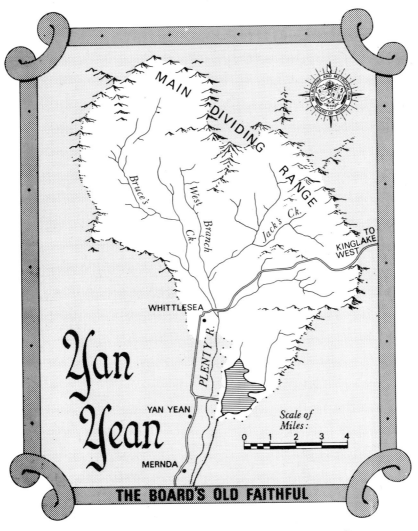

Figure 12.1   River Plenty catchment area, Victoria, Australia

243

disastrous situation. The cracks on these pipelines were the only casualties of importance during the progress of the work.

At a later date, Jackson forecast future practice by saying that he saw no objection 'to having the inside of the tower perfectly watertight and with the valves down inside so that you can go down to them. If I were doing such a thing again, I would have a culvert through the solid, and lay the pipes through the culvert. I would have the sluices within the valve chamber.'[8]

As already stated, the sources of the Plenty river were the streams and springs flowing from Mount Disappointment. At the foot of the mountain the water was sparkling and clean, but before reaching the Yan Yean reservoir it flowed through nearly 4 miles of swamps containing immense beds of decaying vegetation, and the clarity of the water deteriorated. To overcome this defect, Jackson recommended, in a report dated 20 September 1853, that the river should be diverted above the swamps. Two shafts 60–70 ft deep were sunk on the proposed route, and in 1853 tenders were called for a tunnel about 890 yd long; however, the tenders received at that time were so high that the project was abandoned with unfortunate consequences.[9]

The project was a tremendous one for such a small colony with a population of scarcely 100 000, and Jackson recommended that the works should be entrusted to one of the large English contracting firms, such as Brassey and Co. This recommendation was not accepted, however, and he was obliged to execute the work on a piecemeal basis with local contractors. One of these, named Millar, was a former close associate of Lanktree in Belfast (Jackson claimed he had been his partner) and another named Reilly was the Secretary's son-in-law.

The first sod was turned by the Governor, Charles Joseph La Trobe (who was J. F. Bateman's first cousin) on 20 December, 1853, and a canvas city appeared on the site. It had a population of 1000 men, women and children. The men, mainly disillusioned goldminers, were a very turbulent lot and armed police had to be sent from the city to deal with frequent disturbances. There were also labour troubles due to agitation for an 8-hour day.[10] So soon after the discovery of the gold fields it was very difficult to secure good work but Jackson, who must have been a man of very strong character, insisted upon contracts being fully executed. For example, the contractors for the embankment, Messrs. Martindale and Steele, brought pressure to bear on Jackson to relax the depths to which the cut-off trench was to be executed at the ends of the dam, the specified depth being 10–15 ft, but he declined to allow any relaxation.[11] In insisting upon this contract being fully executed in accordance with the specification and drawings, Jackson was no doubt influenced by the appalling consequences of inadequate depths and bad workmanship on an

Figure 12.2 (right)   Valve tower at Yan Yean reservoir, 1857

Matthew B. Jackson

ver. Well. and Inlet Pipes.

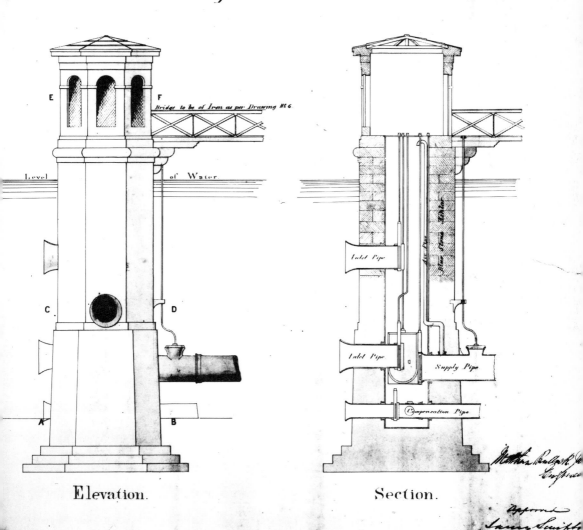

Elevation.

Section.

Figure 12.3 Celebrations at opening of Melbourne's first major water supply, 27 December, 1857

earth dam which he had witnessed at Holmfirth before his departure from England, and on which Rendel had asked him for a report.[12]

Partly due to Jackson's uncompromising attitude towards contracts, and partly as a result of the 8-hour day struggle, some of the contractors lost money or failed to complete their contracts and became bitter enemies of Jackson, including – in particular – Steele and Millar. Lanktree, who had been summarily discharged from Government service towards the end of 1857, was also a bitter enemy.

Cast-iron pipes were sent out from England, and because the roads were too rough for the transport of pipes a wooden tramway was laid along the pipeline route. As Agents for the Colony, William Fairbairn and Sons of Manchester, the founder of which firm was the eminent engineer who was J. F. Bateman's father-in-law, were responsible for procuring and shipping the pipes.

During the construction of the major works the laying of reticulation pipes proceeded, and by 1856 approximately 32 miles of pipes had been laid in many of the main streets. A temporary supply to this pipe system was made available from an elevated cast-iron tank of 150 000 gallons capacity, erected in 1854 on a hill. Steam power was temporarily used to pump water from the Yarra into this tank.

The progress of the Yan Yean scheme was marked by many delays and frustrations and the works were even suspended for a time by the Governor, but at last on 19 December, 1857, the *Argus* reported:

246

The Yan Yean Water Works
The reducing valves (2 in number) which have occasioned so much delay, being now in operation, and everything working satisfactorily, it is proposed to open these works on the 31st inst., when it is expected that His Excellency the Governor will put the finishing stroke to this great enterprise, which has occupied just four years in its prosecution to a successful issue. The water is beautifully clear and icy cold, and the supply almost inexhaustible. The stand-pipes about to be removed from the city will be erected in the suburbs, and those who have neglected to place their houses in connection with the main should lose no time in doing so.

Amidst much rejoicing the water was finally turned on into the city on 27 December, 1857 (Fig. 12.3.).

While Jackson himself was not able to be present, a paper by him on the Yan Yean project[13] was read at the Institution of Civil Engineers on 22 March, 1859. Amongst those who took part in the discussion on the paper were Hawksley, Conybeare, Rawlinson and Maudslay. Proposed by William Fairbairn, seconded by Robert Stephenson and supported by seven other members including William Weallens, Managing Partner of Robert Stephenson and Co., Bateman and Hawksley, Jackson was elected a member of the Institution of Civil Engineers a few days later on 5 April, 1859.

During the construction of the project Jackson had carried an enormous burden of responsibility, but it was after the main works were completed, when he might have expected to enjoy the respect and esteem of his fellow citizens, that his troubles really began.

After the first novelty had worn off the citizens began to look at the water supply critically. As already stated, before reaching the reservoir the water flowed through 4 miles of swamps and rotting vegetation which gave it a disagreeable colour, taste and smell. About the only thing in its favour was that it was less dangerously polluted than the Yarra river. As bacteriology was at that time an unknown science, this aspect was not appreciated and, barely 8 months after the inauguration of the scheme, a correspondent in the *Argus* wrote: 'Would it not be advisable to call a public meeting to denounce such sickening stuff altogether and use the healthy waters of the Yarra?'

Owing also to the softness of the Plenty river water (said by Jackson to have only $2°$ hardness) and the use of lead service pipes, lead poisoning was suspected. In an attempt to provide protection the lead piping, called 'Commissioner's piping' delivered by Fairbairn and Sons, had an internal coating of tin. Unfortunately voltaic action destroyed the tin coating, with the result that water remaining in the pipes overnight became highly charged with lead salts.

The consequence of the agitation against the quality of the water supply was that in October 1858 a Select Committee was appointed 'to enquire into the properties of the Water of the Yan Yean'. After examining Jackson and other witnesses, the Committee's report[14] was published in February 1859. The Committee strongly criticized the Commissioners for not having tapped the river Plenty above the swamps as recommended by Jackson and added: 'So important do your Committee consider this remedy that they regard it as the only feasible remedy for existing evils; and therefore they unhesitatingly recommend its adoption regardless of expense, if this City is to be supplied with unpolluted and wholesome water.' This recommendation was ignored. It was not until some 30 years later that this necessary improvement to the Yan Yean project was carried out.[15] The Committee also recommended that the further use of Commissioner's piping should be strictly prohibited and the Commissioners on their own initiative issued instructions that taps should be opened and water run to waste prior to use. The trouble with discoloration of the water and lead poisoning continued, and a second Select Committee to investigate the water supply was appointed in April 1860. The Committee inspected the Plenty river, and in their report[16] they drew attention to the pollution of the river by Bruce Creek which acquired its many impurities from the sewage of Whittlesea and the surrounding district, also from disturbance, etc. of the water from constant use by geese, pigs and cattle. They recommended that the water from this creek should be diverted.

The Committee sanctioned the use of pure lead service pipes but not Commissioner's piping, and when they discovered that, whilst Jackson had ceased laying any Commissioner's piping himself, he had allowed plumbers to purchase and use a limited amount of it on their own responsibility, they wrote:

> Your Committee cannot too strongly express their condemnation of the conduct of the Commissioners of Sewers and Water Supply and of their engineer, Mr. Jackson, for persisting in defiance of the reiterated recommendation of the former Select Committee in facilitating the sale and use of such piping to the detriment and danger of the health of the Citizens.

For this lapse, which probably affected his standing with public opinion, Jackson cannot be exonerated.

What appears to have been a greater worry to Jackson, and one which seems to have caused him to have a nervous breakdown, was that from time to time bursts occurred on the main pipeline between the Yan Yean reservoir and Melbourne. On 19 May, 1854, less than 5 months after construction had started, he wrote: 'I consider that the whole works may be finished in two years.' He also wrote:

> From the outside of the embankment, one only at present of the pipes . . . will be led dow: to a point, distant about 7 miles from Melbourne, and at a level approaching 300 feet above the lowest part of Melbourne and 150 feet above

the highest; and at this point [Preston] will be constructed a distributing reservoir, with filters etc.[17]

The water level in the Yan Yean reservoir is approximately 600 ft above sea level, and if this distribution reservoir had been constructed the maximum water pressure in the mains would have been limited to approximately 300 ft of water. Before being despatched from Cochran's works in England the cast-iron pipes were all tested at a pressure of 450 ft of water which would have given a margin of 50 per cent more resistance above the static pressure for water-hammer. The pipes in those days were not centrifugally spun and it is a remarkable tribute to the standard of workmanship obtained that such large pipes, varying from 24 to 30 in. diameter, could be manufactured to resist so high a pressure.

Perhaps because the estimated cost of the works and the estimated time to complete them both showed signs of being exceeded, Jackson most unfortunately omitted the distribution reservoir from the first stage of construction, and for breaking pressure on the main pipeline he relied upon the dubious expedient of having the two reducing valves or pressure regulators already referred to; one at the location of the future distribution reservoir site and the other located about midway between this site and the Yan Yean reservoir. This was the first time that such devices had been used on a large pipeline. Under this arrangement the filters were, of necessity, also omitted but Jackson did not regard them as being essential.[18]

In the discussion on Jackson's paper at the Institution of Civil Engineers, Hawksley wisely expressed the opinion that

> pressure regulators were, generally speaking, of little use for the mere regulation of pressure. When the water ceased to flow in any considerable quantity from the lower end of the main, the regulator allowed as much water to pass as would give pressure to the length below; consequently it was no value in regulating pressure and would not save the pipe below from bursting.

Hawksley added that if a pipe burst a regulator 'might so reduce the flow that the issue of water might be comparatively small and thus cause but little damage in the neighbourhood of the accident'.[19] Jackson reported in his paper that when carrying out tests on one of his regulators the disc closed too quickly, with the result that 'immediately on the pipes becoming full, the concussion or recoil was so great as to burst a pipe. This experiment was repeated five times with the same result.' However, Jackson added: 'Since the opening of the Works, the pipes in the lowest position of the city have always been kept partly open so that even at night when it is presumed all the service pipes are stopped, the regulators are not closed'.[20]

Probably because the Commission of Sewers and Water Supply failed to keep its expenditure within its budget and to satisfy the Government auditors, it was dissolved in December 1859 and its responsibilities were transferred to the Board of Land and Works. The staff was also transferred and Jackson's reports were now addressed to J. G. Francis, the Commissioner of Public Works.

In spite of the lowest pipes being left partly open, Jackson was obliged to report to the Commissioners on 28 December, 1859, that there had been a burst on the main pipeline. Having no doubt by this time received Hawksley's comments on pressure-regulating valves, he evidently became a very worried man indeed. Unfortunately the distribution of pipe diameters used, that is to say predominantly 30 in. diameter for the first 6½ miles from the reservoir, predominantly 27 in. diameter for the next 6½ miles and 24 in. diameter for the remaining 6 miles, were such as to maintain high pressures in the pipeline and Jackson, having probably lost faith in the pressure-regulators, may well have rightly concluded that the pressures at the lower end of the pipeline at times exceeded 450 ft. As a concession, and without, apparently, consulting Jackson, the Corporation had been allowed by Francis to use the fire plugs for washing down the streets. Jackson, by then suffering a nervous breakdown, became obsessed with the idea that the water-hammer in the reticulation pipes, and the fluctuations in pressure caused by the opening and closing of these fire plugs, even though they were only 2½ in. diameter, were enough to break the camel's back. When a second burst occurred a few days later he wrote on 4 January to the Commissioner that 'this is the second burst that has taken place in a week, and other portions of the main line of pipes may be almost daily expected to give way'. In both cases the pipes which burst were 27 in. diameter. In his letter he put the blame for these bursts on the watering of the streets by the Corporation, and he made the suggestion that if a large number of fire plugs happened to be closed simultaneously, even the reservoir was not safe unless they were placed under his own control.

On 24 January, 1860, Sinclair, a member of the Legislative Council who as a contractor had made one or two unsuccessful bids for contracts on the Yan Yean project, proposed:

> That a Select Committee be appointed to take into consideration the Reports of the Engineer-in-Chief for the Yan Yean Water Supply on the cause of the recent bursts in the water pipes and to enquire and examine into the stability and general management of the works and supply of water; also as to the sum expended on the works, and the revenue derived therefrom up to 31st December last, the Committee to have power to call for persons, papers and records.

Whilst there were 12 members on the Committee, usually only 3 to 5 members with Sinclair as Chairman attended the sittings. Francis was one of the members but, whilst he was probably active behind the scenes, he took no part in the public proceedings.

250

The Committee first questioned Jackson on the pipeline burst but learnt nothing more from him and subsequently wrote

> that the report of the Engineer-in-Chief of the Water Commission which occasioned the appointment of this Committee was calculated to excite the greatest apprehension in the minds of the public [but] there was no evidence tendered to your Committee to shew that there was any mismanagement of the fire-plugs by the Corporation nor that the bursts in the main pipes had been in any degree affected by the use or abuse of them by the parties so charged with flushing the streets. On the contrary, the Engineer in another document apologises for the alarm-cry raised in his report by stating that the only excuse for writing it was contained in a medical certificate dated 4th January 1860, a copy of which he enclosed to the Commissioner of Public Works.[21]

The Committee satisfied themselves that the cracked pipes through the embankment had been safely repaired and that the embankment was sound, but without giving Jackson any credit for his achievement in their report.

The total cost of the works to the end of 1857, including street reticulation, was £754 206, whereas Jackson's original estimate in 1853 was £438 178. Jackson maintained that his responsibilities were limited to the engineering, and that the proper person to ask questions on financial matters was the former Secretary and Treasurer of the Commission, Lanktree. He also drew attention to many extras not included in his original estimate, such as the cost of management, salaries, legal expenses, purchase of land, service pipes, the temporary water supply (£53 810) and pumping costs of the same, cast-iron plates for sewers (£38 317), the Plenty road (£4663) and 62 miles of reticulation pipe weighing more than 5000 tons all charged indiscriminately against the main vote for the original works. Jackson referred to several cases where contractors had failed to complete their contracts but had been allowed to withdraw without surrendering their securities or cash deposits. He also referred to cases in which unit rates had been changed without his recommendation or agreement. During the 1850s the price of labour rose considerably. In 1850 labourers could only earn 2s. per day; in 1852 their wages had risen to 9s., and, during the construction of the Yan Yean reservoir, labourers were paid 20s. and masons 36s. per day.[22] The Committee did not accept Jackson's arguments and reported that it appeared to them that 'the difference between the amount estimated and that expended has not been satisfactorily explained and that it can only be attributed to reckless and incompetent management'. If the Commission had accepted Jackson's advice to employ a large experienced English contracting firm, the accounts would probably not have got into such a serious state. Jackson made mistakes but he had to contend with considerable difficulties and 'reckless and incompetent management' appears to be too harsh a verdict.

251

The Committee also took evidence from Lanktree[23] and some of the contractors whose evidence against Jackson were shown to be fabrications. Jackson requested that if the Committee members had any doubts on his character they should summon as witnesses some of the former Commissioners for whom he had worked but, shamefully enough, instead of doing so or exonerating him from the serious charges against him they returned a verdict of not proven, as follows:

> Your Committee have, from the strong personal feeling evinced by several witnesses, labored under considerable difficulty in arriving at a satisfactory conclusion as to the various charges made against the Engineer, but your Committee thinks it will fully discharge its duty by directing the attention of the Honourable the Commissioner of Public Works to the evidence taken during the course of the investigation.

Examining this evidence as recorded in the Select Committee's minutes more than a century later, it appears to the author that no charges were substantiated against Jackson and that in every case where a charge had been made the accuser was, in Jackson's own words either 'a man of worthless character and dubious antecedents, as had so strong a motive to wish me out of the way and to invalidate my testimony that his evidence would have been keenly sifted by any honest enquirer'. The situation in which he was placed necessarily incurred the animosity of a great number of persons either in the shape of disappointed tenderers or of persons who were unsuccessful in the carrying out of such contracts as they had undertaken, but he had a right to expect to be protected against such parties instead of the reverse having been the case.

After his return to England Jackson wrote in his own defence what seems an accurate account of the events leading to his departure from the colony, including a not unfair account of the Committee and its proceedings, some excerpts from which are as follows:

> In fulfilment of a duty which I owe to all those gentlemen at whose hands I have received marks of consideration and confidence in Australia, I herewith forward to you the following statement, premising that I would have fulfilled this duty at a much earlier period had I not been prevented by paralysis of body and mind, brought on by the treatment I have received at the hands of certain members of the Victorian Government, who have held office since November, 1859.
>
> I have first to assure you that the apology given by me on my leaving the Colony, to John Millar, and published in the Melbourne papers, was signed by me when I was not responsible for my actions, through mental distress.
>
> I do assure you that I never wronged the man in any respect, and that all the

evidence given by me before the Committee of the House of Assembly, on the Management of the Yan Yean Waterworks, presided over by Mr John Sinclair, was strictly correct. That he (Millar) took contracts on the Waterworks which he was unable to fulfil, is true; that it became my duty by insisting on the fulfilment of the conditions of those contracts, and refusal to allow or certify to certain extras claimed by him, to cause him pecuniary losses and embarrassments, is also true; but that I ever persecuted him, or acted at any time other than the interests of the Sewerage and Water Commission demanded, is utterly untrue; and it is totally false that I ever shewed any favour to any contractor whatever, or acted otherwise than an honest man was called on to do.

I will now endeavour, in as few words as the subject will admit, to lay before you the circumstances of my case, and to furnish you concisely with such facts as will, I doubt not, convince you that I have been the victim of a conspiracy unexcelled in the details of its baseness, and got up for the purpose of invalidating my testimony, of shielding defalcators and their sureties, and concealing frauds and criminal neglect.

In the first place, I would briefly allude to my official connection with the former Secretary to the Sewerage and Water Commission, John Lanktree. Shortly after my appointment as Engineer to the Board, I found myself impeded in the carrying out of the works by his incessant interference with my assistants and duties, while his unceasing attempts to fill-up every vacant office with his own relations and friends (unfortunately too generally successful), became at last so notorious as to attract the notice of the Public Press, which repeatedly commented on the nepotism which existed. This I had no power to prevent; but attempts having been made by him to place contracts for extensive works in the hands of his son-in-law, I at once protested against it, and early in 1855, brought certain charges against him. (Vide Parliamentary Papers moved for by Mr. J. P. Fawkner, in the Legislative Council in April 1855, and ordered by the Council to be printed.) My charges, instead of being replied to and rebutted, were met by countercharges, in which the most frivolous matter was introduced. . . . It will also be seen on referring to those papers that I was entirely exonerated by the Board of Enquiry from all the charges preferred against me by Lanktree, while his conduct was characterized as artful, cunning, and unscrupulous. He was not however then dismissed from office, and on that account I scarcely think I received fair treatment at the hands of the Commissioners, as it was obviously impossible that I could afterwards act cordially with, or feel otherwise than suspicious of a man whose conduct had been so stigmatized.

Jackson then went on to explain that Lanktree had subsequently been discharged from the public service in 1857 for having had financial dealings with contractors but that this affair had been hushed up. When Lanktree's successor, Bury, was appointed Jackson, according to himself, had urged the necessity of regularizing the accounts. This seems to have led to bad feeling encouraged, if not caused, in Jackson's opinion by Francis, the Commissioner, and to have raised a host of enemies in the Government Audit department against him. Francis tried unsuccessfully to get Jackson to resign. The Select Committee under Sinclair, which had suspended its sittings whilst these efforts to get Jackson to resign were being made, then resumed its proceedings. In Jackson's words:

> Every charge made against me was made in my absence, and the knowledge that such charges had been made was carefully kept from me for months; but towards the close of the so-called enquiry (which extended over upwards of eight months) some of the members who had absented themselves becoming cognizant of the fact that the proceedings of the committee were of an infamous nature, attended, and I was then for the first time informed of the charges that had been made, and requested to reply to them – a copy of the original proof-sheets of evidence being furnished to me for the purpose of enabling me so to do. Replies I did furnish, though I had short time left to do it – only three days – to answer and disprove what it had taken months to concoct, and the verdict of the committee was necessarily one that the charges had not been proven – a great moral triumph under the circumstances. When, however, the proceedings of the committee appeared before the public, I found to my astonishment that the evidence as issued was totally at variance with the proof-sheets. New and important changes had been interpolated. The evidence of the witnesses against me had been allowed to be altered in order that denials of my statements might appear to have been made prior to my making them. Evidence that I had given – that Millar had circulated in the colony spurious testimonials bearing the names of eminent men in England, had been struck out, as had also evidence that I had tendered shewing that from the nature of Lanktree's antecedents, both in the colony and prior to his arrival, he ought not to be believed. Portions of documents had also been excised, so that the document purporting to be the report and evidence of the Committee appointed to enquire into the general working of the Sewerage and Water Commission (as issued) is not a correct record.

Jackson endeavoured to get the record put straight but neither the Chief Secretary nor either of Francis's two successors was prepared to act. By this time Jackson was seriously ill, partly due to an accident sustained in Government service in 1855, and also as a result of his responsibilities and anxieties over the last few years. He seems in fact to have had a serious mental breakdown and his friends persuaded him to leave the Colony. Jackson added:

Under these circumstances I did leave the Colony I had so long and faithfully served, and having been followed on board ship by Millar, with a Judge's order obtained by one of the Ministry's, as I was informed, to prevent me leaving the Colony, I did sign the apology to him, which will ever be a subject of regret to me; but I still feel that the infamy of that act does not lie on me but upon the men who had by artifice and fraud reduced me to the wreck I then was.

In his letter Jackson reasonably asks why:

If the Government even thought that I was such a scoundrel as I have since my departure from the colony been alleged to be, (and they had ample opportunities of ascertaining between November 1859, and January 1861), did they not suspend me from office? And am I to conclude that the treatment I received was entirely due to the personal hostility of Mr. Francis, the Commissioner of Public Works? The accusations made against me were no grounds for a reduction of my salary to one half its former amount, but for an ignominious dismissal if true, and if false, as it was known they would be proved to be with a fair inquiry and impartial jurors, for the reverse of a reduction? Why also was I not treated in an open and manly manner? Why was I subjected to treatment such as the meanest felon does not receive? Why was evidence invariably sought for in quarters known to be adverse to me? Why was Sinclair's committee not appointed by ballot if its object was to be to enquire into the character and fitness, & of myself? There is an answer! The Truth was not wanted!!![24]

After Jackson's departure, Melbourne continued for 4 years to have trouble with frequent bursting of mains, and had often to resort to emergency supplies whilst the repairs were carried out. In the year 1864, however, the break pressure reservoir unfortunately omitted in the first stage of the project was constructed at Preston and, after it came into use, no further trouble with bursting mains was experienced.[25]

The Yan Yean reservoir is still a key element of Melbourne's water supply; its embankment now more than 120 years old remains a lasting testimony to the skill and determination of its much-maligned and ill-used engineer.

As described in the next chapter, after the Dale Dyke dam collapsed in 1864, Jackson was one of the few expert witnesses who gave evidence at the coroner's inquest; he was one of the nine engineers who reported on the disaster on behalf of the Sheffield Corporation and he also gave evidence on it before a Select Committee of the House of Commons during June 1865. He played a very active and intelligent part in these proceedings but, except to propose in 1866 an ambitious scheme for the water supply of Sheffield, Rotherham and Doncaster jointly,[26] he apparently took no further part in waterworks engineering afterwards.

13 John Towlerton Leather (1804–85) and the collapse of the Dale Dyke dam

The Sheffield Waterworks Company came into existence under an Act which reached the Statute Book in June 1830. Under the Act assets of an earlier company, including wooden pipes, were taken over, and improvements to the water supply were contemplated by tapping the Wyming Brook, a tributary of the river Rivelin.[1]

John Towlerton Leather (1804–85) was appointed to be the first Managing Clerk, Resident Engineer and Surveyor of the Company at a salary of £300 per annum. Towlerton was the eldest son of James Leather, colliery proprietor of Beeston Park, Yorkshire, and had served his apprenticeship under his uncle George Leather.[2] Subsequently in their first Annual Report dated April 1831 the Management Committee stated that they had decided to dispense with the services of their first engineer and 'to employ Mr. Leather in that capacity, and that under his superintendance, with the occasional assistance of a more experienced Engineer, they hoped the intended Works may be completed'.[3] A contract was also awarded for the supply of cast-iron pipes.

The Act prescribed that 'what should be deemed the flood or spare Waters of the Wyming Brook and its tributary streams and when the same may be taken by the Company without injury to the Millowner'[4] should be decided by two referees, one appointed by the Company and the other by the millowners. The two referees appointed failed to reach a settlement themselves but agreed to leave the matter to the umpirage of James Simpson. It was in compliance with his instructions that the first storage reservoir, subsequently known as the middle one, was built at Redmires (Fig. 13.1). Whilst Towlerton Leather was undoubtedly in charge of the construction of this embankment, the Committee's annual reports are vague as to who designed it. At a later date the reservoir was used for town water supply only but initially it served to also provide compensation water.

The outlet arrangements consist of a 12 in. diameter cast-iron standpipe at the upstream toe of the embankment with two inlets at different levels controlled by single-faced penstocks on each of the inlets coupled to a 12 in. diameter cast-iron pipeline laid in a 4 ft diameter stone-lined tunnel under the embankment.

The Committee referred in their second Annual Report to a service reservoir at

Crook's Moor having been set out by Towlerton Leather, and to a contract having been let for its construction, 'the Plan thereof having been previously submitted to Mr. Clarke, of the West Middlesex Waterworks',[5] and in their third Annual Report they wrote that

> the New Reservoir at Crooks is now also ready for use. . . . The substantial manner in which the work has been executed, under the direction of Mr. J. T. Leather, the Company's engineer, will, it is hoped, meet with the approval of the Proprietors:– the Masonry of the Feed pit, and the Tunnel for carrying off the waste or surplus Water, are especially worthy of attention.[6]

A year later the Management Committee wrote that construction of the first Redmires reservoir had started and added:

> And should the Tenants increase, so as to render even this immense Supply inadequate, an event which will assuredly indicate a high degree of prosperity in your Affairs, your Committee will be found to have provided even for this remote occurrence, by securing Ground for the formation of another large Reservoir immediately adjoining that above described.[7]

Within 15 years, the company was to be embarked on the remote contingency.

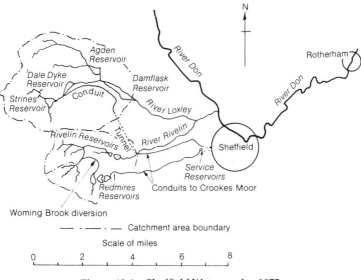

Figure 13.1 Sheffield Waterworks, 1875

By 1836 the Committee wrote on the progress at Redmires that

> the Excavation and Embankment are nearly completed; but with the view of
> still further enlarging the capacity of this Principal Store for future supplies,
> and which it was found might be done without any considerable increase of
> expense, it was considered expedient to erect a strong Wall upon the top of the
> Reservoir Bank.[8]

By this means the crest level was raised about 5 ft (Fig. 13.2) and the storage capacity
was increased by about 50 per cent. The original wall was made of dry rubble but
subsequently, following damage during a storm in 1844, it was replaced with stone
set in mortar.[9]

In their seventh Annual Report the Committee stated that a total of 25½ miles of
cast-iron pipes had been laid and that 'the quantity of Wood Pipes still remaining in
the streets is considerable, but so long as they will answer the end, it will probably
not be thought well to incur the expense of replacing them with Iron'.[10]

In 1846 the Committee reported that

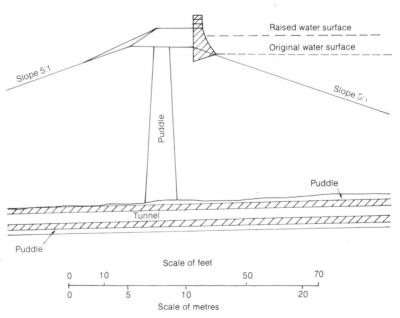

Figure 13.2 First Redmires embankment, subsequently known as the Middle Redmires dam,
1836 (redrawn from contemporary drawing)

the Act for which the Company applied to Parliament last year received the Royal Assent 31st Day of July last. By this Act the Company are to construct Two Reservoirs for the use of the Mills on the Rivelin, and are then to be entitled to the whole of the Wyming Brook and its tributary streams where the level is sufficiently high to admit of them being available. The Act also authorises the construction of two additional Reservoirs on the Moors, for the purpose of storing up Water for the use of the Town.[11] [Fig. 13.1].

J. Towlerton Leather continued to act as the Company's consulting engineer, and the works authorized by the 1845 Act were designed by him but executed by John Gunson, Towlerton having previously given up his position as resident engineer and manager to the company to enable him to undertake contracting, in which business he was very successful.[12]

The dams undertaken at this time were the lower Redmires embankment, for which the land had already been bought, and the two Rivelin embankments. Construction of the second dam on the moors at Redmires authorized by the Act was postponed.

A cross-section of the Lower Redmires embankment is shown in Fig. 13.3. The drawing appears to have been intended for the use of a contractor whose responsibilities excluded the supply and installation of pipes and valves, it being quite common practice for a water authority or company to make themselves responsible for pipework.

The original intention was that the 6 ft diameter vertical shaft at the upstream end of the tunnel should act as a spillway. It can also be deduced that there was a pipeline inside the tunnel, the upstream end of which projected through the wall of the shaft and communicated in some way or other with the water in the reservoir, also that this pipeline was controlled by one or more valves in a valve chamber beneath the downstream toe of the dam.

Construction of the three embankments commenced in 1846. Towlerton Leather reported that considerable difficulty was experienced in obtaining good foundations for the three embankments but that by April 1848 this had been accomplished.[13] Two years later, the Committee reported:

> During the past year, the whole of the Works on the Rivelin have been finished, and the New Reservoir at Redmires has been so far completed as to authorise the Company to appropriate the supply of Water from the Wyming Brook.
>
> In the course of construction of the reservoir at Redmires, several slips of the embankment took place, by which considerable delay was occasioned. The damage, however, was so far repaired that it was considered safe to fill the reservoir, and your Committee have much pleasure in saying that it has been

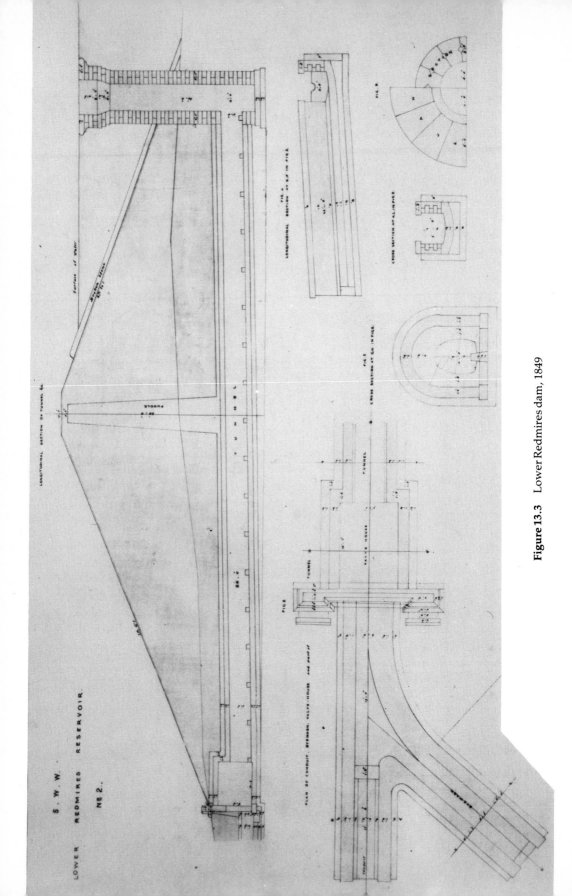

Figure 13.3 Lower Redmires dam, 1849

quite full during part of the winter without any casualty having happened. There remains some additional support to be given to the embankment, to complete the contract.

The Proprietors are aware that the Company are bound by their Act, passed in August 1845, to give a supply of Water to the town of eight hours a day, within five years from the passing of the Act. The Committee . . . hope to fulfil the obligation completely.[14]

However the Committee were disappointed in their expectations of being able to give a regular supply because in November that year some crisis arose which made it necessary to empty the reservoir.[15] According to one report, the water got through the culvert and washed away part of the embankment.[16] Roman cement had been invented by Edgar Dobbs in 1810 and this had been followed in 1824 by Joseph Aspdin's improved patent for Portland Cement,[17] but cements were often of inferior quality, with lias lime which is unsuitable for hydraulic structures, still being used sometimes. The spillway was quite a bold structure for its time and one can suspect not only that the mortar in the stonework joints was inferior but also that there was differential settlement causing cracking.

It was probably at this time that Towlerton Leather decided to abandon the use of the vertical shaft as a spillway and to construct instead a spillway of somewhat similar discharging capacity, that is to say one 25 ft long, which discharges into a bypass channel. The top of the shaft was raised to the crest level of the embankment and with a 20 in. diameter standpipe inside it, it was converted into a valve shaft with two 12 in. diameter inlets from the reservoir at different levels, each inlet being controlled by a sluice valve. It was not until April 1851 that the repairs and alterations were completed and that the reservoir was able to be put back into service again.

When water was stored for compensation water purposes it was considered sufficient to provide a bottom-water outlet only. This theory was applied to both the Rivelin dams designed by Towlerton Leather, where the pipelines were buried beneath the embankments without being enclosed in tunnels and with the valves controlling releases through them sited at the downstream toes of the embankments.

When Towlerton Leather came to design the upper Redmires dam he omitted a tunnel and allowed his pipelines (twin in this case) to be buried in a trench in the foundations of the embankment. His reason for dispensing with a tunnel was based, perhaps, on his unfortunate experience with the Lower Redmires dam tunnel. However, by means of a standpipe in the reservoir with inlets at two different levels, each inlet being controlled by a sluice, and with this single standpipe coupled to the twin-outlet pipelines, he did provide upstream control of releases through the pipelines.

261

Figure 13.4   Aerial view of Dale Dyke dam site

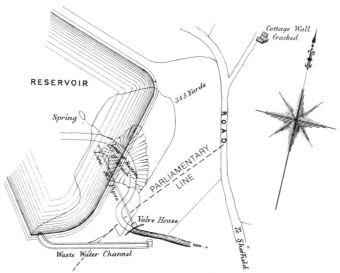

Figure 13.5   The Dale Dyke dam failure in 1864

In 1853 the Water Company obtained Parliamentary powers to construct the Dale Dyke and Agden dams. Powers were also obtained for the Strines embankment but construction of this dam was not put in hand until a later period. In contemporary accounts Dale Dyke dam is sometimes referred to as the Bradfield dam after the name of the nearest village downstream.

The original Dale Dyke embankment was situated 9 miles west of Sheffield on the river Loxley, a tributary of the river Don. On an aerial view of the dam site (Fig. 13.4) the centre line of the old dam, the landslip adjacent to it and a fault some 300–400 yd downstream are indicated in broken white lines. On a plan of the dam (Fig. 13.5), the centre line for the dam initially selected as shown on the Parliamentary plan is marked by a dotted line. The north end of this centre line lay in the middle of the landslip area, and when trial holes were put down on it the strata were found to be disturbed. The dam centre line was therefore moved about 150 yd upstream at the north end, and it was also curved round upstream at the south end.

The embankment was a large one for its time. The maximum height was 95 ft and the crest length was 1254 ft. It had a top width of 12 ft and slopes on both sides of 2½ to 1 (Fig. 13.6). A narrow vertical core of puddle clay 4 ft wide at the top and with a maximum width of 16 ft at ground level, the batters on each face being 1 on 16, was carried down below ground level to a watertight stratum, the maximum depth of the cut-off trench being 60 ft. Above ground level, the puddle clay corewall was supported by two triangular sections of fill. The downstream slope incorporated a stone toe with a maximum height of about 50 ft which contained 24 000 cu. yd of

263

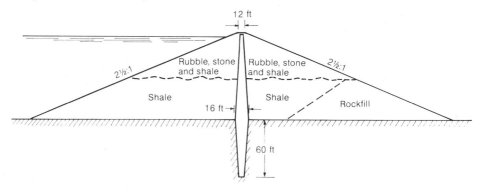

Figure 13.6   Dale Dyke dam, 1863, as deduced from evidence given at the inquest

stone and was intended to prevent slips. An extra 3*d*. per cu. yd, a significant increase in those days, was paid for selecting the stone and placing it. The overflow weir excavated in solid ground at the south end of the dam had a semicircular sill 65 ft long at a level 5 ft below the top of the bank.

In spite of the reservoir being for water supply, Towlerton Leather followed the precedent he had already set himself at the Rivelin dams for the outlet arrangements. A bottom outlet chamber (Fig. 13.7) was constructed, from which twin outlet pipes were laid in a straight line diagonally beneath the embankment. They were cast iron spigot and socket pipes 1½ in. thick and 18 in. diameter, in 9 ft lengths. The sockets were 6 in. deep, narrower at the entrance and were caulked with lead.

The pipes were laid in a trench about 9 ft wide and 8–9 ft deep. To prevent them

Figure 13.7   Outlet chamber after failure of Dale Dyke dam, 1864

from fracturing where they crossed the clay core, the excavation was sloped down from about 100 ft either side of the centre line so that it intersected the bottom of the cut-off trench which was about 30 ft deep at this point. It was backfilled with puddle clay and an 18 in. depth of puddle was placed in the remainder of the pipe trench.[18] Control of the release of water was by means of valves at the exit ends of the pipe-lines housed in a chamber at the bottom of the downstream slope of the embankment.

On 27 May, 1853, J. F. Bateman appeared before the Select Committee on the Dewsbury, Batley and Heckmondwike Waterworks Bill and was asked whether he was also concerned at Bradford to which he replied 'I was originally; I have been replaced there, I was concerned at Sheffield which is also in the same district.'[19] One is left wondering whether it was under the influence of Bateman that Towlerton Leather was encouraged to bury pipelines beneath embankments and to have downstream control of the release of water through them.

The works were commenced on 1 January, 1859. In April 1860 Towlerton Leather reported:

> The works of the Dale Dyke reservoir have been retarded in some degree, in consequence of the difficulties experienced in arriving at a satisfactory foundation in the middle of the valley, for the puddle wall, which difficulties have been enhanced by the severity of the past winter. There is now, however, every prospect of favourable change and it is hoped that the works will be vigorously prosecuted during the ensuing season.[20]

The cut-off trench was completed in 1861 and the placing of fill began in the autumn of that year. On 20 April, 1863, Towlerton Leather wrote:

> I am happy to report that notwithstanding the more than ordinary difficulties which have been encountered in the construction of the Dale Dyke reservoir, the embankment is now so far completed as to be ready for the reception of the Water, and the Waste Weir, which is not quite finished, may be soon so in the course of a few weeks from the present time, and the Works throughout are well and substantially executed.[21]

To divert the river during the construction period, an artificial channel above the intended top water level of the reservoir had been excavated on the south side of the valley and the reservoir commenced filling when a heavy flood destroyed this diversion channel in June 1863. Filling proceeded intermittently. By 10 March, 1864, the water level was 2 ft 3 in. below the crest of the weir and still rising. During the latter part of the afternoon of 11 March, a horizontal crack along the downstream slope near the crest of the dam was observed, and at 11.30 p.m. the same evening, by which time the reservoir was practically full, the embankment collapsed suddenly with no further warning (Fig. 13.8). The circumstances surrounding this collapse are reviewed subsequently. Nearly 250 people lost their lives, and there was considerable damage to property including some in the city of Sheffield.

An inquest was opened on 13 March at the Union Workhouse but after evidence of identification had been taken on four of the victims it was adjourned until 23 March. The Mayor sent a request to the Home Secretary, Sir George Grey, that a Government Inspector should be sent to enquire into the cause of the disaster, and Robert Rawlinson arrived at Sheffield on 1 March. Two days later he went up to the dam site with the coroner and began taking evidence. Rawlinson reported to Grey:

> For the purpose of making the embankment the engineer has allowed the sandstone rock to be bared on the inside of the reservoir. This rock . . . is jointed and open so as to admit water. The coroner and I have seen water rising out on one side of the valley and sinking in on the other side, just within the broken embankment. This is sufficient evidence that the reservoir leaks and with a great head of water before bursting must have leaked much more.

He also wrote that the pipes were laid 'in an improper manner'. He described large stones up to 4 ft long in the embankment and stated: 'these stones have been tipped

Figure 13.8   Breach in Dale Dyke dam, 1864

so that they form a loose rubble-heap, through which the river flows at present unchecked'.[22] Rawlinson quickly reached his own conclusions as to the cause of the accident but he was concerned that he had been asked by the coroner not only to give evidence at the inquest but also to act as adviser to him and the jury. He asked the Home Secretary to send a legal representative to join him and he wrote: 'I foresee great difficulty in such a course and fervently desire to have legal advice to guide me. It cannot be proper for the same individual to advise the coroner as to the questions which may be put to witnesses tendered by the Company for examination and then himself give evidence.'[23] The Home Secretary overruled Rawlinson's scruples but, instead, pressed on him the services of another engineer to assist him. As a result Nathaniel Beardmore,[24] nominated by the immediate past President of the Institution of Civil Engineers (the President being overseas), joined him.

Rawlinson also expressed the opinion that nothing would be gained by attempting to incriminate the engineers or the Water Company and that the aim of the inquest should be 'to obtain facts so as to arrive at reliable conclusions for future use'. On the other hand, he also seemed very worried that possibly 'all sorts of evidence will be tendered, feeling will be imported into the evidence, if not checked, and with this I ought not to be mixed up.'[25]

On a subsequent visit to the dam site before the inquest was resumed Rawlinson also met the jury, and there is little doubt that they were influenced by him to take a lenient attitude towards the engineers and the Water Company, also to be selective in the witnesses called to give evidence. Having regard to the state of hydraulic engineering knowledge at the time, this may not have resulted in any miscarriage of justice, but it had strange consequences. Unlike the inquest after the failure of the Bilberry dam, at which many people connected with the construction of the embankment in one capacity or another – including witnesses of the accident – gave evidence, after the failure of the Dale Dyke dam only five persons, of whom only one had been engaged on the construction of the dam and had witnessed its collapse, gave evidence. At the end of the second day of the resumed inquest the coroner was anxious to probe deeper into the cause of the accident. He injudiciously said, however, that the jury had already made up their minds to find no-one guilty of manslaughter, and as the purpose of an inquest is to determine the cause of death and whether anyone is criminally responsible, the Water Company's legal representative – by declaring that it would therefore be a waste of time for him to call any witnesses – was able to bring the proceedings to a sudden end.[26]

The five witnesses, in order of first appearance before the Coroner, were J. Towlerton Leather; John Gunson – who as the Water Company's engineer had been responsible for the construction of the embankment; Matthew B. Jackson – who, after leaving Australia, had taken up residence in Sheffield; Rawlinson; and Beardmore.

When questioned about the embankment, Towlerton Leather displayed a good deal of ignorance as to the materials that had been used in the construction of the shoulders and confessed that he did not know whether they had been put in by barrows or waggons. Either with or without his knowledge, the fill material appears frequently to have been placed in much thicker layers than the maximum thickness of 3 ft he specified. The possibility and potential consequences of unequal settlement in the shoulders of the embankment obviously did not worry him. As regards the clay puddle corewall, he was much more careful. He submitted in evidence a good specification for the puddle clay and he evidently attached the greatest importance to having a properly constructed puddle clay corewall on a watertight foundation. However, as will be demonstrated later, he was completely unconscious of the dangers of differential settlement in the clay core and, having seen for himself during one of his rare visits to the site that the corewall was founded on watertight strata, he was content to leave the rest of the work to Gunson, whom he trusted.

Gunson claimed that the materials he used for building the dam were very good, also that the finer materials had been placed next to the clay puddle wall. However it is significant that, whereas for the other dams – previously constructed – it had been found necessary to instal drains to draw off surplus water from the puddle trenches, the material used for the Dale Dyke dam was so porous that the water escaped through the fill without it being necessary to instal any drains. The material placed next to the puddle clay corewall must, therefore, have been relatively coarse. In addition, Gunson gave evidence on the collapse of the embankment and the events leading up to it, which will be referred to later.

Jackson visited the dam site on 14 March, less than 48 hours after the accident, and expressed the opinion that either: (a) the extra pressure caused by the depth of water on the filling of the reservoir occasioned a fracture of one or more of the pipes beneath the dam and forced the water through the fracture into the earth forming the outside slope of the embankment, thus inducing a settlement and a slip of the outside slope immediately preceding the burst; or (b) the same cause, i.e. the extra depth of water and pressure, occasioned a leakage alongside the outside of the pipes between their surface and the puddle, and had the same effect. He had also noted that there were railway waggons which had evidently been used for construction on the embankment. He pointed out that if one used waggons and rails, the waggons always travelled in the same direction and over the same parts until the roads were shifted, giving rise to thick layers and unequal consolidation. On the other hand, he considered that tipping carts used in conjunction with continuous layers not exceeding 2 ft in thickness greatly improved consolidation.

Rawlinson said that no waterworks embankment ought to have a line of pipes laid through an embankment in such a way as to preclude any possibility of inspection or repairs if failure takes place, or means of renewal if the pipe wears out! An engineer, he held, should be master of his work, not the work master of him. He went on to advocate 'a tunnel or culvert through the solid stratification on one side of the valley and perfectly free from the loose earth of the embankment. Within that culvert or tunnel the outlet pipes are ultimately laid. Provision is made for closing the pipes inside the reservoir.'

Commenting by inference on the methods used for constructing the dam, Rawlinson also said:

> We have been told this reservoir embankment was made exactly as the Agden embankment. From the mode of tipping the waggons and the materials tipped, I have no hesitation in coming to the conclusion that the substance of that bank is as porous as a sieve. The specification limits the tips to three feet each in thickness, the tips at present in work are at least double that height. This method of working rolls the largest stones continually, to the foot of the tips and makes, in fact, a rubble embankment open and porous in layers.

Nathaniel Beardmore stated that he substantially agreed with what Rawlinson had said. Nevertheless, he considered the puddle wall to be 'of most excellent workmanship and I think that the immense depth excavated must have removed danger from springs.' In his opinion, the buried pipelines were the most likely source of trouble.

Subsequently, Rawlinson and Beardmore wrote a joint report to Sir George Grey which followed much the same lines as the evidence they gave and is critical both of the design and the construction of the dam. They gave it as their opinion that failure was most probably due to leakage from a fractured pipe with consequential erosion.

After finding that the deaths were due to drowning as a result of the bursting of the reservoir, the jury expressed the opinion that

> there has not been that engineering skill and that attention to the construction of the works, which their magnitude and importance demanded; that, in our opinion, the Legislature ought to take such action as will result in a governmental inspection of all works of this character; and, that such inspection should be frequent, sufficient and regular; that we cannot separate without expressing our deep regret at the fearful loss of life which has occurred from the destruction of the Bradfield reservoir.[27]

It was to be 66 years before Government introduced legislation on reservoir inspection.[28]

There was no official enquiry as to the cause of the disaster. Perhaps because the victims were all of the labouring class and without votes, the Sheffield Members of

269

Parliament put no pressure for one on the Home Secretary; their constituents were more likely to be shareholders of the Water Company.

By the time of the Tay Bridge collapse, in 1879, the working class in the towns had been enfranchised (Act of 1867), there was a greater awareness of public opinion, and the Home Secretary was forced to give instructions for an official enquiry to be held. As a consequence, although the death toll did not exceed that of Bilberry, the smaller of the two dam disasters, and there was no damage to third-party property, it is remembered, whereas both Bilberry and Dale Dyke are quite forgotten.

The Sheffield Water Company had retained Thomas Hawksley, J. F. Bateman, James Simpson, T. E. Harrison and John (later Sir John) Fowler. Fowler at the age of 16 had been apprenticed to Towlerton Leather and he was probably biased in his favour. They disagreed with Rawlinson and Beardmore on the quality of the workmanship in the dam. In a joint report they expressed the opinion that the Dale Dyke dam collapsed as a result of a landslide, and that it was an unavoidable accident.[29]

The Sheffield Corporation, which wished to buy out the Water Company, engaged no less than nine engineers to report individually on the dam. The nine were Sir John Rennie, Charles B. Vignoles, David Stevenson, Peter Barlow, William Lee, John Murray, Henry Coneybeare, James Leslie and Matthew B. Jackson. In essence these engineers agreed with Rawlinson and Beardmore that the bank had been faultily constructed, that the depths of the tips were too great, that building material ought not to have been taken from inside the reservoir and that the burying of pipelines beneath embankments was bad practice. Jackson was also of the opinion that 'the site of the embankment was not judiciously chosen as it appears to have been placed in the immediate neighbourhood of ancient slides, of strong springs and of suspicious indications of faults in the strata' and it did not appear to him that sufficient examination of the site had been made before commencing work.[29]

Subsequently, Messrs Hawksley, Bateman, Fowler, Leslie, Jackson and Murray,[30] were called upon to give evidence during May and June 1865 before a Select Committee on a proposed Water Bill which, in the event, did not reach the Statute Book but which gave these engineers an opportunity to continue the debate on the causes of the failure of the Dale Dyke dam.

Subsequent to the inquest the pipelines buried under the dam had been tested under pressure and Jackson changed his opinion regarding them. In answer to a question on them, he said: 'the pipes are not broken. . . . I think there cannot be any very serious leakage from the joints themselves, or otherwise it would have been detected during the test that was applied.'[31] The other engineers maintained the opinions that each of them had previously expressed.

On the basis mainly of the evidence given by Gunson at the inquest, it is now necessary to look closer at events prior to the collapse of the embankment. On 10 March, 1864, following a fortnight of heavy rainfall there had been a gale warning, and the following day Gunson visited the reservoir in the afternoon to observe the effect of the waves on the embankment; the water level had risen to 1 ft 3 in. below the crest of the weir.

At the inquest Gunson stated that, although he stood watching the embankment all the afternoon, he did not observe the least sinking. He stated that he was in a direct line, and level with the top of the embankment, and if there had been anything at the top he would have seen it if it had been out of the true line. There was no wave wall on the embankment and because of the spray that was blowing over it he did not cross it. Being convinced that all was well, Gunson then went home.[26] Whilst the recent rain would have tended to conceal the evidence, if Gunson had examined the toe of the dam before going home he would have found probably some muddy leakage taking place.

In a letter quoted by Samuel Harrison, editor–proprietor of the *Sheffield Times*, one of the Bradfield villagers, employed on the construction of the dam, wrote: 'Another important fact, well known here, but which I have not so far seen any inquiry into is, that a large spring of water issued from the foot of the embankment where the breach has occurred, and was conveyed away by a drain.'[32] Erosion had probably been going on a long time without being noticed.

About 5.30 p.m. a workman employed by the Waterworks Company had to cross the embankment to go to his residence and, the wind still being strong, he walked along at some distance below the crest where he was protected from the full force of the gale. Presumably the grass had not yet started to grow on the newly completed crest and as he proceeded along he noticed a crack in the side of the embankment. A mounted messenger was sent to recall Gunson and the valves were opened. Gunson got back after nightfall, about 10 p.m. In his evidence Gunson described the crack as being horizontal and he estimated that it was about 10–12 ft down the slope from the top of the dam.

An employee of the waterworks company who was present wrote:

> I went up to the reservoir about eight o'clock, I measured the crack on the bank: in half an hour's time it did not enlarge more than one eighth of an inch. About ten o'clock I measured the crack again; it had then enlarged about a quarter of an inch. A two-foot rule would pass down the crack about 20 inches. Messrs. Gunson and Craven [contractor's representative] arrived between 10 and 11 o'clock. At that time, I went on the embankment. Those persons on the bank then observed the crack, which was about an inch wide in the widest place.[29]

In his evidence Gunson stated that when he arrived he could just get his fingers into the crack edgeways. Unfortunately, neither Gunson nor the waterworks employee stated the length of the crack. Gunson's first impressions on the cause of the crack were as follows:

I thought it was the action of the wind and the waves that had been beating against it all the afternoon, and that it might have loosened the material that the inner slope of the top of the embankment is composed of, above the water mark: and if that had been the case, I thought it would be like taking the inner slope of the puddle wall from it, and cause a slight crack outside.

Gunson decided to relieve the water pressure against the crest of the embankment by blowing up the top stones of the weir. He described what happened next:

After putting the shot in, I said to the workmen, 'We will go carefully back and examine it again', and I thought of measuring from the top to the crack to see whether it was above or below the surface water of the reservoir. We walked over the crack and all seemed perfectly right just as it did when we had passed over before, all the men and the rest of us, perhaps half an hour before. I had a lantern in my hand, and when I got to the end and saw what was there, I said to Swindon [his inspector] 'George, good God, the water is over the embankment'. It came right under my feet and dropped down the crack.

Gunson went down the slope below the valve house to see if he could get some idea of the quantity of water passing over which initially was 'no great current'. He continued his evidence:

After I had been at the bottom a short time, I turned me round to go out, and cast my eye up the embankment, and could see an opening about 30 yards wide, perhaps, just as though we had blasted a way in the middle of the embankment, and in another moment one tremendous rush came and shook the ground under my feet.[26]

A huge gap was quickly cut in the embankment down to the level of the top of the bottom outlet chamber (Fig. 13.7) on the upstream side and down to river level on the downstream side (Fig. 13.8). The time was approximately 11.30 p.m. Ironically, the shot in the weir went off after the break in the dam had been made.[26] According to one report the water level in the reservoir was within 3 in. below the crest of the weir at the time the accident occurred. Jackson reported that when he first arrived at the dam site

there was the high water mark of rack the same as rack on the sea shore which ran in an even straight line about six feet from the top of the embankment, which showed me that the water never washed over the top till after the bank slipped and settled down, and then only over a portion of it.[33]

During the afternoon of 11 March, 1864, Gunson failed to detect any damage to the dam, yet within 8 hours it had collapsed. Any explanation as to how the disaster occurred must take into account the horizontal crack near the top of the downstream side of the dam and the remarkable speed with which the dam failed.

By condemning the burying of pipelines beneath embankments with their controls on the outside, a practice which Bateman nevertheless continued to use, Rawlinson made a major contribution to the safety of reservoirs but, in view of the pumping test referred to by Jackson (which evidently gave a satisfactory result) it does not appear that in this case the buried pipelines caused the collapse.

On the other hand the Hawksley landslide theory is difficult to accept. The dam, it must not be forgotten, failed immediately the reservoir became practically full for the first time, and as Jackson asked: 'Was this the precise moment for a natural and unavoidable landslip to occur?'[34]

Amongst the reports of the engineers and other documents ordered by the House of Commons on 13 February, 1866, to be published were some statements obtained by Jackson from three of the men who had been working on the dam, one of them being the Waterworks Company employee already referred to. One witness stated that, during excavation of the cut-off trench, a powerful spring was encountered which was successfully bottomed.

> The pumps were one 13-inch and three of 12-inch each diameter. There were times when all this could not keep the water down. The old springs stopped when the water gushed into the trench; they flowed again when the puddle got to the surface.

Another witness, however, wrote:

> I and my brother were both in the puddle trench at the time when they commenced puddling. We saw a spring at the bottom of the puddle trench. It was in the inner angle of the trench next to the dam.

The spring, whether bottomed or not, must have presented an immediate threat to any weakness in the puddle clay in the cut-off trench.

The statement obtained by Jackson from the Waterworks Company employee also included the following:

> Several weeks, or a month, before the bursting, I observed the pitching inside the bank had settled forming a hollow, as near as I can tell, about the place where the hole was first blown through, just above the surface of the water at that time, I suppose this was about 10 or 12 feet below the level of the waste weir when I observed this sinking of the pitching. I was standing on the bank about opposite, inside the mason work, inside where the water enters the

273

pipes, when I was watching the water boil through the bank at a distance of about 30 yards from it.[29]

Gunson did not report any depression in the pitching nor any whirlpool but when he was giving his evidence the Coroner, who was very dictatorial, hardly allowed him to do more than answer directly the questions put to him, and no question about either was raised. This reported evidence, which has an authentic ring about it, suggests that one must look at the embankment itself and not a land-slide for the cause of the disaster.

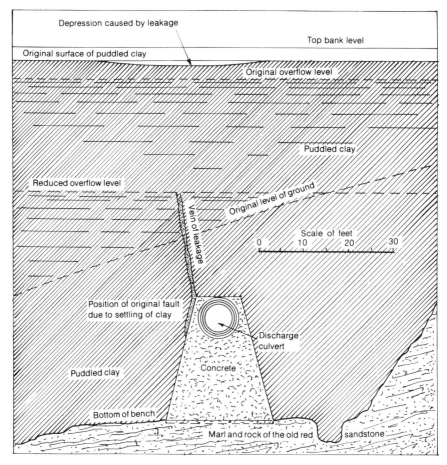

Figure 13.9 Shear failure and leakage due to improperly formed discharge culvert through puddle wall of reservoir (reproduced from article by G. F. Deacon on water supply in 10th edition of *Encyclopaedia Britannica*)

When weighted with the clay above it the lower part of a block of clay invariably becomes a denser mass, particularly puddled clay with its high liquid content. If, therefore, one part is held up by unyielding rock or concrete whereas an adjoining part has no support but the clay beneath it, a fracture occurs as shown in the example in Fig. 13.9.

Figure 13.10 is printed from a microfilm found recently by the Author amongst some microfilms of nineteenth century drawings owned by Watson–Hawksley. It shows a longitudinal section of the cut-off trench of the first Dale Dyke dam. It can be seen that below the centre part of the embankment which was washed away there was a near-vertical step 35 ft high on one side of a flat top and another step 10 ft high on the other side. These abrupt unsymmetrical changes in depth of the cut-off trench, which were not revealed at the inquest nor in subsequent discussions, must have caused rupture in the puddle clay wall, most probably before the clay corewall reached its full height.

According to the same Waterworks Company employee interviewed by Jackson

> Mr Gunson and the contractors sent for drills and powder to blow out a stone from the top course of the waste weir. Whilst the men were engaged drilling, a man was trying to cut out a stone with wedges. It was observed that the water was lowering faster than the pipes could draw it off. This was named to the contractors. They thought it was not so; but they noticed themselves after-wards, and they were satisfied that it was lowering. Then they sent a man along the bank with a light to see whether the water was escaping. He came running back to say there was a hole blown through. Mr Gunson and George Swinden and others immediately went over the top of the embankment. I went as far as I thought safe, and saw the water boiling through. I stood about ten minutes and then the top fell in, which appeared to stop the water a minute or two, until the water ran over the top in sheets of foam. An immense gap was speedily opened . . .'[29]

The evidence points to the water having escaped through a breach at the base of the corewall as a consequence of the clay in the cut-off trench having been ruptured. In an earlier study[35] the author attributed the collapse to other causes but in view of the evidence of a powerful spring having been encountered during excavation of the cut-off trench and the extraordinary configuraton of the bottom of the trench, he is now of the opinion that there is no need to look any further for the basic cause of the accident.

In 1887 A. R. Binnie wrote:

> Formerly it was the custom to finish off the bottom of the trench longitudinally into long level benches or planes divided by abrupt vertical steps of greater or

275

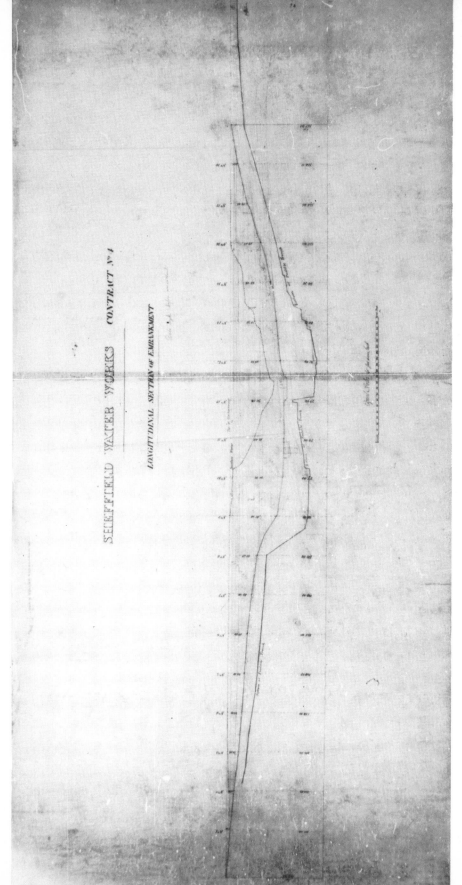

Figure 13.10 Sheffield Waterworks – contract No. 4 – longitudinal section of embankment

less height; but this is a very dangerous practice, for it must be remembered that clay puddle is a very plastic and compressible substance, and apt to crack under unequal strain, consequently it has been found that, owing to the unequal depth of puddle which occurs at the steps, the superincumbent weight has caused that on the deeper side to settle more than on the higher, and so produce a vertical crack or fault in the puddle which has led to serious consequences; the practice now is to form the bottom of the trench into long inclines, and so avoid abrupt changes of depth in the puddle.[36]

On the left bank there is a road along the valley, named Dale Road. At the time when the original dam was being built there were some cottages (which no longer exist) immediately north of the dam site above this road, on and close to the edge of the ancient landslide (Fig. 13.5). When the dam collapsed some movement of the ancient landslide, sufficient to cause cracks in the walls of these cottages, occurred. Hawksley and his supporters used this evidence of cracking of the cottage walls to support their theory that the dam had been destroyed by the ancient landslide moving again.[29]

However, as a consequence of reservoir impounding, the piezometric levels in the river bed foundations beneath the dam must have been raised considerably on the upstream side of the cut-off trench and, when the dam collapsed, the speed with which the load was removed from the foundations in this particular area almost certainly exceeded the speed with which the piezometric levels were able to adjust themselves. As a consequence of this rapid drawdown, some movement of the dam foundations, which also affected the adjacent landslip area, probably occurred. In other words this movement is believed to have been a consequence of, and not the cause of, the collapse.

There can be no doubt any longer as to the basic cause of the accident but the steps leading to the rapid destruction of the dam remain, to some extent, a matter for conjecture. Cavities formed on the upstream side of the thin clay corewall in a similar way to what occurred at the Bilberry and the Upper Roddlesworth embankments[37] may have risen rapidly as occurred on the Messaure dam[38] and the horizontal crack seen by Gunson may have been due to consequential reduced support against the clay core on the upstream side or it may have been a manifestation of the undermining of the clay corewall or a combination of both. Once the crest fell in at one place, erosion under wave action would have quickly widened the breach and destruction swift and terrible would have followed.

Appendix:

Particulars of dams mentioned in text

The reservoirs of all the dams listed that still exist are now used for water supply with or without releases of water for compensation purposes. With the exception of Vyrnwy, which is a masonry dam, and the original Abbeystead and Loch Katrine structures, which no longer exist, all the dams listed are earth dams.

Dam	Year of Act	Year of completion	River	Nearest town	Height above lowest foundation (m)	Length of crest (m)	Volume content of dam (10^3 m^3)	Gross capacity of reservoir (10^3 m^3)	Present owner	Engineering by	Original main purpose
Thornton	1847	1854	Tr. Soar	Leicester	13	509	120	1473	Severn–Trent Water Authority	Thomas Hawksley	S
Eccup[1]	1837	1842	Eccup Beck	Leeds						George Leather & Son	S
Bilberry[2]	1837	1845	Digley Brook	Holmfirth	20	90		310		George Leather	P
Holme Styes	1837	1840	Ribble	Huddersfield	20	183		304	Yorkshire Water Authority	George Leather	P
Boshaw Whams	1837	1840	Dean Dyke	Huddersfield	18	488		220	Yorkshire Water Authority	George Leather	P
Whittle Dean, Northern	1845	1848	Whittle Burn	Newcastle upon Tyne	10	122	178	115	Newcastle and Gateshead Water Co.	James Simpson	S
Whittle Dean, Western	1845	1848	Whittle Burn	Newcastle upon Tyne	12	195	340	265	Newcastle and Gateshead Water Co.	James Simpson	S
Whittle Dean, Lower	1845	1848	Whittle Burn	Newcastle upon Tyne	16	140	40	450	Newcastle and Gateshead Water Co.	James Simpson	S
Barrow No. 1	1846	1850		Bristol		793		654	Bristol Waterworks Co.	James Simpson	S
Chew Magna	1846	1847	Winford Brook	Bristol	9	92		91	Bristol Waterworks Co.	James Simpson	C

Name	Year 1	Year 2	Stream	Place					Authority	Engineer	
Sherborne, Upper	1846	1850	Chew	Wells	20	114		469	Bristol Waterworks Co.	James Simpson	C
Sherborne, Lower	1846	1850	Chew	Wells	9	124		109	Bristol Waterworks Co.	James Simpson	C
Barrow No. 2	1862	1864	Dundrey Stream	Bristol	9	1006		858	Bristol Waterworks Co.	James Simpson	S
Barrow Bridge³	1862	1864	Dundrey and Elwell Streams	Bristol	12	137		150	Bristol Waterworks Co.	James Simpson	C
Ynysyfro	1846	1848	Ynysyfro Brook	Newport	13	250	86	323	Welsh National Water Authority	James Simpson	S
Horse Coppice	1861	1864	Bollinhurst Brook	Stockport	18	178	69	332	North West Water Authority	James Simpson	S
Glencorse	1819	1822	Glencorse Burn	Edinburgh	24	165	66	1671	Lothian Regional Council	Telford	C
Threipmuir	1843	1847	Bavelaw Burn	Edinburgh	7	283	43	2359	Lothian Regional Council	J. Jardine	C
Harlaw	1843	1848	Bavelaw Burn	Edinburgh	21	155	56	736	Lothian Regional Council	J. Leslie	C
Clubbiedean	1847	1850	Bonaly Burn	Edinburgh	17	188	53	255	Lothian Regional Council	J. Leslie	S
Torduff	1847	1851	Bonaly Burn	Edinburgh	26	157	136	481	Lothian Regional Council	J. Leslie	S
Bonaly	1847	1851	Bonaly Burn	Edinburgh	10	256	28	200	Lothian Regional Council	J. Leslie	S
Loganlea	1847	1851	Logan Burn	Edinburgh	18	116	78	538	Lothian Regional Council	J. Leslie	C
Harperrig	1856	1859	Water of Leith	Edinburgh	13	30	55	4091	Lothian Regional Council	J. Leslie	C
Crosswood	1863	1868	Crosswood Burn	Edinburgh	15	614	67	793	Lothian Regional Council	J. Leslie	C

Dam	Original main purpose	Engineering by	Present owner	Gross capacity of reservoir (10^3m^3)	Volume content of dam (10^3m^3)	Length of crest (m)	Height above lowest foundation (m)	Nearest town	River	Year of completion	Year of Act
Edgelaw	C	J. & A. Leslie	Lothian Regional Council	1218	71	72	29	Edinburgh	Fullerton Burn	1880	1874
Gladhouse	S	J. & A. Leslie	Lothian Regional Council	8240	116	308	25	Edinburgh	South Esk	1879	1874
Rosebery	C	J. & A. Leslie	Lothian Regional Council	1727	134	143	26	Edinburgh	South Esk	1880	1874
South Monikie	S	J. Leslie	Tayside Regional Council	1270				Dundee		1848	1845
North Monikie	S	J. Leslie	Tayside Regional Council	795				Dundee		1855	1853
Crombie	S	J. Leslie	Tayside Regional Council	720	107	610	18	Dundee	Crombie Burn	1869	1866
Lintrathen	S	J. & A. Leslie	Tayside Regional Council	9741	46	335	11	Dundee	Melgam	1875	1870
Hewenden	C	J. Wignall Leather	Yorkshire Water Authority	314		210	15	Bradford	Hewenden Beck	1844	1841
1st Chellow Dean	S	J. Wignall Leather	Bradford Metropolitan Authority	195		110	17	Bradford	Chellow Dean	1844	1841
2nd Chellow Dean	S	J. Wignall Leather	Bradford Metropolitan Authority	141		82	13	Bradford	Chellow Dean	1851	1841
Grimwith	C	J. Wignall Leather	Yorkshire Water Authority	3082		213	25	Pately Bridge	Dibb	1864	1854

Name			Stream	Town					Authority	Engineer	
Lower Barden	1854	1874	Barden Beck	Skipton	22	686		2251	Yorkshire Water Authority	J. Wignall Leather	S
Chelker	1854	1858	Calder Banks Gill	Skipton	12	620		1170	Yorkshire Water Authority	J. Wignall Leather	S
Silsden	1854	1858	Great Gill Beck	Keighley	29	171		653	Yorkshire Water Authority	J. Wignall Leather	C
Stubden	1858	1862	Denholme Beck	Bingley	25	174		453	Yorkshire Water Authority	J. Wignall Leather	S
Doe Park	1858	1866	Denholme Beck	Bingley	18	155		488	Yorkshire Water Authority	J. Wignall Leather	C
Rivington (Lower)	1847	1857	Douglas	Horwich	18	1152		6785	North West Water Authority	T. Hawksley	S
Rivington (Upper)	1847	1857	Yarrow	Horwich	11	597		919	North West Water Authority	T. Hawksley	S
Angelzarke	1847	1857	The Goit	Chorley	14	1081		4169	North West Water Authority	T. Hawksley	S
Rake Brook	1847	1857	Roddlesworth	Blackburn	26	454		330	North West Water Authority	T. Hawksley	C
Lower Roddlesworth	1847	1857	Roddlesworth	Blackburn	25	180		415	North West Water Authority	T. Hawksley	C
Upper Roddlesworth	1860	1865	Roddlesworth	Blackburn	21	363		739	North West Water Authority		C
Vyrnwy	1880	1891	Vyrnwy	Shrewsbury	44	357	199	59666	Welsh National Water Authority	T. Hawksley & G. F. Deacon	S
Dale Dyke (Reconstruction)	1867	1875	Dale Dike	Sheffield	25	274		2210	Yorkshire Water Authority	T. Hawksley	S
Strines	1852	1871	Strines Dike	Sheffield	29	305		2332	Yorkshire Water Authority	T. Hawksley	S
Damflask	1852	1896	Loxley	Sheffield	28	290		5267	Yorkshire Water Authority	T. Hawksley	C

Dam	Year of Act	Year of completion	River	Nearest town	Height above lowest foundation (m)	Length of crest (m)	Volume content of dam (10³m³)	Gross capacity of reservoir (10³m³)	Present owner	Engineering by	Original main purpose
Waskerly	1866	1872	Waskerly Beck	Durham	27	732	685	2045	Northumbrian Water Authority	T. Hawksley	S
Smiddy Shaw	1860	1875		Durham	14	960		1386	Northumbrian Water Authority	T. Hawksley	S
Tunstall	1866	1879	Leeshaw Water	Crook	25	366	551	2364	Northumbrian Water Authority	T. Hawksley	S
Cowm	1866	1877	Tr. Spodden	Rochdale	16	332	122	1076	North West Water Authority	T. Hawksley	S
Lough Island Reavy	1835	1840	Muddock River	Banbridge	12			8000		J. F. Bateman	P
Hurst	1838	1840	Hurst Brook	Manchester	20	158	72	167	North West Water Authority	J. F. Bateman	P
Dingle	1843	1850	Three Nooks Shaw Brook	Bolton	12	424		359	North West Water Authority	J. F. Bateman	S
High Bullough	1846	1850	Limestone Clough	Chorley	12	301		250	North West Water Authority	J. F. Bateman	S
Kentmere Head	1845	1848	Kent	Kendal	18	254		1245	James Cropper & Co.	J. F. Bateman	P
Bilberry (Reconstruction)	1853		Digley Brook	Holmfirth	16	80			Yorkshire Water Authority	J. J. Bateman	P
Digley	1937	1954	Digley Brook	Huddersfield	49	262	443	3370	Yorkshire Water Authority	G. H. Hill & Son	S

Name			Location	River					Authority	Engineer	
Woodhead	1847, 1863	1876	Glossop	Etherow	29	140	218	5367	North West Water Authority	J. F. Bateman	C
Torside	1847	1857	Glossop	Etherow	31	270	378	6701	North West Water Authority	J. F. Bateman	C
Rhodeswood	1847	1855	Glossop	Etherow	21	194	203	2273	North West Water Authority	J. F. Bateman	S
Vale House	1865	1869	Glossop	Etherow	30	139	66	1563	North West Water Authority	J. F. Bateman	C
Bottoms	1865	1872	Glossop	Etherow	33	276	233	2345	North West Water Authority	J. F. Bateman	C
Hollingworth	1847	1854	Glossop	Hollingworth	21	250	85	300	North West Water Authority	J. F. Bateman	S
Arnfield	1847	1854	Glossop	Arnfield Brook	20	952	251	977	North West Water Authority	J. F. Bateman	S
Thirlmere	1879	1894	Keswick	St John's Beck	20	224	27	40714	North West Water Authority	G. H. Hill	S
Waulkmill Glen	1845	1848	Glasgow	Brock Burn	18	186		1048	Strathclyde Regional Council	W. Gale	S
Ryat Linn	1845	1848	Glasgow	Brock Burn	11	140		340	Strathclyde Regional Council	W. Gale	S
Balgray	1845	1854	Glasgow	Brock Burn	16	412	102	3370	Strathclyde Regional Council	W. Gale	S
Loch Katrine	1855	1859	Stirling	Achray Water				25500	Strathclyde Regional Council	J. F. Bateman	S
Bollinhurst	1861	1872	Stockport	Bollinhurst Brook	17	246	89	384	North West Water Authority	G. H. Hill	S
East Hallington	1863	1872	Newcastle	Tr. Erring Burn	12	413	59	3115	North West Water Authority	J. F. Bateman	S

Dam	Year of Act	Year of completion	River	Nearest town	Height above lowest foundation (m)	Length of crest (m)	Volume content of dam ($10^3\,m^3$)	Gross capacity of reservoir ($10^3\,m^3$)	Present owner	Engineering by	Original main purpose
Vartry	1845	1868		Dublin	20					P. Neville	S
Daisy Green[4]		1849	Tinkler's Brook	Darwen	15			54		J.F. Bateman	S
Abbeystead[5]		1852	Wyre	Lancaster	7	30		164		R. Rawlinson	S
Lower Lliw[6] (original)	1860	1867	Lliw	Swansea	27	182		464		R. Rawlinson	S
Blaenant-Ddu[7]	1860	1878		Swansea						G. Couzens	S
Vehar No 1		1858	Goper	Bombay	26	254	219	47800	Municipal Corporation of Greater Bombay	H. Conybeare	S
Vehar No 2		1858		Bombay	13	169	41		Municipal Corporation of Greater Bombay	H. Conybeare	S
Vehar No 3		1858		Bombay	15	285	93		Municipal Corporation of Greater Bombay	H. Conybeare	S
Yan Yean		1857	Plenty	Melbourne	9	960		28700	Melbourne & Metropolitan Board of Works	M.B. Jackson	S
Middle Redmires	1830	1836	Fairthorn Clough	Sheffield	15	689		854	Yorkshire Water Authority	J. Towlerton Leather	C

Lower Redmires	1845	1849	Fairthorn Clough	Sheffield	12		628	Yorkshire Water Authority	S
Upper Rivelin	1845	1848	Rivelin Brook	Sheffield	12		228	Yorkshire Water Authority	C
Lower Rivelin	1845	1848	Rivelin Brook	Sheffield	18	305	768	Yorkshire Water Authority	C
Upper Redmires	1845	1854	Fairthorn Clough	Sheffield	17		1560	Yorkshire Water Authority	S
Dale Dyke[8]	1852	1863	Dale Dike	Sheffield	29	380	3240	Yorkshire Water Authority	S
Agden	1852	1869	Agden Dike	Sheffield	29	458	2860	Yorkshire Water Authority	S

NOTES

1   Original dam demolished. Present dam of later date.
2   Original dam overtopped and destroyed in 1852.
3   Abandoned in 1882.
4   Dam demolished in 1979. The pipeline, which was found to be in good shape, had an internal diameter of 18 in. and, contrary to Bateman's usual practice, it was not embedded in concrete. Except for some minor pitting and scaling, the cast-iron of the pipes had remained in excellent condition.
5   After having been raised once, Rawlinson's dam was demolished. The present interesting structure, which is 20 m high, is a masonry dam with concrete backing in two arches, one buttressed and the other forming a spillway, designed by James Mansergh and completed in 1881.
6   Original dam was demolished and reconstructed to the designs of Binnie & Partners during 1976–78.
7   In 1919 the reservoir was taken out of service because seepage into mine workings below had reached a quantity which had become unacceptable.
8   Original dam destroyed in 1864.

Notes and References

INTRODUCTION

1 Edwin Chadwick (hereafter referred to as EC) to Macvey Napier, editor of the *Edinburgh Review*, 11 October, 1842. (Quoted with amendments to punctuation by S. E. Finer in the *Life and Times of Chadwick*, 1952

CHAPTER 1

By courtesy of the Library of University College London the author has been able to study the papers of Sir Edwin Chadwick and the figures in parentheses are reference numbers to these papers.

1 For general information about Chadwick's career reliance has been placed largely on the biographies by Finer, S. E. *The Life and Times of Sir Edwin Chadwick*, Barnes and Noble, New York/Methuen, London, 1952 (reprinted, 1970) and Lewis, R. A. *Edwin Chadwick and the Public Health Movement 1832–1854*. Longmans Green, 1952.
2 Chadwick, E. *The Sanitary Condition of the Labouring Population of Gt. Britain*, 1842 (republished 1964 by Edinburgh University Press), pp. 113 and 114.
3 General Board of Health Report on the Supply of Water to the Metropolis 1850, pp. 190 and 191.
4 *The Times*, 24 July, 1849.
5 Chadwick, E., *op. cit.*, p. 223
6 *Ibid.*, pp. 423 and 424.
7 Health of Towns Commission, First Report, July 1844, vol. II, p. 211.
8 *Ibid.*, pp. 241 and 242.
9 Quoted in *Centenary of the Shaw's Water Companys Works 1827–1929*, published by the Corporation of Glasgow.
10 Health of Towns Commission, First Report, July 1844, vol. II, p. 2.
11 *Ibid.*, pp. 17, 23 and 35. Wicksteed adhered doggedly to his opinion that constant supply was impractical and subsequently published a pamphlet with the title 'Analysis of the Evidence in Favour of the Constant Supply System given before the Health of Towns Commission by T. Wicksteed 1846'.
12 Health of Towns Commission, First Report, July 1844, vol. II, p. 275.
13 Letter, Thomas Hawksley (TH) to Edwin Chadwick (EC), 25 May, 1845 (960).
14 General Board of Health Report on the Supply of Water to the Metropolis, 1850, pp. 25–7.
15 Health of Towns Commission, First Report, July 1844, vol. II, pp. 88 and 89.
16 *The Liverpool Journal*, 14 September, 1844.
17 *The Liverpool Journal*, 17 August, 1844.

18 From James Simpson to the Commissioners of Paving and Sewering. The Town of Liverpool, dated 24 April, 1844, published in the *Liverpool Chronicle*, 28 August, 1844.
19 *The Liverpool Journal*, 24 August, 1844.
20 EC to TH, 1 September, 1844 (2181/4) and TH to EC, 2 September, 1844 (960).
21 *The Liverpool Journal*, 31 August, 1844.
22 EC to T. Hawksley, 23 May 1845 (2181/10).
23 EC to T. Hawksley, 18 July 1845 (2181/11).
24 EC to Lord Francis Egerton, 1 October 1845 (683).
25 De Rance, C. E., *The water supply of England and Wales*. Edward Stanford, 1882, pp. 197 and 198.
26 TH to EC, undated (960).
27 EC to TH, 5 June 1844 (2181/3).
28 EC to TH, 2 July 1844 (2181/3).
29 Gale J. M. On the Glasgow Waterworks. *Proc. Instn Civ. Engrs in Scotland*, 1863–64, vol. VII, p. 24.
30 It was not until the death of his father in June 1851 that Lord Ashley became the 7th Earl of Shaftesbury but, to avoid confusion, he is referred to in this book as Shaftesbury throughout.
31 Letters dated 16 July, 1844, to the Bishop of London and Lords Shaftesbury and Ebrington (2181/3).
32 EC to Dr Southward Smith, 23 July, 1844 (2181/3).
33 Health of Towns Commission, First Report, July 1844, vol. II, pp. 75 and 76.
34 Maitland F. W. *Township and borough*, Cambridge University Press, 1898; and Martin G. *The town*, Reader's Union/Studio Vista, 1965, p. 67.
35 TH to EC, 9 February, 1845 (960).
36 Ditto.
37 Health of Towns Commission, First Report, July 1844, vol. II, p. 93.
38 EC to TH, 11 August, 1844 (2181/5).
39 TH to EC, 2 September, 1844 (960).
40 EC to TH, 4 September, 1844 (2181/4).
41 TH to EC, 13 October, 1844 (960).
42 EC to TH, 22 October, 1844 (2181/5).
43 EC to TH, 27 February, 1845 (2181/7).
44 EC to TH, 10 March, 1845 (2181/10).
45 EC to TH, 21 May 1845 (2181/10).
46 EC to TH, 10 July, 1845 (2181/11).
47 TH to EC, 11 July, 1845 (960).
48 At the time there was a great deal of public interest in atmospheric railways and in a debate on them at the Institution of Civil Engineers in April 1845 Hawksley caused a sensation by boldly declaring 'that the atmospheric principle was inapplicable to the traffic of a long line' (*Min. Proc. Instn Civ. Engrs*, vol. IV, 1845, p. 284). Within 3 years on the South Devon Railway, for which I. K. Brunel was the engineer, the whole idea was proved a complete failure.
49 EC to TH, 12 July, 1845 (2181/11).
50 EC to TH, 21 July, 1845 (2181/11).
51 EC to TH, 5 July, 1845 (2181/11).
52 TH to EC, 5 August, 1845 (960).
53 EC to TH, 31 August, 1845 (2181/11).
54 EC to TH, 6 September, 1845 (2181/11).
55 EC to TH, 11 September, 1845 (2181/12).
56 TH to EC, 25 September, 1845 (960).
57 EC to TH, 26 September, 1845 (2181/13).
58 TH to EC, 5 October, 1845 (960).
59 EC to Lord Egerton, 4 October, 1845 (683).
60 The comments are written on a copy of 'The Improvement of Leicester – A Report setting forth a plan proposed by the Towns Improvement Company' (48).

61 EC to Raikes Curry, 27 September, 1845 (580).
62 EC to TH, 27 October, 1845 (2181/12).
63 TH to EC, 16 October, 1845 (960).
64 As compared with engineering inspectors subsequently employed under the 1848 Health Act at 3 guineas per day, surveyors were at this time demanding 7½ guineas per day.
65 TH to EC, 23 October, 1845 (960).
66 EC to TH, 25 October, 1845 (2181/12).
67 TH to EC, 14 January, 1846 (960).
68 Obituary. *Min. Proc. Instn Civ. Engrs*, vol. CXVII, 1893–94, p. 364.
69 EC to TH, 6 November, 1844 (2181/8).
70 EC to TH, 11 October, 1845 (960).
71 EC to Lord Egerton, 1 November, 1845 (683).
72 Rolt L. T. C. *George and Robert Stephenson*, Longmans, 1960, p. 291.
73 EC to Lord Egerton, 2 April, 1846 (2181/15).
74 Bernard Shaw, *Major Barbara*.
75 TH to EC, 16 October, 1845 (960).
76 TH to EC, 23 October, 1845 (960).
77 EC to TH, 3 November, 1845 (2181/12).
78 TH to Holland, 8 February, 1846 (960).
79 Bateman J. F. La Trobe *History and Description of the Manchester Waterworks*, E. & F. N. Spon, 1884, p. 57
80 EC to Lord Egerton, 13 January, 1846 (2181/13).
81 EC to Lord Egerton, 28 March, 1847 (683).
82 EC to Lord Egerton, 20 February, 1849 (683).

CHAPTER 2

1 General Board of Health Report on the Supply of Water to the Metropolis, 1850, p. 183.
2 *Ibid.*, p. 209.
3 *Ibid.*, pp. 209 and 210.
4 EC, to Lord Carlisle, 1 November, 1849 (1055).
5 Communications from the General Board of Health and reports of Superintending Engineers in respect of Pipe Sewers 1854–5, vol. XLV, p. 49 (quoted by Lewis, *op. cit.*, p. 335).
6 General Board of Health Report on the Supply of Water to the Metropolis, 1850, pp. 191–2.
7 TH to EC, 13 October, 1847 (960).
8 General Board of Health Report on the Supply of Water to the Metropolis, 1850, pp. 190 and 191.
9 William Congreve's poem, *The Mourning Bride*.
10 *The Sheffield & Rotherham Independent*, 16 November, 1850.
11 Anonym. *Engineers & officials*: an historical sketch of the progress of 'Health of town works' (between 1838 and 1856) in London and the Provinces. Edward Stanford, 1856, p. 128.
12 Charles May to EC, 7 July, 1852 (1375).
13 Parliamentary Papers 1851, XV, Oq. 13, 599; 13, 608.
14 EC to Charles May, 20 July, 1852 (1375).
15 EC to the Dean of Durham, 23 July, 1852 (2031).
16 Letter to the Most Hon. The Marquis of Chandos, MP, 22 April, 1853.
17 *Min. Proc. Instn Civ. Engrs*, vol. XIV, 1854–55, p. 291. This discussion with James Simpson in the presidential chair 'On the Flow of Water through Pipes' by James Leslie, a paper of no lasting scientific merit, was made the occasion for attacks against Chadwick and the Board of Health by Robert Stephenson and others also.
18 *Min. Proc. Instn Civ. Engrs*, vol. XII, 1852–53, p. 25 et seq.
19 Hodder, E. *The Life and Work of the Seventh Earl of Shaftesbury K.G.* Cassell, 1886, vol. II, pp. 442 and 443.

20 *Ibid.*, p. 443.
21 *Min. Proc. Instn Civ. Engrs*, vol. CXVII, 1893–94, pp. 370–1.
22 Battiscombe G. *Shaftesbury 1801–1885*. Constable, 1974, p. 233.
23 Macdonnell Sir J. *Political Economy Club Journal*, 5 July, 1905.
24 Letter, J. S. Mill to James Henderson, August 1868.

CHAPTER 3

1 Beckwith F. The Population of Leeds, *Thoresby Soc.*, vol. XLI, 1967.
2 Rimmer W.G. Working Men's Cottages in Leeds 1770–1840, *Thoresby Soc.*, vol. XLVI, Part 2, 1967, p. 197.
3 See also, for some details not given by the Statistical Society, the *Leeds Mercury*, 2 November, 1839.
4 The Engineer was J. Wignall Leather.
5 E. Chadwick, *op. cit.*, p. 225
6 Fraser D. Improvement in Early Victorian Leeds. *Thoresby Soc.*, vol. LIII, Part 1 (1970), p. 80.
7 Beckwith F. Robert Baker, *University of Leeds Review*, vol. 7, No. 1 (June 1960), p. 40.
8 A full account of this rivalry is given in D. Fraser's article, The politics of Leeds Water. *Thoresby Soc.*, vol. LIII, Part 1, 1970.
9 *Leeds Intelligencer*, 29 October, 1836.
10 Undated prospectus for Leeds Waterworks.
11 House of Commons Committee on the Liverpool and Manchester Railway 1825; George Leather's evidence 421, 430–1. Hadfield C. and Skempton A. W. *William Jessop Engineer*, David and Charles, London, 1979, p. 178.
12 Hadfield C. *The Canals of Yorkshire and North East England*, vol. 1, David and Charles, London, 1972–3.
13 Lewis M. J. T. *Dunham Bridge: a memorial history*. The Society for Lincolnshire History and Archaeology, Sleaford, 1978.
14 'Statement of Facts in reply to Two Anonymous Letters' by John W. Leather, 1838.
15 The following account of the water supply during the 18th and first half of the 19th century is largely taken, by kind permission of Mr R. S. Peppard, from his unpublished dissertation in the Brotherton Library, University of Leeds, 'The Growth and Development of Leeds Waterworks'.
16 Stewart A. P. and Jenkins E. *The Medical and Legal Aspects of Sanitary Reform*, 1866 (republished 1969 by Leicester University Press), p. 64.

CHAPTER 4

1 *The Times*, February 16, 1852.
2 Pierce, C. (ed.) *A History of the Holmfirth Reservoir Commissioners*. Holmfirth Local History Research Group, 1972, p. 1.
3 The area was not surveyed geologically until after the Bilberry dam was built (J. R. Dakyns and C. Ward, 1870) and there are therefore no contemporary observations on the site geology. It is covered by a regional 1 in. (Sheet 86) and 6 in. maps (Sheet 272 NW, Bromehead 1926–27) and by a general geological map of the adjacent Digley reservoir. (Morton E., 1936, in Woodhead T. H. 1939. *History of the Huddersfield Water Supplies*, Handbook X. Tolson Memorial Museum Huddersfield.) These maps differ slightly in that Morton has assigned the Readycon Dean and Heyden Rock grits of the regional maps to a single sandstone unit, the Pule Hill Rock, and has shown an enlarged shale outcrop south-east of the dam.
   The Bilberry reservoir is situated in the Kinderscout Grit, a major unit of the Millstone Grit Series (Upper Carboniferous) which forms the Holme Valley inlier (Bromehead C. E. N., Edwards W., Wray D. A. and Stephens J. V. (1933). *The geology of the country around Holmfirth*

and Glossop (explanation of sheet 86): Memoirs of the Geological Survey of England and Wales.) The grit is typically coarse with shaly partings, and the rock at the reservoir is described in the regional memoir as a pebbly grit. Stratigraphically it must be close to the top of the Kinderscout Grit as the small shale inlier 200 m south-east of the dam contains the marine goniatite fossil diagnostic of the succeeding Middle Grit Group. Accounts of repairs to the culvert beneath the dam embankment refer to the excavation of a drift in shale from the downstream side to near the centre of the dam. The thickness and extent of this shale bed is not known.

The Kinderscout Grit dips shallowly east, and steeper dips of 13° ESE and 20° SE have been measured respectively in the right abutment of the dam and in the right bank 130 m downstream. No faults are indicated in the Marsden Clough valley. The ENE-trending Digley Mill fault to the south does not affect strata at the dam. The parallel major fault 650 m north of the reservoir, one of the Harridge–Bradshaw series of fractures, is the only other major structural feature in the area. Faulting is related to the post-Carboniferous, mostly pre-Pennine fold movements. A photograph in the memoir, of Kinderscout Grit higher up Marsden Clough, shows that it is vertically jointed. For the above geological description the author is indebted to Mr I. M. Kirkpartick.

4 Morehouse H. *History and Topography of the Parish of Kirkburton*, printed for the author by H. Roebuck, Huddersfield, 1861, p. 231.
5 Obituary of Sir James Falshaw. *Min. Proc. Instn Civ. Engrs*, vol. XCIX, 1889–90, p. 383.
6 *The Times*, 16 February, 1852.
7 The words in parentheses are inserted from a contemporary account of the inquest by the Commissioners' solicitors, the remainder being quoted from the *Leeds Mercury*.
8 Wood C. J. Tunnel outlets from reservoirs, *Min. Proc. Instn Civ. Engrs*, vol. LIX, 1879–80, pp. 37–49.
9 Morehouse H. S., *op cit*. p. 231.
10 Although at a time when commissions and promotions in the army were obtained by purchase, Moody's rank at the age of 39 was only that of Captain, he had already had a distinguished career as professor of fortifications at the Royal Military Academy during 1839 and as the first Governor of the Falkland Islands from 1840 to 1846. During his subsequent career he was Lieutenant Governor of British Colombia and he retired in 1868 with the rank of Major General. (Ref. *Proc. Instn Civ. Engrs*. vol. XC, 1887, pp. 453-5).
11 Moody was presumably referring to the height measured from the bottom of the cut-off trench which suggests that the latter was about 30 ft deep.
12 Bateman J. F. Discussion on reservoir outlets. *Min. Proc. Instn Civ. Engrs*, vol. LIX, 1879–80, p. 66.
13 Before commencing the reconstruction of the Bilberry embankment described in Chapter 9, J. F. Bateman made some record drawings of the breached embankment. These drawings appear to be lost but, fortunately, for his inspection of the Bilberry reservoir under the Reservoirs (Safety Provisions) Act 1930 in 1933, E. J. Silcock used Bateman's drawings for preparing his own drawings, and from Silcock's drawings kept in the files of the Yorkshire Water Authority, it has been possible to draw Fig. 4.4.
14 Vaughan P. R., Kluth D. J., Leonard M. W. and Pradoura H. H. M. Cracking and erosion of the rolled clay core of Balderhead dam and the remedial works adopted for repair. *Proceedings of the 10th International Congress on Large Dams* (Montreal 1970), vol. I, pp. 73–93.
15 Chapter 8, pp. 140–1.

CHAPTER 5

1 The Charter is given in full by Sisley R. *The London Water Supply*, Scientific Press, London, 1899, pp. 175–86.
2 Dickinson H. W. *The Water Supply of Greater London*. Printed for the Newcomen Society at Courier Press, Leamington Spa and London, 1954, p. 71.
3 Simpson J. Presidential Address. *Min. Proc. Instn Civ. Engrs*, vol. XIII, 1853–54, p. 12. As

regards Glasgow the only treatment of the drinking-water supply at the time was natural filtration through one bank into tunnels below the level of the river Clyde (see Gale J. M. On the Glasgow Waterworks, *Proc. Instn. Engrs in Scotland*, vol. VII, 1863–64, p. 23). Simpson may have been encouraged by the success of the treatment to reproduce it artificially or he may be referring to other privately owned waterworks in Glasgow.

4a The *Journal of Gas Lighting and Water Supply*, February 1855 *et seq.* summarized in *Engineers and Officials* by Edward Stanford, 1856, p. 190.
4b Dickinson, *op. cit.*, pp. 112 and 113.
5 Memoir, James Simpson. *Min. Proc. Instn Civ. Engrs*, vol. XXX, 1869–70, p. 457.
6 Engineer's Report to the Directors of the Lambeth Water Works November, 1848, pp. 7–10.
7 *Ibid.*, pp. 10 and 11.
8 Dickinson, *op. cit.*, p. 83.
9 The following account is largely taken from Rennison R. W., *Water to Tyneside*, published 1978 by the Newcastle and Gateshead Water Company.
10 EC to TH, 28 February 1845 (2181/7).
11 Simpson, J. Report on an Increased Supply of Water to the City of Aberdeen, 1855, pp. 17 and 18.
12 Jones F. C. *The Bristol Waterworks Company 1846–1946*. St. Stephen's Bristol Press, 1946, pp. 1–14.
13 Hadfield C. and Skempton A. W., *William Jessop. Engineer*. David & Charles, 1979, pp. 222–42.
14 Jones, *op. cit.*, pp. 15 and 16.
15 Health of Towns Commission, First Report, July 1844, vol. II.
16 Letter, EC to TH, 5 July, 1845 (2181/11).
17 One director who attended the meeting was Dr Budd, the co-discoverer with Dr Snow that cholera was a water-borne disease. Previous to the meeting he had recommended that Simpson should fill the appointment of Engineer to the new water company.
18 William Chadwell Mylne, FRS (1781–1863), a descendant of the King's master masons in Scotland and the son of Robert Mylne who built Blackfriars Bridge, succeeded his father as Engineer to the New River Company in 1811.
19 Thomas Wicksteed, to whom reference has already been made, was Engineer to the East London Water Company, the Southwark and Vauxhall Water Company and the Kent Water Company.
20 Jones, *op. cit.*, p. 19.
21 Simpson J. Discussion on Bridge Aqueduct at Roquefavour. *Min. Proc. Instn Civ. Engrs*, vol. XIV, 1854–55, p. 202.
22 *Ibid.*, p. 220.
23 *Ibid.*, p. 220.
24 *Ibid.*, p. 222.
25 De Rance C. E. *op. cit.*, pp. 354–55.
26 Stewart A. P. and Jenkins E., *The Medical and Legal Aspects of Sanitary Reform*, 1867 (republished 1969 by Leicester University Press), p. 60.
27 Private communication from the late Thomas Hawksley, great grandson of the first Thomas Hawksley and former dam consultant to the Bristol Waterworks Company, to the author.
28 Humphreys, W. H. The York Waterworks. *Trans. Assoc. Water Engrs*, 1910, vol. XV, p. 73.
29 The contract, including the specification and the drawings, has been carefully preserved by the York Waterworks Company and is in excellent condition.
30 Bateman J. F., *op. cit.*, pp. 22–4.
31 Guild A. E. *History and Description of Newport Waterworks*, County Borough of Newport, 1956, pp. 2 and 3.
32 Information supplied by North West Water Authority.
33 Father of the founder of the consulting engineering firm Sir Alexander Gibb and Partners.
34 Memoir, James Simpson. *Min. Proc. Instn Civ. Engrs*, vol. XXX, 1869–70, p. 457.
35 Galton D., Simpson J. and Blackwell T. E. *Report to First Commissioner of Her Majesty's Works*

and *Public Buildings on Main Drainage of the Metropolis*, 31 July, 1857.
36 Obituary. *Min. Proc. Instn Civ. Engrs*, vol. XXVIII, 1868–9, p. 360.
37 EC to F. O. Ward, 12 October, 1849 (2055).
38 The first filter Bed 1829. Extract from Faulkner's *Chelsea* 1829, vol. II, p. 357.

> In reference to the Chelsea Water-Works, and the plans then in progress as mentioned in vol. I, p. 48, it is now gratifying to be able to record the fact that the great Filter Bed constructed with so much ingenuity and skill by Mr Simpson, the Engineer to the Company, is now in full action, having completely realised the Company's most sanguine hopes and expectations; and henceforth Chelsea, Westminster, and the parts adjacent, in the Chelsea Water Works district, will be supplied with water free from all impurities.

CHAPTER 6

For scrutinising the various Minute Books of the Dundee Water Company and extracting relevant information from them, also for obtaining copies of James Leslie's reports, the author is greatly indebted to Dr D. K. Harrison of Dundee University.

1 Scott-Dodd M. A. 'A History of the Water Supply of Edinburgh'. MS, 1978.
2 Cockburn H. *Memorials of His Time*, Adam and Charles Black, Edinburgh, 1856, p. 352.
3 *The Scotsman*, 10 October, 1857. Cockburn gives a more sympathetic description of the water caddies in *Memorials of His Time*, pp. 351–3.
4 *The Scotsman*, 10 October, 1857.
5 Telford T. Report to the Council on the means of improving the supply of water for the City of Edinburgh. Printed for Archibald Constable and Company, Edinburgh, 1813.
6 Binnie G. M. The evolution of British dams. *Trans. Newcomen Society*, 47 (1974–76), 215 and 216.
7 Leslie A. The Edinburgh Waterworks. *Min. Proc. Instn Civ. Engrs*, 1882–83, vol. LXXIV, p. 96.
8 *The Scotsman*, 10 October, 1857.
9 The description of the Pentlands works in the following paragraphs is based on Leslie A. The Edinburgh Waterworks. *Min. Proc. Instn Civ. Engrs*, vol. LXXIV, 1882–3, pp. 95–100.
10 *Min. Proc. Instn Civ. Engrs*, vol. XVIII, 1857–8, p. 389.
11 An example is 'Specification of the Manner of Constructing the Reservoirs at Craighton Muir for Dundee Water Company', dated 20 August, 1845.
12 *Min. Proc. Instn Civ. Engrs*, vol. XVIII, 1857–8. Footnote to p. 390.
13 Bateman J. F. Report dated 4 February 1869 to the Corporations of Edinburgh, Leith and Portobello.
14 Colston J. *The Edinburgh and District Water Supply*. Printed for private circulation by the Edinburgh and District Water Trustees, 1890, p. 127.
15 *Ibid.*, p. 147.
16 *Ibid.*, p. 146.
17 Information supplied by Lothian Regional Council Water Services.
18 (a) As shown on the map (Fig. 6.1) the scheme included reservoirs at Gladhouse, Edgelaw and Rosebery, the first being for town supply and the other two for compensation water. In addition, Portmore Loch with its top water level raised 10 ft and the upper part of the Tweedale Burn were to be exploited for town supply, also filters were to be constructed at Alnwick Hill. The Gladhouse and Rosebery dams were similar in design to the Harperrig and Edgelaw dams respectively.
18 (b) Leslie A., The Edinburgh Waterworks. *Min. Proc. Instn Civ. Engrs*, vol. LXXIV, 1882–3, p. 96.
19 McIldowie G. L. The Construction of the Silent Valley Reservoir, Belfast Water Supply. *Min. Proc. Instn Civ. Engrs*, 1934–35, vol. 239, p. 465.
20 Baxter G. *The Dundee Water Commissioners*, 1913. General particulars of the works carried out by the Dundee Water Company are given in this report.

21 Report to the Directors of the Dundee Water Company by James Leslie, Civil Engineer, on the *Best Source from which a Supply of Water can be obtained by the Town of Dundee*, dated 10 August, 1844.
22 Minute books of the Dundee Water Company for General Meetings (1845–69) and Directors' Meetings (1844–54 and 1854–66), and Minute books of the Dundee Water Company for General Meetings (1845–69) and Directors' Meetings (1844–66).
23 Baxter, *op. cit.* (see note 20), p. 20.
24 Bateman J. F. (1870) *Report as to additional water supply for Dundee*.
25 *Ibid.*, p. 7.
26 *Ibid.*, p. 4.
27 *Ibid.*, pp. 5 and 6.
28 *Ibid.*, p. 8.
29 Bateman, J. F. *Observations on the Various Routes which have been proposed for conveying water from Lintrathen to Dundee to which are attached Letters on the Same Subject by William Robertson Esq.* January 1872. Letters contain several references to Easton Gibb.
30 Stewart J. W. *Report relative to the Conveyance and Distribution of the First Instalment of the Lintrathen Water*. Edinburgh, 17 July 1873. First paragraph refers to when he was consulted in October 1871.
31 Leslie J. and Stewart J. W. *Dundee Water Commission – Report with Estimates as to Conveying Water from Loch of Lintrathen to Dundee*, December 1871, p. 1.
32 Bateman, *op. cit.* (see note 29), p. 3.
33 *Ibid.*, p. 7.
34 Obituary of James Leslie. *Min. Proc. Instn Civ. Engrs*, vol. C, 1889–90, p. 389.
35 Stewart, *op. cit.* (see note 30).
36 Baxter, *op. cit.* (see note 20).

CHAPTER 7

1 Obituary of J. Wignall Leather, *Min. Proc. Instn Civ. Engrs*, vol. LXXXIX, 1887, p. 475.
2 George Oxley to J. Wignall Leather, 29 June, 1850.
3 George Oxley to J. Wignall Leather, 6 June, 1850.
4 George Oxley to J. Wignall Leather, 27 June, 1850.
5 Obituary of J. Wignall Leather. *Min. Proc. Instn Civ. Engrs*, vol. LXXXIX, 1887, p. 476.
6 Binnie A. R. *Rainfall, reservoirs and water supply*. Constable, 1913 (incorporating and updating *Water Supply*. The Royal Engineers Institute, 1887), p. 87.
7 Glossop R. The invention and development of injection processes, Part II, 1850–1960, *Geotechnique*, vol. XI, p. 259.
8 Bateman J. F., Report to Waterworks Committee of the Bradford Corporation, 8 February, 1865.
9 *Ibid.*
10 Wood C. J. Tunnel outlets from storage reservoirs. *Min. Proc. Instn Civ. Engrs*, vol. LIX, 1879–80, pp. 37–49.
11 Binnie A. R. *Water supply, op. cit.*, pp. 82–5.

CHAPTER 8

1 Obituary. *Min. Proc. Instn Civ. Engrs*, vol. CXVII, 1893–94, p. 364.
2 *Ibid.*
3 Linsley S. M. *Ryhope Pumping Station*. The Ryhope Engines Trust, 1973, p. 11.
4 *Ibid.*, Introduction.
5 Obituary. *Min. Proc. Instn Civ. Engrs*. vol. CXVII, 1893–94, p. 364.
6 Piper, D. *The Companion Guide to London*. Collins, 1964, p. 168.
7 The Presentation of Engineering Evidence – First Lecture, 20 June, 1946. 'The Giving of Evi-

dence before a Parliamentary Committee, in the High Court'; and 'Before an Arbitrator' by Lord MacMillan of Aberfeldy – Institution of Civil Engineers.

8 MS, n.d., on Private Bills, quoted by Lewis, *op. cit.*, p. 135.
9 Chapter 13.
10 *The Architect and Contract Reporter*, 29 September, 1893.
11 *Dundee Advertiser*, 26 September, 1893.
12 The following accounts of the events leading to the construction of the Rivington and Vyrnwy Schemes and of Hawksley's quarrel with the Liverpool Borough Council are taken by kind permission of Mr Frank Harris, Principal Lecurer in History and Mr R. J. O. Roe, from an unpublished dissertation of the City of Liverpool College of Higher Education by the latter on 'Water into Liverpool – 1848–1902', written in 1976. The first part, on the Rivington scheme, is based principally on contemporary accounts in the *Liverpool Mercury* and on contemporary pamphlets. The second part, on Vyrnwy, is based principally on reports by Duncan, Jackson, Hawksley, Bateman and Deacon, and articles in the *Porcupine* and the *Liverpool Mercury*.
13 Extracted by Roe from the Memorial to the Highways Board, September 1845, p. 2. *Liverpool Water Supply Pamphlets and Reports*, vol. I.
14 Findings of inquiry based on initial address by James Reay, *Liverpool Water Supply Pamphlets and Reports*, vol. I (October, 1845), p. 2.
15 Roe, R. J. O. 'Water to Liverpool 1848–1902', 1976 (unpublished). (See note 12.)
16 Stephenson R. *Report on the Supply of Water to the City of Liverpool*. Bradbury and Evans, London, 1850.
17 Description of the Rivington Watershed of the Liverpool Corporation Waterworks. *Trans. Instn Water Engrs.* vol. VII, 1903, pp. 169–74.
18 Duncanson, Correspondence on Reservoir Outlets. *Min. Proc. Instn Civ. Engrs*, vol. LIX, 1879–80, p. 78.
19 Adamson R. A. *History of the Rivington Works*, Liverpool Corporation Waterworks Internal Report, March 1935, p. 1.
20 *Ibid.*, p. 19.
21 *Ibid.*, p. 20.
22 *Ibid.*, p. 20.
23 Information from North West Water Authority.
24 *Porcupine*, 17 August, 1872, vol. XIV, p. 307.
25 Jackson J. Future Supplies of Water to Liverpool. Report to the Water Committee, 1874. *Liverpool Water Supply Pamphlets and Reports*, vol. 2.
26 Hawksley T. *loc. cit.*
27 Bateman J. F. Borough of Liverpool – New Water Supply, 14 August 1874.
28 Bateman J. F. *Metropolis Water Supply from the Sources of the River Severn*. Wacher and Son, Westminster, 1865.
29 *The Irish Times*, 14 April, 1879 – found by Roe in Town Clerk's newscuttings, April–December 1879.
30 Lapworth H. The Geology of Dam Trenches. *Trans. Instn Water Engrs.* vol. XVI, 1911.
31 Extract from a letter by Hawksley to Alderman Bennett, published in *Liverpool Mercury*, 22 July, 1885.
32 *Liverpool Mercury*, 22 July, 1885.
33 *Liverpool Mercury*, 20 July, 1885.
34 Extract from a letter by Hawksley to the Town Clerk, published in *Liverpool Mercury*, 18 June, 1885.
35 The *Liverpool Daily Post*, 26 September, 1893.
36 Yourdi G. N. Reservoir outlets to earthen embankments. *Trans. Assoc. Water Engrs*, vol. XV, 1910, pp. 39–53.
37 Askwith R. Discussion on 'Reservoir outlets to earthen embankments'. *Trans. Assoc. Water Engrs*, vol. XV, 1910, p. 49.
38 Askwith R. Description of the Weardale and Consett Waterworks. *Trans. Assoc. Water Engrs*, vol. XIV, 1909, pp. 62–4.

39 Fishwick, *Rochdale Jubilee, A Record of Fifty Years Municipal Work, 1856–1906*. George Falkner & Sons, 1906, pp. 98 and 99.

40 Glossop R. The invention and development of injection processes. Part II: 1850–1900. *Geotechnique*, vol. XI, 1960, p. 259. In correspondence with the author Glossop has agreed that contrary to what he wrote in this article the Cowm embankment was grouted before the Tunstall embankment.

41 Terrey W. *History and Description of the Sheffield Water Works*, 1908, pp. 34–36 (Printed by desire of the Water Committee, Sheffield Corporation)

42 International Commission on Large Dams Register of Dams.

43 Lloyd D. The reliable yield of a reservoir impounding for town supply. *Water and Water Engineering*, July 1946, p. 396.

44 De Rance C. E. *The water supply of England and Wales*. Edward Stanford, 1882, p. 500.

45 Lloyd *op. cit.*, p. 397.

46 Binnie A. R. On mean or average annual rainfall and the fluctuations to which it is subject. *Min. Proc. Instn Civ. Engrs*, vol. CIX, 1891–92, p. 3.

47 Obituary. *Min. Proc. Instn Civ. Engrs*, vol. CXVII, 1893–94, p. 364.

CHAPTER 9

1 Bateman J. F. *On the present state of our knowledge on the supply of water to towns*. British Association for the Advancement of Science, 1855.

2 Russell P. E. 'John Frederic La Trobe Bateman FRS Water Engineer (1810–1889)'. University of Manchester MSc. thesis, 1980. The author is greatly indebted to Mr Russell for permission to use his work.

3 Comenius A. *Didacta Magna*, 1657; quoted by Dodd R. in *Design and technology in the school curriculum*. Hodder, London, 1978; also quoted by Russell, *op. cit.*

4 Russell, *op. cit.*

5 *Min. Proc. Instn Civ. Engrs*, vol. XCVII, 1889, p. 392.

6 Hayward R. A. 'Fairbairn's of Manchester'. University of Manchester MSc. thesis, 1971; quoted by Russell *op. cit.*

7 Fairbairn ,W. 'Reservoirs on the River Bann in the County of Down' Ireland for more effectually supplying the Mills with Water (1836), *op. cit.*

8 *Min. Proc. Instn Civ. Engrs*, vol. I, 1837–41, pp. 168–70.

9 *Min. Proc. Instn Civ. Engrs*, vol. VII, 1848, pp. 251–74

10 *Min. Proc. Instn Civ. Engrs*, vol. I, 1837–41, pp. 168–70.

11 Smyth J. *Construction and working of the Bann reservoir*. John Falconer, Dublin, 1871, p. 16.

12 *Min. Proc. Instn. Civ. Engrs*, vol. I, 1842, p. 169.

13 Smyth, *op. cit.*, pp. 12–17.

14 Information supplied by North West Water Authority.

15 International Commission on Large Dams Register of Dams.

16 An Act for more effectively supplying with Water the Town of Bolton, etc., 1843.

17 Swales J. K. Repair works in connection with the Belmont reservoir of the Bolton Corporation. *Trans. Instn Water Engrs*, vol. XXXI, 1926, pp. 203–14.

18 An Act for better supplying with Water the Town of St. Helens etc. 1843 – Purchase of existing waterworks, use springs in Township of Eccleston.

19 A Bill dated 1844 was prepared but no Act followed.

20 Blackburn Waterworks Act 1845 – works authorized included five small reservoir embankments, completed 1847–49.

21 Chapter 1, p. 24.

22 EC to Bateman, 3 October, 1845 (1184). EC to Raikes Currie, 3 October, 1845 (580).

23 EC to Bateman, 25 October, 1845 (2181/12).

24 Chorley Waterworks Act 1846 – the reservoir authorized was subsequently taken over by the Liverpool Corporation and became the High Bullough Compensation water reservoir.

25 Wilson P. N. Kendal reservoirs. *Transactions of the Cumberland and Westmorland Antiquarian and Archaeological Society*, vol. LXXIII, 1973, pp. 329–31.
26 The Kendal Reservoirs Act, 1845. Probably as a consequence of improvement in conditions on the river Kent about to take place, Chadwick asked Bateman for an estimate for a water supply. The Kendal Union Gas and Waterworks Company's Act 1846 with Bateman as Engineer followed.
27 Figure 9.4 is reproduced from Fig. 6 in 'Kendal reservoirs' by the late Lord Wilson, *Transactions of the Cumberland and Westmorland Antiquarian and Archaeological Society*. vol. LXXIII, 1973, pp. 336–47.
28 The author is indebted to Mr James Cropper of James Cropper and Co., Kendal, for a copy of this specification.
29 Wilson, *op. cit.*, p. 346.
30 Communication from Mr James Cropper.
31 The *Leeds Mercury*, 28 February, 1852; Statement on Holme Styes Reservoir made by Captain Moody.
32 From files of the Western Division of the Yorkshire Water Authority.
33 Letter quoted by Russell, *op. cit.*
34 Specification for the Reconstruction of the Bilberry Reservoir May 1854, J. F. Bateman, CE.
35 Messrs, Joseph Aspinall and Sons and the Directors of the Holme Reservoirs Indenture and Deed of Covenants, dated 15 March, 1867, Engineer Geo. H. Hill.
36 The Holme Reservoirs, Statutory Report under the Reservoirs (Safety Provisions) Act 1930, by E. J. Silcock, MICE, Qualified Civil Engineer, 12 August, 1933.
37 Huddersfield Corporation Waterworks, Bilberry reservoir, Statutory Report under the Reservoirs (Safety Provisions) Act 1930, by James P. Beveridge, MICE, MIWE, Chartered Civil Engineer, 4 November, 1943.
38 Woodhead, T. W. *History of the Huddersfield Water Supplies.* County Borough of Huddersfield; the Tolson Museum, 1939.
39 Beveridge J. P. Pictorial Record of the Flooding in the Holme Valley on the 29th May 1944. (Not published). Observations by more than 40 eyewitnesses of the storm were also recorded.
40 Bateman J. F. *History and Description of the Manchester Waterworks.* T. J. Day, Manchester/ Spon, London, 1884, p. 32.
41 *Ibid.*, p. 31.
42 Bateman J. F. 'Observations on the relationship which the fall of rain bears to the water flowing from the ground', *Memoirs of the Manchester Literary and Philosophical Society* (Man. Mem) (1) 7 (1846), 157–190; quoted by Russell, *op. cit.*
43 British Association for the Advancement of Science Report (1844) Transactions of the Sections, p. 100.
44 EC to John Shuttleworth, 9 October, 1844 (2181/5). John Taylor (1779–1863) was an eminent mining engineer. He was one of the founders of the British Association on 26 June, 1832, holding the office of treasurer until September 1861. In 1798 he became Manager of Wheal Friendship Mine at Tavistock and built the 4½ mile long Tavistock canal, of which 1½ miles are in tunnel, between Tavistock and Morwellham. (References: *DNB*, IV, 457; and Booker F. *The story of Morwellham*. Dartington Amenity Research Trust, Dartington, Totnes, Devon, 1970.)
45 Bateman J. F., *op. cit.*, pp. 9–17.
46 *Ibid.*, pp. 56 and 57.
47 Russell P. E., *op cit.*
48 Act 10–11, Vic. cap. cciii, Manchester Corporation Waterworks, 1847.
49 Report by Bateman J. F. to the Water Committee of the Manchester Corporation (Water Cttee), dated 9 January, 1858.
50 Sandeman E. The Derwent Valley Waterworks. *Proc. Instn Civ. Engrs.* vol. 206, 1917–18 Pt II pp. 155 and 156
51 Walters R. C. S. *The nation's water supply.* Ivor Nicholson and Watson, 1936, p. 107.

52 Bateman to Water Cttee, 2 October, 1849.
53 Bateman, *Manchester Waterworks*, p. 121.
54 Bateman to Water Cttee, 18 December, 1850.
55 Bateman to Water Cttee, 23 April, 1851.
56 Bateman, *op cit.*, p. 122.
57 Bateman to Water Cttee, 19 February, 1851.
58 Bateman, *op. cit.*, p. 168.
59 Bateman to Water Cttee, 13 December, 1854.
60 Report By J. F. Bateman for the Council of the Manchester Corporation, January 1855.
61 Bateman to Water Cttee, 22 February, 1855.
62 Bateman, *op. cit.*, p. 132.
63 Bateman to Water Cttee, 5 April, 1855.
64 Bateman, *op. cit.*, p. 132.
65 Redford, A. *The history of local government in Manchester*, vol. II. Longmans, 1939, p. 202.
66 Bateman, to Water Cttee, 30 May, 1860.
67 Chapter 4, p. 64.
68 Bateman, *op. cit.*, p. 172.
69 Bateman to Water Cttee, 9 June, 1858.
70 Bateman to Water Cttee, 9 June, 1858.
71 Clark J. F. F. Discussion on case records of cement grouting by Perrot *et al.* in *Grouts and drilling muds in engineering practice.* Butterworth, 1963, p. 112.
72 Bateman, *op. cit.*, pp. 111 and 112.
73 *Ibid.*, p. 130.
74 Bateman to Water Cttee, 7 October, 1868.
75 Bateman to Water Cttee, 30 May, 1860.
76 Bateman to Water Cttee, 6 October, 1874.
77 Creber W. F. H. Manchester waterworks. *Trans Instn Water Engrs*, vol. XXXI, 1926, p. 24.
78 Bateman; *op. cit.*, p. 130.
79 Three letters from Thomas Telford with Introduction and Notes by R. A. Paxton, 1968, p. 10. Printed privately.
80 Bateman, *op. cit.*, pp. 143–6.
81 Bateman, *op. cit.*, p. 215.
82 Walters, *op. cit.*, p. 100.
83 Bateman to Water Cttee, 19 November, 1884; quoted by Russell, *op. cit.*
84 *Min. Proc. Instn Civ. Engrs*, vol. CCXII, 1920–21, p. 424.
85 1885 according to the obituary of J. F. LaTrobe Bateman in *Min. Proc. Instn Civ. Engrs*, vol. XCVII, 1889–90, p. 393.
86 Russell, *op. cit.*
87 Burnet J. *History of the Water Supply to Glasgow*, Glasgow Corporation Waterworks, 1869, pp. 3–17.
88 *Ibid.*, pp. 17–25.
89 Gale J. M. On the Glasgow Waterworks. *Instn Engrs in Scotland*, vol. VII, 1863–64, pp. 44 and 45.
90 Letter from William Gale to Henry Austen, quoted in General Board of Health, Report on the Supply of Water to the Metropolis, Appendix III, pp. 89 and 90.
91 Loch Katrine water is famed throughout the world for its purity and quality but it has one serious defect: it is aggressive to a variety of metals including iron, copper and lead. Its plumbosolvency propensity is particularly serious and has been well documented. Although acute lead poisoning is unlikely to occur as a result of consuming plumbosolvent water, cases have been reported where chronic lead poisoning has been associated with lead-contaminated water. In the present Loch Katrine supply, lime is added to the water and the use of lead pipes and lead cisterns in new work has been discontinued since 1968. (Reference: Richards W. N., Britton A. and Cochrane A. 'Reducing Plumbosolvency – the effect

of added lime on the Loch Katrine supply to Glasgow. *J. Instn Water Engrs & Scient.*, **34** (July 1980), 315–33.)
92 Gale, *op. cit.*, pp. 25–7.
93 *Ibid.*, p. 55.
94 Sutherland J. R. Glasgow Corporation Waterworks. *Trans. Instn Water Engrs*, vol. 29, 1924, pp. 53–6.
95 Eleven shafts were sunk on a tunnel 2325 yd long and upwards of 500 ft under the top of the ridge.
96 Extract from speech delivered on 23 October, 1859, by J. F. Bateman at a banquet given in his honour to commemorate the completion of the Loch Katrine Waterworks.
97 Obituary on J. F. La Trobe Bateman. *Min. Proc. Instn Civ. Engrs*, vol. XCVII, 1888–89, p. 394.
98 By the author's grandfather Sir Alexander Binnie, on behalf of the London County Council. He was a pupil of Bateman.
99 Russell P. John Frederick La Trobe-Bateman (1810–89) Water Engineer, *Trans. Newcomen Soc.*, 52 (1981). Chart and maps.
100 For objections to this practice, see comments by Tulloch in Chapter 11, p. 233.
101 Chapter 10, p. 205.
102 Neville P. On the water supply of the city of Dublin. *Min. Proc. Instn Civ. Engrs*, vol. XXXVIII, 1873–74, p. 12.
103 Wood C. J. Tunnel outlets from storage reservoirs. *Min. Proc. Instn Civ. Engrs*, vol. LIX, 1879. Discussion by Binnie, p. 72.
104 *Ibid.*, pp. 60 and 61.
105 *Ibid.*, p. 63.
106 The Daisy Green reservoir, near Darwen, of the North-West Water Authority. The pipeline had an internal diameter of 18 in. and contrary to Bateman's normal practice it was not embedded in concrete. The pipeline was found to be in good shape and, except for some minor scaling and pitting, the cast-iron of the pipes had remained in excellent condition.
107 Wood, *op. cit.*, pp. 44 and 45.

CHAPTER 10

1 Obituary on Sir Robert Rawlinson. *Min. Proc. Instn Civ. Engrs*, vol. CXXXIV, 1897–98, pp. 386–391.
2 R. Rawlinson to Edwin Chadwick, 30 September, 1852 (1645).
3 Rawlinson R. On the drainage of towns. *Min. Proc. Instn Civ. Engrs*, vol. XII, 1852, p. 25.
4 *Ibid.*, pp. 77–8.
5 Rawlinson R. (1865) Report, Sheffield and Bradford reservoirs.
6 Rawlinson R. (1865) Report, Rochdale and other waterworks reservoirs.
7 Mansergh J. Discussion on the Geelong and Sandhurst water supplies. *Min. Proc. Instn Civ. Engrs*, vol. LVI, 1878–79, Part II, p. 169. James Mansergh FRS (1834–1905) is chiefly remembered as the engineer responsible for the masonry dams in the Elan and Claerwen valleys constructed at the beginning of the 20th century for Birmingham Water Supply.
8 Except as regards the conclusions the following account is largely taken, by kind permission of Mr Dennis Earp, Divisional Manager, Gower Division of the Welsh National Water Authority, from an unpublished report 'History of Lower Lliw Reservoir 1860–1978', by P. G. de Lande Long of Binnie and Partners.
9 Rawlinson Report, as quoted in *The Cambrian*, 26 October, 1860.
10 *The Cambrian*, 24 January, 1862.
11 *The Cambrian*, 11 January, 1867.
12 'Notes on the Construction and Repairs to the Lliw Embankment', by Edward Cousins, MICE, 31 August, 1880.
13 Extract from the *Builder*, reported in *The Cambrian*, 4 June, 1869.
14 The same Major Tulloch who was in Bombay (see Chapter 11, p. 232).

15 Letter to *The Cambrian*, 28 February, 1873.
16 Reported in *The Cambrian*, 11 April, 1873.
17 *The Cambrian*, 7 and 8 May, 1874.
18 Cousins E. Address to British Association at Swansea on 'The Construction and Repairs of the Lliw Embankment', also published in *The Cambrian*, 31 August, 1880.
19 *The Cambrian*, 3 August, 1880.
20 *The Cambrian*, 3 April, 1883.
21 *The Cambrian*, 11 May, 1883.
22 *The Cambrian*, 12 October, 1883.
23 *The Cambrian*, 16 November, 1883.

CHAPTER 11

The author is indebted to Mr William Phillips, Chief Resident Engineer on behalf of Binnie and Partners (India) Ltd, on the Bhandup Complex for the water supply of Bombay from 1975 to 1980, for a copy of Major Tulloch's report of 1872, reprinted in 1964, and for the photograph of the superstructure of Vehar Valve Tower (Fig. 11.2).

1 *Min. Proc. Instn Civ. Engrs*, vol. XXXII, 1871, p. 167.
2 Parliamentary Paper, 'Sheffield Reservoirs', 13 February, 1866, p. 17.
3 *Min. Proc. Instn Civ. Engrs*, vol. XXXII, 1871, p. 170.
4 Parliamentary Paper, 'Sheffield Reservoirs', 13 February, 1866, p. 17.
5 The *Bombay Times*, 18 January, 1856.
6 Longmate N. *King Cholera*. Hamish Hamilton, 1966, p. 242.
7 Conybeare, H. Description of the Works, recently executed, for the Water Supply of Bombay, in the East Indies. *Min. Proc. Instn Civ. Engrs*, vol. XVII, 1858, p. 557.
8 Tulloch H. *The water supply of Bombay*. 1872 (reprinted 1964 by Town Printery), Banda, Bombay, p. 7.
9 *Ibid.*, p. 11.
10 *Ibid.*, p. 12.
11 Quoted in the *Bombay Times*, 18 January, 1856.
12 Tulloch, *op. cit.*, p. 14.
13 Quoted in the *Bombay Times*, 18 January, 1856.
14 Tulloch *op. cit.*, pp. 18 and 19.
15 *The Engineer*, 21 November, 1856.
16 Conybeare, *op. cit.*, p. 565.
17 *Ibid.*, p. 561.
18 *Ibid.*, p. 566.
19 He is the same Major Tulloch who has already been referred to in the previous chapter. By 1893 he had succeeded Rawlinson as Chief Engineering Inspector.
20 Tulloch H. Report on the Vehar Lake Dams, dated 25 July, 1871.
21 Tulloch H. *The water supply of Bombay*, footnotes to pp. 36 and 37.
22 Binnie A. R. *op. cit.*, p. 82.
23 Tulloch, *op. cit.*, footnote to p. 23.
24 *Ibid.*, p. 23.
25 *Ibid.*, p. 27.
26 *Ibid.*, p. 29.

CHAPTER 12

The author is very much indebted to Mr Michael Oddie, Director of Binnie and Partners Pty. Ltd. in Australia for sending him copies of three reports of Select Committees of the Government of

Victoria during the period 1858–60, publications of the Melbourne and Metropolitan Board of Works, contemporary drawings by Matthew B. Jackson and others, contemporary newspaper accounts and other contemporary documents on which this chapter is based.

1 Jackson's letter dated 31 May, 1853, to the Commissioners of Sewers and Water Supply printed as Appendix X in Victoria 1859–60; Report from the Select Committee upon Yan Yean Water Supply, ordered by the Legislature Council to be printed 13 September, 1860.
2 The Stephensons had two firms: Robert Stephenson and Co. which manufactured locomotives, stationary engines and other machinery, and George Stephenson and Son, which undertook surveying and civil engineering design work. Until Robert Stephenson moved the design firm to Westminster in 1836, both firms had been based in Newcastle. By Jackson's own evidence he was exclusively involved on civil engineering rather than mechanical projects from the commencement of apprenticeship in 1845, and this suggests that after the design work was moved to Westminster, Stephenson retained a design capability based on the Newcastle office.
3 Jackson's letter of application for appointment of Chief Engineer dated 31 May, 1853.
4 In his letter dated 31 May, 1853, Jackson wrote: 'I was further employed on designs for the South Australian Railway, from the city to the port, and I may say that it was in consequence of my being so employed that I left England; as the whole of the designs sent home for approval by Mr Cartwright Wills, the engineer, were condemned'. According to the particulars given on a form required by his proposer and supporters when Jackson was elected a Member of the Institution of Civil Engineers, he subsequently became Consulting Engineer to the Melbourne and Hobson's Bay Railway Company.
5 Matthew B. Jackson arrived in Melbourne on the *Tulloch Castle*. According to the shipping records, he travelled steerage, his age was 27 and his profession was iron merchant! No explanation for the last entry can be given.
6 The account of the period prior to 1854 is based partly on Gibbs G. A. *Water supply systems of the Melbourne and Metropolitan Board of Works*, 1915 and partly on Seeger R. C. The history of Melbourne's water supply, *The Melbourne and Metropolitan Board of Works Federation Journal*, 1948.
7 Jackson, M. B. On the water supply to the City of Melbourne, South Australia; comprising a brief description of the Melbourne Gravitation Water works. *Min. Proc. Instn. Civ. Engrs*, vol 18 (1858–9), p. 372. J. F. Bateman also had trouble with cracked pipes on one of the Longdendale Valley embankments and repaired them in a similar manner. Thomas Hawksley also had cracked pipes in the Rivington embankment but how he repaired them is not recorded.
8 Dale Dyke or Bradfield reservoir inquest. Second Day, 24 March, 1864. Questions 990 and 991. Evidence of House of Lords, vol. 33.
9 Victoria 1858–59; Report from the Select Committee upon Water from the Yan Yean reservoir, printed 16 February, 1859. Question 1436.
10 A century of water supply – The Yan Yean scheme . . . Melbourne's first piped-water supply, pamphlet issued by the Melbourne and Metropolitan Board of Works in 1957, p. 6.
11 Victoria 1859–60; Report from the Select Committee upon Yan Yean Water Supply, printed 13 September, 1860. Question 1028.
12 *Ibid.*, Questions 1316–18.
13 Jackson, 1859, *op. cit.*
14 Victoria 1858–59; Report from the Select Committee upon Water from the Yan Yean reservoir, printed 16 February, 1859.
15 The Toorourrong reservoir and clear water channel, completed 1884.
16 Victoria 1850–60; Report from the Select Committee on the Yan Yean purification, printed 2 August, 1860.
17 Jackson, M. B. *Water Supply to the City of Melbourne*. The Commissioner of Sewers and Water Supply, Melbourne, 1854, pp. 6 and 7. One of the advantages claimed by Jackson for his scheme was that 'by erecting a number of hydraulic cranes along the wharf on the principle

patented by W. G. Armstrong Esq. C. E. of Newcastle-upon-Tyne, and which are coming into general use at home, ships lying alongside the wharf can be discharged in one-sixth part of the time which is now occupied'.

18 By controlling development in the catchment area, and by using chlorination, the need for filtration has been avoided to the present time (1980).

19 Jackson, 1859 *op. cit.*, pp. 387 and 388.

20 *Ibid.*, pp. 376 and 377.

21 Report from the Select Committee upon Yan Yean Water Supply ordered by the Legislative Assembly to be printed 13 September, 1860.

22 Gibbs, *op. cit.*, p. 11.

23 Jackson was accused by Lanktree of having grossly exaggerated his previous experience and responsibilities in his letter of application for the appointment of Chief Engineer. In the letter as printed (Appendix X in Report from the Select Committee upon Yan Yean Water Supply, 13 September 1860) two separate paragraphs have obviously been consolidated by the printer into one paragraph, with the consequence that Jackson's reference to being employed 'either as designer or outdoor superintendant in charge' while working for Hasking is made to appear as applying to all his activities whilst with Robert Stephenson and Co.

24 Open letter 25 September 1861 from Manchester.

25 Seeger, *op. cit.*, p. 31.

26 Jackson M. B. *A Scheme for the Supply of Water to the towns of Sheffield, Rotherham-cum-Kimberworth and Doncaster with provision for the future supply of Chesterfield.* Westminster, 1866.

CHAPTER 13

1 Committee for the Management of the Affairs of the Sheffield Waterworks Company (Cttee SWC), First Annual Report dated 6 April, 1831.

2 Obituary. *Min. Proc. Instn Civ. Engrs*, vol. LXXXIII, 1885–86, pp. 433–6.

3 Cttee SWC, First Annual Report, dated 6 April, 1831.

4 *Ibid.*

5 Cttee SWC, Report dated 11 April, 1832.

6 Cttee SWC, Report dated 3 April, 1833.

7 Cttee SWC, Report dated 7 April, 1834.

8 Cttee SWC, Report dated 11 April, 1836.

9 When stability considerations permit, one can sometimes obtain relatively cheap additional storage in much the same way by steepening the slopes in the vicinity of the crest of a dam as was done *ab initio* at Manglu dam in Pakistan. Binnie *et al.* Mangla, *Proc. Instn Civ. Engrs*, 1967, vol. 38, Fig 28 on p. 73.

10 Cttee SWC, Report dated 3 April, 1837.

11 Cttee SWC, Report dated 13 April, 1846.

12 For a summary of John Towlerton Leather's career as a contractor in railway and maritime enterprises, which appears in no way to have been adversely affected by the collapse of the Dale Dyke dam, reference can be made to his obituary in *Min. Proc. Instn Civ. Engrs*, vol. LXXXIII, 1885–86, pp. 433–6.

13 Report dated 9 April, 1848, by J. Towlerton Leather to the Committee of the Sheffield Water Company.

14 Cttee SWC, Report dated 17 April, 1848. As mentioned in Chapter 1, p. 12, Chadwick had been unsuccessful in making the water company responsible for giving a constant supply.

15 Cttee SWC, Report dated 12 April, 1852, reads *inter alia*:

> The fall of rain for the whole year, within the Company's gather, having been several inches below the average and also, from one of the Reservoirs at Redmires having to be emptied for the purpose of being repaired from about the end of November 1850 to the end of the following March thereby limiting the Company's storage, at the most favour-

able period for storing, to only one of the large Reservoirs, it was found advisable as a matter of precaution, to abridge the usual hours of supply towards the close of the year.

See also Note 16.

16 Matthew B. Jackson, who had been trained in England and who was the engineer for the Yan Yean water supply scheme for Melbourne built 1855–57 (see Chapter 12) had to appear before a Select Committee in Melbourne and was asked a question to which he replied:

> Engineers adopt different ways of taking the pipes away from the reservoirs. At Manchester the pipes gave way. At Sheffield, on the contrary, they put the pipe in a culvert – the water got through and washed part of the bank away, and if the reservoir had been the extent of the Yan Yean one, it would have been a very serious affair.

When the lower Redmires reservoir is full, the water level comes above the level of the culvert beneath the middle Redmires embankment, and if it had been this culvert which let the water through it would have been necessary to empty both reservoirs to enable it to be repaired. Only one reservoir was emptied, and it is therefore concluded that it was the newly constructed culvert below the lower Redmires embankment which gave trouble.

17 *Manual of British Water Supply Practice*, 2nd edn, with Supplement. Heffer, 1958, p. 5.

18 The inlet ends of the old pipelines still exist. They are in an open-topped masonry chamber a short distance upstream from a weir constructed in the 1930s which submerges them to a depth of about 10 ft. No trace can now be found of the outlets but the pipes are evidently blocked as no water escapes through them.

19 House of Lords Records Office. Select Committee on Dewsbury, Batley and Heckmondwike Bill (1853).

20 Report dated April 1860, by J. Towlerton Leather to the Committee of the Sheffield Water Company.

21 Report dated April 1863 by J. Towlerton Leather to the Committee of the Sheffield Water Company.

22 Robert Rawlinson to Sir George Grey, 15 March, 1864 (Public Record Office).

23 Robert Rawlinson to Sir George Grey, 18 March, 1864 (Public Record Office No. HO45-OS/ 7656).

24 Nathaniel Beardmore (1816–72), engineer for works for draining and navigating River Lee, 1850; published writings on hydraulic engineering.

25 Robert Rawlinson to Sir George Grey, 18 March, 1864.

26 Sheffield Waterworks (Bradfield Innundation) Bill 1864. House of Lords Record Office. Evidence of House of Lords, vol. 33.

27 *Ibid.* A lively account of the inquest is given by Amey G. in *The Collapse of the Dale Dyke Dam 1864.* Cassell & Co. Ltd, 1974.

28 Reservoir (Safety Provisions) Act 1930.

29 Bradfield Reservoir Report (Sheffield Reservoirs), 13 February, 1866. House of Commons Parliamentary Papers, 1866, (25), LX, 365 (hereafter referred to as HC 1866).

30 John Murray's experience had been mainly in maritime and river works.

31 Special Report from the Select Committee on Waterworks Bill; together with the Proceedings of the Committee, Minutes of Evidence, Appendix and Index. House of Commons Parliamentary Papers 1865 (XII), 445 (hereafter referred to as SR 1865).

32 Harrison S. A Complete History of the Great Flood at Sheffield. The *Sheffield Times*, 1864, p. 24.

33 SR 1865 (see note 31), Q. 1381.

34 HC 1866 (see note 29), p. 30.

35 Binnie G. M. The collapse of the Dale Dyke dam in retrospect. *Q. Engng Geol.*, 1978, II, 305–25.

36 Binnie A. R. *Water Supply*, The Royal Engineers, 1887, p. 39.

37 Described in Chapter 4, pp. 65–8 and Chapter 8, pp. 140–1.

38 Nilsen T. Discussion 8th Int. Congr. Large Dams, Edinburgh, 1964, 5, p. 463. Cavity was in a non-cohesive moraine core.

Index

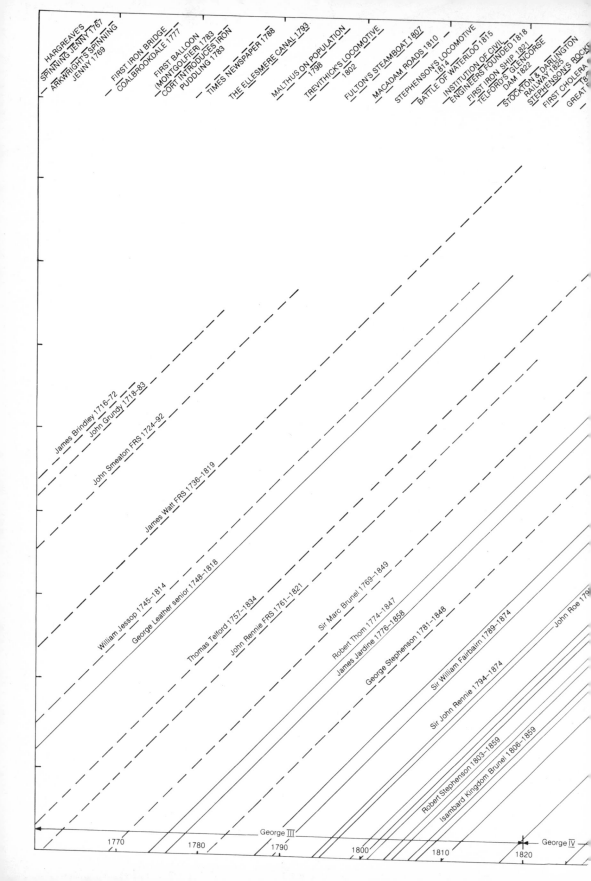

HARGREAVE'S SPINNING JENNY 1767
ARKWRIGHT'S SPINNING JENNY 1769
FIRST IRON BRIDGE COALBROOKDALE 1777
FIRST BALLOON (MONTGOLFIER) 1783
CORT INTRODUCES IRON PUDDLING 1783
TIMES NEWSPAPER 1788
THE ELLESMERE CANAL 1793
MALTHUS ON POPULATION 1798
TREVITHICK'S LOCOMOTIVE 1802
FULTON'S STEAMBOAT 1807
MACADAM ROADS 1810
STEPHENSON'S LOCOMOTIVE 1814
BATTLE OF WATERLOO 1815
INSTITUTION OF CIVIL ENGINEERS FOUNDED 1818
FIRST IRON SHIP 1821
TELFORD'S GLENCORSE DAM 1822
STOCKTON & DARLINGTON RAILWAY 1825
STEPHENSON'S ROCK...
FIRST CHOLERA...
GREAT...

James Brindley 1716–72
John Grundy 1718–83
John Smeaton FRS 1724–92
James Watt FRS 1736–1819
William Jessop 1745–1814
George Leather senior 1748–1818
Thomas Telford 1757–1834
John Rennie FRS 1761–1821
Sir Marc Brunel 1769–1849
Robert Thom 1774–1847
James Jardine 1776–1858
George Stephenson 1781–1848
Sir William Fairbairn 1789–1874
Sir John Rennie 1794–1874
John Roe 179...
Robert Stephenson 1803–1859
Isambard Kingdom Brunel 1806–1859

George III

George IV

1770   1780   1790   1800   1810   1820